Greenberg's® Guide to
LIONEL® TRAINS
1945-1969

Volume III, Sets

By Paul V. Ambrose

Greenberg Publishing Company, Inc.
Sykesville, Maryland

Copyright © 1990
by Bruce C. Greenberg

Greenberg Publishing Company, Inc.
7566 Main Street
Sykesville, MD 21784
(301) 795-7447

First Edition
First Printing

Manufactured in the United States of America

Greenberg Publishing Company, Inc. offers the world's largest selection of Lionel, American Flyer, LGB, Ives, and other toy train publications as well as a selection of books on model and prototype railroading, dollhouse miniatures, and toys. For a copy of our current catalogue, please send a large self-addressed stamped envelope to the address above.

Greenberg Shows, Inc. sponsors the world's largest public train, dollhouse, and toy shows. They feature extravagant operating model railroads for N, HO, O, Standard, and 1 Gauges as well as a huge marketplace for buying and selling nearly all model railroad equipment. The shows also feature a large selection of dollhouses and dollhouse furnishings. Shows are currently offered in metropolitan Baltimore, Boston, Ft. Lauderdale, Cherry Hill in New Jersey, Long Island in New York, Philadelphia, Pittsburgh, Tampa, and Wilmington in Delaware. Greenberg Auctions, a division of Greenberg Shows, Inc., offers nationally advertised auctions of toy trains and toys. Please contact our shows manager at (301) 795-7447 for further information. To receive our current show listing, please send a self-addressed stamped envelope marked "Train Show Schedule" to the address above.

ISBN 0-89778-172-4 (Hard Cover)
ISBN 0-89778-173-2 (Soft Cover)

Library of Congress Cataloging-in-Publication Data
Greenberg, Bruce C.
   [Guide to Lionel trains, 1945-1969]
   Greenberg's guide to Lionel trains, 1945-1969.
      p. cm.
   Includes index.
   Contents: v. 3 Sets / by Paul V. Ambrose.
   ISBN 0-89778-172-4 (v. 3). -- ISBN 0-89778-173-2 (soft) (v. 3)
   1. Railroads--Models. 2. Lionel Corporation. I. Title.
TF197.G667 1990
625.1'9--dc20
                                                          90-3917
                                                          CIP

TABLE OF CONTENTS

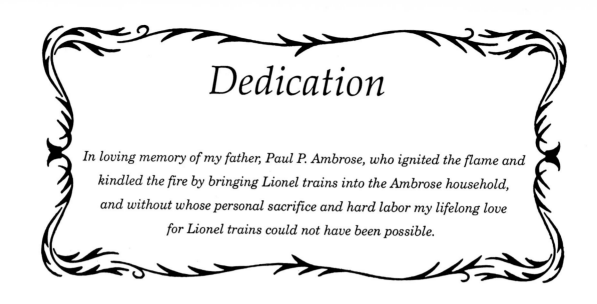

Dedication

In loving memory of my father, Paul P. Ambrose, who ignited the flame and kindled the fire by bringing Lionel trains into the Ambrose household, and without whose personal sacrifice and hard labor my lifelong love for Lionel trains could not have been possible.

Acknowledgments

The topic of catalogued sets has been an interest of mine for many years. Knowing what has to be said, however, and saying it are two entirely different things. More time and energy were expended on this book than I ever imagined, and I can only hope that the readers will find it worthwhile.

My sincerest gratitude goes to **Barbara Morey** of the Greenberg staff, who toiled with me on a day-to-day basis for over a year to get this work in print. Aside from her technical, editorial and spelling prowess, she deserves a special commendation for being able to read my handwriting.

All of the photographs in this book, unless otherwise noted, were taken by **Bruce Greenberg**. **Maureen Crum** designed the cover of this book, and did much of the paste-up work. **Donna Price** reviewed the manuscript several times for consistency and accuracy, and made several suggestions regarding the page layout. **Dallas Mallerich** was a most helpful in-house Lionel consultant, as was **Dwayne Lindsay**. **Samuel Baum** supervised the production of this book.

Robert Swanson has intensively studied Lionel trains made from 1945 through 1947 and is the authority on these years. He graciously contributed the chapters on these years for this volume. He reviewed other chapters as well and clarified some "gray" areas in the period of the late 1940s.

Drew Bauer carefully and methodically reviewed all the text and made many very helpful suggestions. **Cindy Lee Floyd** contributed to the **Introduction**. Several other experienced Lionel collectors graciously reviewed the manuscript prior to publication. They include **Thomas Austern, Warren Blackmar, Philip Catalano, M.D., Neil Fagan, Michael Ocilka, Robert Osterhoff, Harold Powell, Chris Rohlfing, Michael Sabatelle, I. D. Smith,** and **William Holden. Larry Nuzzaci** also assisted with this book.

Nicholas DeGrazia, president of Lionel Trains, Inc., graciously permitted us to use page 19 of the 1948 catalogue for the cover of this book. He also granted permission to use the photographs on pages 6 and 7 of the 1946 catalogue and page 15 of the 1947 catalogue in the text.

There were several others who were most helpful and courteous in the pursuit of information. We appreciate very much the assistance of **B. Myles, M. Sokol,** and **P. Sigrist** who generously allowed us to photograph and study their collections. Thanks also to **Howard Holden** and **Roland LaVoie** for allowing us to use photographs of their sets, and to **Donald Corrigan** for the photographs of the billboards. **Bob Morgan** and **Ed Prendeville** of Train Collector's Warehouse allowed me to roam at will through their inventory in order to corroborate data. Being able to examine so many items under one roof was a blessing. Their open-door policy extended throughout the decade of the 80s. **Harry Lovelock** and **Randy Okun** willingly shared information as well as their collections with us.

Paul V. Ambrose
September 1990

INTRODUCTION

Purpose

The purpose of this book is to provide a comprehensive listing with current prices for Lionel outfits in O, O27, and Super O Gauges produced from 1945 through 1969. We also include certain variations which have been authenticated. In a few cases we ask our readers for further information where data is uncertain. The terms *outfit* and *set* are used interchangeably in the text. The word *outfit* appeared as a descriptive term in the 1946 Lionel catalogue. Its use was continuous, though not always constant, throughout the postwar era.

Determining Values

Toy train values vary for a number of reasons. First, consider the **relative knowledge** of the buyer and seller. A seller may be unaware that he has a rare variation and sell it for the price of a common piece. Another source of price variation is **short-term fluctuation** which depends on what is being offered at a given train meet on a given day. A related source of variation is the **season** of the year. The train market is slower in the summer and sellers may at this time be more inclined to reduce prices if they really want to move an item. Another important source of price variation is the relative strength of the seller's **desire to sell** and the buyer's **eagerness to buy**. Clearly a seller in economic distress will be more eager to strike a bargain. A final source of variation is **the personalities** of the seller and buyer. Some sellers like to quickly turn over items and, therefore, price their items to move; others seek a higher price and will bring an item to meet after meet until they find a willing buyer.

Outfit values in this book are based on *obtained* prices, rather than asking prices. Generally, the prices reported here represent a price perceived as a fair value by the buyer of the most common variation, unless specifically stated otherwise. They may sometimes appear lower than those seen on trains at meets for two reasons. First, items that sell often sell in the first hour of a train meet and, therefore, are no longer visible. (We have observed that a good portion of the action at most meets occurs in the first hour.) The items that do not sell in the first hour have a higher price tag and this price, although not representing the selling price, is the price observed. A related source of discrepancy is the willingness of some sellers to bargain over price.

Another factor which may affect prices is reconditioning done by the dealer. Some dealers take great pains to clean and service their pieces or sets so that they look their best and operate properly. Others sell the items just as they have received them, dust and all. Naturally, the more effort the dealer expends in preparing his items for sale, the more he can expect to charge for them. This factor may account for significant price differences among dealers selling the same equipment.

Many Like New items have been uncovered under a layer of dust. Keep in mind that dust, in most instances, can be removed while dents and chipped paint cannot. Sellers often tend to "over-clean" their merchandise. Keep a watchful eye for items that have been given a coat of wax, and for those that have had their wheels polished. This practice may be acceptable to some for Very Good items but it is never acceptable for a Like New grade. Be aware of anything that is the color silver, and note that most red-painted and red heat-stamped items are extremely sensitive to dust and cleaning.

From our studies of train prices, it appears that mail order prices for used trains and outfits are generally higher than those obtained at train meets. This is appropriate considering the costs and efforts of producing and distributing a price list and packing and shipping items. Mail order items may sell at prices above those listed in this book. A final source of difference between observed prices and reported prices is region.

We receive many inquiries as to whether or not a particular item or outfit is a "good value." This book will help answer that question; but, there is NO substitute for experience in the marketplace. *We strongly recommend that novices do not make major purchases without the assistance of friends who have experience in buying and selling trains.* If you are buying a set and do not know whom to ask about its value, look for the people running the meet or show and discuss with them your need for assistance. Usually they can refer you to an experienced collector who will be willing to examine the outfit and offer his opinion.

Condition

For each outfit, we provide two price categories: **Very Good** and **Like New**. The novice collector, however, should be aware that there are other categories commonly used as well, and we have included them here for reference. As a guide, the following definitions may be used to determine an item's condition.

FAIR — Well-scratched, chipped, dented, rusted, or warped.

GOOD — Scratches, small dents, dirty.

VERY GOOD — Few scratches, exceptionally clean, no major dents or rust. Must include the outfit box and component boxes where applicable, with allowance for normal wear. It is always preferable, though not mandatory, to have box liners and associated paperwork along with miscellaneous items such as lubricant and smoke pellets. O27 and O Gauge track are optional because they have minimal resale value in Very Good condition, but Super O track should be included along with the related uncoupling/operating items. Although desirable, low-end transformers are not mandatory while better transformers such as a 1033 are required.

EXCELLENT — Minute scratches or nicks, no dents or rust, all original with less than average wear.

LIKE NEW — Only the faintest signs of handling and wheel wear with crisp, vibrant colors that show no evidence of polishing. The outfit box and component boxes where applicable must be in comparable condition with no major rips or tears. A Like New box must have all the end flaps, ears, and coupler protection flaps attached. Like New condition *must* include all box liners, instruction sheets, miscellaneous items, and the appropriate track and/or transformer. Super O track and related items, and transformers with whistle/horn controllers have substantial resale value.

The decision to purchase or not to purchase always rests with the buyer. Some buyers' criteria are more stringent than others. Keep in mind that some collectors frown upon the inclusion of track in outfits because track is quite apt to cause damage to the far more valuable boxes.

MINT — Brand new, absolutely unmarred, all original and unused, with the outfit box, and component boxes where applicable, and with any additional items that came with the set, such as instruction sheets, factory inspection slips, billboards, track, manuals, etc.

In the toy train field there is a great deal of concern with exterior appearance and less concern with operation. If operation is important to you, then ask the seller whether the train runs. If the seller indicates that he does not know whether the equipment operates, you should test it. (For items in Mint condition it is *not* recommended that you even test run the equipment.) Most train meets have test tracks provided for that purpose.

We have included the Like New classification in this edition because of the small but important and ever-increasing trade in pre-1970 items in higher grades. The prices shown for Like New form a basis for transactions of these items. This is reasonable in light of the substantial confusion in the minds (or perhaps simply difference of opinion) of both sellers and buyers as to what constitutes "Mint" condition. How do we define Mint? Among very experienced train enthusiasts, a

Mint piece means that it is brand new, in its original box, never run, and extremely bright and clean with crisp component boxes. An item may have been removed from the box and replaced in it but it should show no evidence of handling. A piece is not Mint if it shows any scratches or evidence of discoloration. It is not uncommon, however, for an absolutely brand-new item to show signs of handling and to even have some touch-up paint. These instances occurred at the factory, and many a dirty, greasy hand picked up an item and left finger marks on what would otherwise be absolutely perfect merchandise. Paint touch-ups were quite prevalent and are most apparent on GG-1s. The shells were often stacked one on top of the other at the factory before they were mounted on a chassis but after the side ladders were attached! No wonder the paint was sometimes chipped.

It is the nature of a market for the seller to see his wares in a very positive light and to seek to obtain a Mint price for a Like New item. In contrast, a buyer will see the same item in a less favorable light and will attempt to buy a Mint set for the price of one in Like New condition. It is our responsibility to point out this difference in perspective **and** the difference in value implicit in each perspective, and to then let the buyer and seller settle or negotiate their different perspectives.

Sets which are determined to be truly Mint in condition — by both the buyer and seller — will bring a substantial premium above the prices shown for Like New. Again, we strongly recommend that novices exercise extreme caution, since restored, fraudulent, and reproduction items are all quite prevalent in the marketplace.

We do not show values for items in Fair or Restored condition. **Fair** items are valued substantially below Very Good. We have not included **Restored** either, because such items are not a significant portion of the market for postwar trains.

Pricing Criteria

As we have indicated, prices in this book were derived from large train meets or shows and from experienced collector input. Many factors were considered in determining set values. First and foremost was the box data. A set that came from the factory with component boxes is of greater value than the same or a comparable set that was shipped without component boxes. For example, the Super O General outfit 2528WS from 1959 is priced $150 higher when acquired with component boxes as opposed to being obtained without boxes in Type B display-style packaging. Most of the General items are readily available, yet their individual component boxes are scarce. The scarcity of the outfit box itself was also taken into account. Outfit 12700 from 1964 is worth $100 more than the comparable outfit 12710, which even included an LW transformer as an extra component, because of the scarcity of set box 12700. Outfits that contained a 1033 transformer or one with a whistle/horn controller such as 1053 bring a premium over those shipped with a 1012 or 1015. Also considered was the type of track included in the set. A circle of Super O along with several straight sections and a No. 37 uncoupling section add approximately $50 to the value of the set.

An example of how a Like New condition set with component boxes was priced is as follows:

The 209 New Haven passenger set 1608W is very scarce. Because top-of-the-line outfits, whether O27, O, or Super O, were made in far lesser quantities than the low- and medium-range sets, their outfit boxes command a high value.

209 New Haven AA	$1000
2432 Vista Dome	90
2432 Vista Dome	90
2434 Pullman	120
2436 observation	100
1053 transformer	25
track and miscellaneous paper	25
outfit box	350
TOTAL	$1800

If you have trains to sell and you sell them to a person planning to resell them, you will not obtain the prices reported in this book. Rather, you should expect to achieve between 50 and 70 percent of these prices for ordinary items. For highly desirable items in Like New condition, a higher percentage of the price is often obtained because the demand exceeds the supply. Basically, for your items to be of interest to a buyer who plans to resell them, he must purchase them for considerably less than the prices listed here.

Information Sources

Seeking advice is especially important because of the ever-present danger posed by fakes and frauds. Not long ago, the Train Collectors Association, the largest train collecting organization in the United States, published the details of a chemical dyeing process which can alter a common plastic locomotive cab or freight car's color into an apparently real and "rare" but spurious color. While it is not the purpose of this book to be judgmental about this matter, we urge our readers to exercise extreme caution when purchasing Lionel postwar outfits with equipment purported to be a "factory error" or preproduction because of a difference in color or graphics. Even box reproductions are now commonplace. The Factory Prototypes and Errors chapter, in *Greenberg's Guide to Lionel Trains, 1945-1969, Volume II*, contains entries which are known to be genuine factory errors. Readers should consult expert opinion before contemplating any such purchase. Extreme caution is advised.

The Lionel collector and operator has several additional sources for toy train information. The selection of Greenberg publications available for your library includes Guides to prewar, postwar, and modern era trains; operating and repair manuals; catalogues; and an upcoming encyclopedia with expanded information on postwar items. In addition to the many Lionel references, we also publish books on many other major and minor train and toy manufacturers.

Reporting Postwar Variations

The main reason for the success of *Greenberg's Guide to Lionel Trains, 1945-1969, Volume I* has been the response and interest of you, the collector and enthusiast. Over the years collectors from all over the United States and Canada have written with comments, suggestions, and advice. These contacts have enabled Volume I to become more accurate and thorough. We are very pleased with the eagerness with which readers have responded, and hope that they will continue to do so with our set Guide.

The decision-making process concerning proposed new listings or revisions is surprisingly complex — and sometimes quite agonizing. Sometimes a variation or set component is difficult to establish, and follow-up letters asking for specific information reveal that the component is not in fact a new variation. At other times a really odd item or set component may strain one's credibility — yet the variation is genuine. In general, there are three major criteria used by the editors before listing a new entry, or before amending an existing one:

(1) CREDIBILITY: Obviously, we are not referring to the trustworthiness of the enthusiast! That is something we assume all along. Rather, we are trying to answer the classic question of the skeptic: "How do you know this outfit came as such from the factory?" Perhaps someone else will be able to furnish data to show that this set component or outfit box is really a factory variant.

(2) CORROBORATION: Many times the type of proof sent along with the report is crucial. Photographic evidence is a *must*. Of equal importance is independent verification by other knowledgeable collectors.

(3) COMPLETENESS: Several possible variations may not have been included because of incomplete reports. It is not enough to say that one has a 6560 crane car with no smokestack on the cab for a particular set. There are several different 6560 cranes — which one is being reported? However, if the correspondent says that his crane is "the same as (B) in Volume I, but has no stack," he has given us the proper basis for comparison. Many major variations and box descriptions turn upon a minor item — and so does the value. The more complete your descriptions, the better.

If you wish to report a new entry or correction to us, please use the reporting sheet enclosed with this book. We appreciate very much your cooperation, enthusiasm, and good will in helping us document Lionel train production. As has been our custom, we will acknowledge any comments noted in this Guide as your observation. Every letter to us will be answered.

Various sections of the book will help you with trucks, component boxes, and outfit box descriptions, along with complete appendices of every postwar set and catalogued engine, and at long last, an explanation of the mystery years 1955, 1956, and 1957.

Important References

Volume I is your streamlined reference to *regular production* postwar motive power and rolling stock. It does not include errors and prototypes. Errors and prototypes are listed in a detailed chapter in Volume II. Both Volumes contain references to sets that will be of interest to readers of this guide.

How to Use This Guide

All of the trains Lionel produced during the postwar period operated on three-rail track with a measurement of 1-1/4 inches between the running rails. This track is commonly known as O Gauge. Track was, however, produced in three varieties: O27, regular O, and Super O. Each of these types of track has its own unique characteristics and is not readily interchangeable. O27 Gauge was made of a lightweight metal, and eight curved track sections form a circle with a diameter of 27 inches. Regular O Gauge track was made of heavier metal, and eight curved track sections form a 31-inch circle. Super O was a specialized track system introduced by Lionel in 1957 and consisted of realistic plastic ties with T-shaped running rails. The center rail was replaced by a thin copper blade that allowed electrical contact. Twelve sections of curved Super O track form a circle with a diameter of 38 inches. All O27 items could be run on O Gauge track, and most on Super O, but the converse is not true. Larger O Gauge items such as the 773 Hudson and 2500 series passenger cars cannot run on O27 track. They require at least a 31-inch circle of track offered by O Gauge.

Sets produced during this period contained only one type of track, not a mixture, and are referred to by that track. Most O27 sets were less expensive than both O Gauge and Super O, but the top-of-the-line O27 outfits were often substantially more expensive that the introductory O and Super O sets. Super O sets, however, were considered to be Lionel's premium merchandise.

This Guide is organized by individual years 1945 through 1969. Each listing begins with the outfit number, type of track, and original retail price of the set. For readability of the text, this price is shown simply as **Retail**. The designation **No Retail** indicates that no suggested retail price was given for this set. A list of the set contents is followed by a discussion of the set, when appropriate, and **Very Good** and **Like New** prices concludes each listing.

The term *Advance Catalogue* refers to the catalogues that were sent to dealers and distributors of Lionel trains, while the *consumer catalogue* indicates catalogues that were widely available to the public. Occasionally a set shown in an Advance Catalogue was never produced, or production was altered before it was ever available to modelers. Such discrepancies are pointed out in the appropriate listings.

The reader will notice that considerable attention has been given to outfit and component boxes. To the serious collector, authentic boxes are essential to the credentials of an outfit, and an outfit is not really complete without the appropriate boxes.

The contents of outfits are listed as Lionel listed them — by their catalogue stock number, which sometimes included a suffix, or by the number that appears on the proper component box. They are *not* listed by the number that is stamped on the car. For example, the 6362 rail truck is stamped "636255", but that number never appeared in the catalogue or on a component box; the flatcar with vans and a Midge toy tractor from 1966 is listed as "6431" because that was the catalogue number and the number of the component box even though the car was stamped "6430". Likewise, the N & W work caboose was stamped "641957" but came in a box numbered "6419-100", and the hopper car that was often catalogued and boxed as "6476" in the late 1960s sometimes was stamped "6076" or "6176". Some box suffixes are definitely a means of color identification such as with the 6562 gondola with canisters — "-1" was gray, "-25" was red, and "-50" was black. Suffixes such as "-60" and "-85" that appeared on some boxes from the 1957-1958 era are for the most part unidentifiable, while other suffixes such as "-100" and "-125" from the mid-1960s often denoted load or coupler type.

Since much of this book examines Lionel trains in an original way, it has been necessary to coin new terms in order to clearly categorize this material. Readers will find the **Glossary** and the nomenclature chart in the **Prologue** helpful in understanding these terms.

The following steps show how to use the Appendices:

❖ IF YOU KNOW THE CONSUMER CATALOGUE OUTFIT NUMBER and wish to verify the contents, use **Appendix B** to find the listing. It will also tell you the engine contained in the outfit and the year(s) in which the set was catalogued. Simply turn to the appropriate chapter to locate the desired set, which is presented in numerical sequence.

❖ IF YOU KNOW THE THREE-DIGIT OUTFIT NUMBER, refer first to **Appendix C**, which will tell you the engine that headed the set and the corresponding consumer catalogue outfit number. Then follow the steps mentioned above.

❖ IF YOU WISH TO FIND INFORMATION ABOUT A PARTICULAR ENGINE, refer to **Appendix D**. It will give you a sequential listing of all catalogued postwar engines, the outfit(s) they headed, and the year(s) in which they were catalogued. Appendix D provides the collector with an overview of how frequently a particular engine headed an outfit, which is important in determining relative value. (For example, the 2037 steam engine headed sixteen outfits while the 2016 headed only one.)

❖ In order to satisfy strong collector interest, **Appendix E** lists all of the postwar passenger sets by type.

❖ **Appendix F** lists scarce and collectable rolling stock and cabooses, and the outfit(s) in which they were included.

PROLOGUE

This book treads upon virgin territory and is based upon factual data, not hypothesis. It was compiled primarily from first-hand information that I have collected through the years. I have personally observed and annotated the contents of nearly 400 different postwar Lionel outfits for this book that I believe to be factory correct. Secondary information was taken from both the Advance and consumer Lionel catalogues, original instruction sheets, and internal Lionel documents. I consider myself qualified to undertake such a project; my ongoing love affair with Lionel trains started in 1950 at the age of three.

I must stress one major tenet — "Know thy product." Much of what is presented to the hobbyist as a set is nothing more than some trains in a box. A set, to be a set, must be correct in every facet, i.e., properly dated items, correct trucks, component boxes where applicable, etc. Regrettably, most are not.

Authenticity of Product

It is well known that not much with Lionel was written in stone. One must remember that Lionel was first and foremost a business, and a business must show a profit to stay in business. One of the means of monitoring profits was to avoid taking charge-offs for obsolescence. Obsolete items, whether trucks, boxes, finished stock, or even paint, were all used until depleted. With this in mind, Charts III and IV provide a framework for dating rolling stock boxes and trucks, and help the collector to avoid making significant errors. However, exceptions within this framework do occur. For instance, coil couplers can be found on some 1949 production stock; staple-end trucks have been found on some 1953 items; and 6427 cabooses, vintage 1958 with bar-end trucks, were still being depleted in 1960. But there are also some absolutes: for example, 1955 sets must have boxes with the stock number printed on all four sides; 1956 sets will not have any cars with AAR trucks; and it is impossible for 1958 sets to have any solid orange perforated-front boxes. There is no substitute for knowledge; it enables collectors to determine whether an outfit is factory-correct or an after-the-fact put-together. Keep in mind that most corrugated engine boxes, transformer boxes, instruction sheets, and even Lionel wrapping paper are datable, and do not underestimate the value of original in- struction sheets. They contain a wealth of information such as coupler type, reversing sequence, and other particulars.

The Lionel Corporation, as would any other business, opted to reuse as many dies and manufacturing techniques as possible with only minor alterations. For example, the SP-type caboose that was introduced in late 1947 used basically the same die as those made in 1969. Although that was a 22-year span, a 1950s-era caboose has no place in a 1960s set. Similarly, the 6464 series boxcar had four major body molds that span a sixteen-year period and numerous chassis varia- tions, and all are interchangeable! A 6464-250 Western Pacific from 1966, however, could not have been factory issued with bar-end metal trucks. All F-M and most F-3 and Alco cabs and chassis are also interchangeable. A 2023 Union Pacific cab does not belong on a 2032 Erie chassis, nor a 209 New Haven shell on a 218 Santa Fe frame. Quite often an early-issue F-M such as the 2341 Jersey Central is offered on a 2322 Virginian chassis. Why? What better way to increase the value of the scarce Jersey Central than by substituting a cleaner, more common late-Virginian chassis.

Outfit Numbering

Understanding outfits is not as complex as one might imagine. As one pages through a catalogue, it becomes evident that outfits were usually presented in numerical sequence by gauge and price points, the catalogue showing the lowest-priced outfits in the front and progressing to ever more expen- sive sets toward the end. Therefore, the rule of thumb is that the higher the outfit number in a given year, the higher the price. A notable exception to this convention is evident in the year 1950, in which some of the higher numbers designated lower-priced sets. It is also interesting to note that the better O27 sets were often substantially more expensive than the introductory O Gauge and then Super O outfits.

The charts and comments included in this section should provide useful guidelines for the study of Lionel sets. From 1945 through 1960 all outfits ending with odd numbers were freight sets while even-numbered endings designated passen- ger sets. Exceptions to this numbering system are shown in the following low-end freight sets: 1112 (1948), 1500 (1953-1954), 1000W (1955), 1542 (1956), 1590 (1958), and 1124 (1961 Advance). A plausible explanation for some of these exceptions is indicated, for example, by outfit 1112, which was the companion set to outfit 1111 from the new Scout series introduced in 1948. These freight sets were the first issues in a brand-new series of numbers that was to have been reserved exclusively for low-end and/or promotional sets. Please refer to the chronology of outfit numbers in **Appendix B**.

In 1955 Lionel again strayed from its regular numbering system and promoted outfits 1000W along with 1001 as "special value" freight sets, whereas 1542 and 1590 were late additions to the product line, to meet a specific price point, and were given the lowest available outfit number in the regular series. This is evidenced by the fact that the 1542 outfit from 1956 did not even make the early editions of the Advance Catalogue. Also note that 1541 and 1589 were the last outfit numbers to be used in 1955 and 1957 respectively; therefore 1542 and 1590 were the lowest available numbers in 1956 and 1958.

All outfits from 1946 through 1961 that began with a "1" were O27 sets while those that began with a "2" were either O Gauge or Super O sets. It was not until 1962 that Lionel began to use a five-digit outfit numbering code. This story is explained in the 1962 Advance Catalogue. It states that all train outfit numbers would begin with the numeral "1", while the second, third, and fourth digits would be the actual set number, and the fifth digit would designate the type of packaging. This fifth digit is helpful in 1962 and 1963 but becomes extraneous in 1964 through 1969 as all the fifth digits became "0". Even these five-digit outfit codes tell a specific story that can be traced through 1969. Remembering that all train outfits began with a "1", then the following hold true:

- All O27 sets had a second digit "1".
- All O sets had a second digit "2" except in 1962 when 12502 and 12512 were O27 outfits available in gift packs.
- All Super O sets had a second digit "3".

Outfit Packaging

All O27 sets, except the gift packs 12502, 12512, and the 1800 series from 1959 through 1961, included track and transformer while their O and Super O Gauge counterparts, with some exceptions in the 1964-1966 era and in outfit 2555W from 1960, included only track.

Lionel's packaging during this period was excellent and always contained everything necessary to operate and maintain a train set right in the outfit box. These items included wire, lockon, oil, lubricant, and when necessary, SP smoke pellets along with a wooden plunger, smoke fluid, power bus connectors, and even a battery in some years, as well as the appropriate item(s) to uncouple and/or operate the contents. Lionel began to include billboards with all their sets in 1950 and followed this practice into the mid-1960s.

As an aside, a dry cell battery can and often does cause major damage to engines if carelessly left in place for extended periods of time. It is most frustrating to find an otherwise fine piece of motive power that has been damaged because of battery corrosion. Lionel on occasion shipped items from the factory with a battery included. This practice was most prev-

alent during the years 1955-1957. Items known to have been shipped with batteries are the five-stripe GG-1s, F-M units, Geeps, the motorized 400 and 404 Budd units, and the 1961 reissue of the GG-1. Painful though it may be, sealed examples of the aforementioned engines should be opened and checked for batteries.

An instruction manual was included with all but the lowest-end sets, which had their own special instruction sheets, through 1954. From 1955 on, the manual was reserved solely for top-of-the-line O27, O Gauge, and then Super O outfits while low and moderate O27 sets were given a generic instruction sheet that was predicated upon the contents, i.e., type of transformer, method of uncoupling, diesel or steam, etc. In 1959 Lionel started to print some specific numbered outfit instruction sheets for the low and moderate O27 sets. When O Gauge outfits were reintroduced in 1964, most were given a generic instruction sheet numbered "12700". The introduction of Super O in 1957 required yet another sheet, and Lionel complied. All Super O sets included instructions explaining this rather complex track system, and some sets, most notably the 2555W "Father and Son" set and those with unique track plans in 1960, included still another special instruction sheet.

Other miscellaneous items included in sets were a service station directory, an accessory and/or consumer catalogue beginning in 1954, and various sheets informing the consumer that the 1008 camtrol was attached to a piece of straight track in 1958, as well as instructions, beginning in 1960, that advised the model railroader to "Lubricate Car Axles." Warranty cards and merchandise order forms also began to appear in 1961.

Substitutions

One of the problems in studying catalogued sets and accurately listing their contents is that Lionel dealers sometimes took liberties with set contents in order to make a sale. A well-known instance of component switching occurred in 1957 when the Canadian Pacific passenger set was issued. As sent from the factory this set contained an AA pair of F-3 diesels, three Skyline 500 Vista Dome cars, and the Banff Park observation car. However, many customers wanted more variety in the passenger cars, so dealers frequently substituted Blair Manor and Craig Manor Pullman cars for two of the Skyline 500 Vista Domes.

The Lionel factory also took their share of liberties. Variables such as quality control problems, material shortages, and the non-delivery or substitution of essential accent pieces such as helicopters or cable reels often came into play during production. Sometimes when an item intended for a particular set was prematurely depleted, Lionel replaced that item with a similar one. For example, when the supply of the 6464-50 M St. L boxcars intended for outfit 1535W in 1955 was prematurely exhausted, Lionel decided to complete the production run by substituting the now scarce 6468 tuscan double-door automobile boxcar. Likewise, substitutions were also made when production changes occurred during the period between catalogue issue and the actual shipment of merchandise. These facts are very evident in outfit 2223W from 1954 which is known to have come with either the maroon- or gray-roofed Lackawanna, the 6464-100 with a blue or yellow feather, and the 3482 operating milk car with a small "3472" stamped on the lower right of the car body. Sealed outfit boxes could also hide a multitude of sins. Outfits were the means by which Lionel was able to deplete overstocked boxes; they simply restamped such boxes to use in packaging sets. Remember that Lionel's business was making toys and trains, not fine collectibles that required precise specifications in every phase of the manufacturing and packaging process; we, as collectors, have made them collectable.

Promotion of Outfits

A major facet of Lionel's marketing strategy was to sell outfits, and they were promoted as such in the catalogues and by the salesmen. It was also much simpler to ship and control inventory on outfits than it was on individually-boxed items. Lionel's cost structure made it good business acumen for the dealer to order outfits, since outfits cost an average of 25 percent less than the total of the component pieces. It was also to the advantage of the retail customer to purchase an outfit because he definitely would get more product for his money. When necessary an outfit was broken up, then as today, in order to sell the desired individual item(s).

The marketing of outfits is further evidenced by the fact that master cartons are scarce, and in many instances rare. Master cartons, also known as LTS [the letters "LTS" are an abbreviation for locomotive and tender set] or double boxes, are the corrugated containers that were used to box separate-sale engines, either diesel or steam, and tenders. Even the General and 200 series Alcos came in master cartons when available for separate sale. The engine and tender were in most instances component boxed inside the master carton, although a notable exception to this practice is that the early Alco pairs and some steam engines and tenders from the mid-1960s were not component boxed. Why are these master cartons so scarce? Simply because dealers and their customers bought outfits, and outfits, except for the early 1950s Alco sets, did not include master cartons. What rational person would spend $30 for a 685 LTS when he could have the whole set for $39.95? How many 2383 Santa Fes have you seen? Plenty, no doubt, but I would bet that you have seen very few 2383 master cartons.

The Importance of Boxes

I must again stress the importance of boxes. A collectable item is not complete without its original box, if one exists. A collectable book with its jacket, for example, brings a premium, and the same principle applies to trains. Generally speaking, a component box adds 10 to 15 percent to the value of an item, and a crisp outfit box adds another 15 to 20 percent to the value of the components. The condition of the box should be at least commensurate with the item(s) it contains. These numbers are of major concern as they can increase the total value of the set by as much as 35 percent! There are some

outfit boxes that are so scarce that they are worth as much as 35 to 40 percent of the value of their more common contents.

For example, ten years ago a complete boxed set could be purchased for roughly a 20 percent discount below the value of the components. Boxed sets were usually broken up and sold separately because the individual items brought more than the total package. Today a collector may expect to pay a 20 percent premium; that is a turnaround of 40 percent!

It is also a simple fact that there are more trains than boxes in the marketplace. Not too many years ago outfit and component boxes were excess baggage. They were often one step away from the door, which meant the trash can. Dealers found them burdensome at train meets; it was far easier to wrap items in paper than it was to continually remove and replace them in boxes. Many collectors also shunned boxes because of storage problems, and how many of us have heard from a parent or spouse to "Get rid of those darn boxes." Many boxes have been damaged because of improper care. Have not nearly *all* of us stored boxes in damp basements?

The Infamous "X"

The rubber-stamped "X" that sometimes appeared on both steam and diesel engine and tender flaps remains a mystery. It is known that the "X" suffix on rolling stock boxes did mean "something different" as evidenced by variations that came in boxes stamped "6257X", "3620X", "6560X", and "6468X". If one were to question ten knowledgeable collectors, as many as ten different explanations for the significance of the "X" would be offered. The "X" suffix is most often seen on items from the 1948-1958 era, but it also appears on some later production. It is widely believed that the rare, orange cab 2338 Milwaukee Road Geep and the 2321 maroon roof Lackawanna came with a rubber-stamped "X" as did the scarce N & W long-striped tender. This, however, is not always true. Examples of the maroon roof Lackawanna have surfaced in regular 2321 corrugated boxes. In addition, I had the opportunity to witness the opening of a sealed 2338 corrugated box with a rubber-stamped "X" — it contained the common black cab version. Perhaps this "X" was the method of marking some items designated for separate sale. Numerous items with an "X" suffix have been observed throughout the years in master cartons.

Assessing Value

The less expensive Lionel sets and components have been neglected in previous research on toy trains, and this is unfortunate, since these sets represent some of Lionel's most creative and important marketing efforts. One must remember that during Lionel's heyday, the trains of Louis Marx threatened the low end of Lionel's pricing structure without letup, and especially in the mid-1950s Lionel's marketing creativity was sorely tested. These low-end sets outsold the more expensive sets by many times; they were the means by which people were brought into Lionel Land. Because of their low pricing and stiff competition, Lionel had to put special efforts into the engineering of these sets because, quite literally, pennies counted!

The low-end Lionel sets have been dismissed by many collectors as "junk" all too often, but before the collector assails Lionel for making "cheap" trains, then or now, he had better remember the place these trains held in Lionel's marketing strategy. It is highly unlikely that The Lionel Corporation would have survived as long as it did if it had made only its more expensive trains. In recent years there has been increasing interest in the low-end sets, which is regarded by many as a healthy development.

In real estate the phrase of paramount importance is "location, location, and location." In the field of train collecting the words are "condition" and "rarity." There is no substitute for condition, other than rarity, in the collecting field. Even common items bring a premium when they are in Mint, boxed condition. The easiest items or outfits to resell are top-condition pieces in clean component boxes. In addition, "Like New" and "Mint" examples of trains, as with other collectibles such as stamps and coins, will appreciate at a much faster pace than "Good" or "Excellent" items, proving themselves to be the best long-term investments.

In today's marketplace, I most strongly urge you to *scrutinize* your purchases. Most sellers overgrade their merchandise, and unfortunately, fakes are now rampant and are rapidly tainting our hobby. In addition there exists a condition among collectors in all hobbies that I refer to as "the Santa Claus syndrome." This syndrome clouds normal judgment and can cause collectors to view pieces of highly questionable authenticity, as well as sometimes downright fraudulent examples, as legitimate, because they *want* to believe, just like a child with Santa Claus. I urge you to be a "Doubting Thomas," and keep in mind an old adage, "If it is too good to be true, it probably isn't."

It is presumed by the author that a certain amount of prior knowledge of postwar Lionel trains exists with the reader. Whether a novice or an experienced collector, *Greenberg's Guide to Lionel Trains, 1945-1969, Volumes I and II* would be most valuable companions when reading this work as they give explicit and expanded information on Lionel trains and associated items.

I earnestly suggest reading the introduction to each year before delving into the chapter. The introduction will give you an overview of the entire year and explain some of the constants as well as the variables that were pertinent. Furthermore, I suggest that the reader browse through Charts I-IX included in this Prologue as they paint a relatively clear picture of the progression of events in Lionel's postwar era.

Chart I

A Quick Reference Guide to Set Gauges catalogued 1957 through 1969

(1945 offered its only outfit, 463W, in O Gauge; from 1946 through 1956 both O27 and O Gauges were offered. Super O was introduced in 1957.)

Year	O27	O	Super O	Year	O27	O	Super O
1957	Yes	Yes	Yes	1964	Yes	Yes	Yes
1958	Yes	No	Yes	1965	Yes	Yes	Yes
1959	Yes	No	Yes	1966	Yes	Yes	Yes
1960	Yes	No	Yes	1967	No production.		
1961	Yes	No	Yes	1968	Yes	No	No
1962	Yes	No	Yes	1969	Yes	No	No
1963	Yes	No	Yes				

Chart II

Nomenclature for Postwar Paper-type Boxes

A. Art Deco:	The original postwar component box with bold blue lettering that touched the tops and bottoms of the blue frames and outlines.
B. Early Classic:	The most notable box of the postwar era introduced in 1948 for the O27 line with smaller lettering; the city names "New York", "Chicago", and "San Francisco"; and with the stock number printed on all four sides.
C. Middle Classic:	Same as Early Classic, except the city name of "San Francisco" was eliminated. It was used from mid-1949 through 1955.
D. OPS Classic:	Same as Middle Classic, but with the inclusion of the OPS stamp. It was used in 1952.
E. Late Classic:	Same as Middle Classic, except that the stock number was eliminated from the four sides. It was used from 1956 through 1958.
F. Bold Classic:	Same as Late Classic, but with a much bolder-faced print on the end flaps. It was used for part of the1958 product line.

This photograph shows examples of the many styles of paper boxes used during the postwar period. Top to bottom, left to right: (1) side view, Art Deco; (2) side view, Early Classic; (3) side view, Middle Classic; (4) top view, OPS Classic; (5) side view, Late Classic with the stock number deleted from the sides; (6) end view, Bold Classic; (7) end view, Late Classic; (8) top view, Perforated Picture; (9) bottom view, same for both Orange Perforated and Orange Picture; (10) top view, Orange Perforated; (11) top view, Orange Picture; (12) bottom view, Cellophane Front; (13) top view, Cellophane Front; (14) side view, early version of Hillside Orange Picture that showed only the new corporate name "The Lionel Toy Corporation"; (15) side view, standard version of Hillside Orange Picture; (16) top and bottom views, same for both Hagerstown and Hillside Checkerboard; (17) end view, Hagerstown Checkerboard; (18) end view, Hillside Checkerboard.

G. Glossy Classic: A scarce box that surfaced in 1958. It was made in the Classic design, but was printed on coated stock similar to what was introduced in 1959. The 3424 Wabash brakeman, for example, occasionally came in this type of box.

H. Orange Perforated: A dramatic change in graphics that was a total departure from the classic design. The box was orange coated stock that had a tear-out perforated front panel. It was used in 1959 and 1960.

I. Perforated Picture: This box occasionally surfaced in 1961 and 1962. It was not regularly used, but was simply a means by which to deplete unfinished, perforated-front "raw" stock. It sometimes appears with a rolling stock item, but its use was most prevalent for early issue Presidential passenger cars.

J. Orange Picture: A variation of the Orange Perforated without perforations and with a picture of a steam and F-3 locomotive on the front, and the city names "New York" and "Chicago". It was used from 1961 to 1964 and included the phrase "The Lionel Corporation".

K. Hillside Orange Picture: Similar to Orange Picture, but "Hillside" replaces "New York" and "Chicago". It was used for part of the 1965 product line and included the new corporate name, "The Lionel Toy Corporation".

L. Cellophane Front: This was Lionel's attempt to make package contents visible by adding a cellophane window to the front of the box. The stock number was no longer printed on the end flaps as part of the manufacturing process; it was now rubber stamped and was used in 1966.

M. Hagerstown Checkerboard: Another dramatic change in graphics. This 1968 box had a Lionel checkerboard pattern with "Hagerstown" printed at the bottom of the end flaps and a rubber-stamped stock number.

N. Hillside Checkerboard: Same as Hagerstown Checkerboard, except that "Hillside" replaced "Hagerstown" in 1969.

Chart III

A Quick Reference Guide to Dating Rolling Stock Boxes

1945: Art Deco type with bold lettering. Many boxes were overstamped prewar issues.

1946: Art Deco type with bold lettering.

1947: Same as 1946, but with Toy Manufacturers Association logo.

1948–early 1949: Introduction of the Early Classic box of the postwar era with smaller lettering; the stock number printed on all four sides; and the city names "New York", "Chicago", and "San Francisco".

Mid-1949–1954: Same as 1948 to early 1949, but "San Francisco" eliminated.

1952: Same as mid-1949 to 1954, but with the OPS stamping.

1955: Same as mid-1949 to 1954, but with some major design, size, and liner changes.

    A. Liners eliminated from all steam engines, not to reappear until the reissue of the 773 Hudson in 1964.

    B. Liners eliminated from all tenders.

    C. Liners eliminated from all the F-3 power and tender units.

    D. Liners eliminated from all the 2500 series passenger cars.

    E. Redesigned smaller single-piece cardboard insert for the 6419 work caboose and for the new-issue 6119 series work cabooses.

    F. Wraparound liner eliminated from the diesel switchers in favor of two small cardboard filler pieces.

    G. Redesigned, less complex single-piece cardboard insert for the 6560 cranes.

1956–1957: Same as 1955, but the stock number was eliminated from the four sides.

1958: Same as 1955, but some with bolder-faced type on the end flaps.

1959–1960: Solid orange with tear-out perforated front.

1961–1964: Orange and white with picture of a steam and F-3 locomotive on the front, and the city names "New York" and "Chicago". Earliest issues were a distinctly darker orange.

1965: Same as 1961-1964, but "Hillside" replaces "New York" and "Chicago" and with the new corporate name, "The Lionel Toy Corporation".

1966: Cellophane see-through front.

1967: No production.

1968: Lionel checkerboard pattern with "Hagerstown" on the end flaps.

1969: Same as 1968, but with "Hillside" on the end flaps.

Chart IV

A Quick Reference Guide to Dating Trucks

1945–mid-1946:	Staple-end truck with early coil coupler mounted with a pivot stud and a horseshoe clip.
Mid-1946–1947:	Same as 1945 to mid-1946, but with a late coil coupler.
1948–1949:	Staple-end truck with a magnetic coupler without the extra hole in the activator flap.
1950–late 1951:	Same as 1948-1949, but with the extra hole in the activator flap.
Late 1951–1954:	Introduction of the bar-end truck with a pivot stud and magnetic coupler.
1955:	A transition year that saw the introduction of both the new bar-end truck mounted with a push clip and the extended tab coupler.
1956:	Same as 1955, but with a silver knuckle pin.
1957–mid-1961:	Another transition period that began with the phasing out of metal trucks on O27 rolling stock, and the introduction of the early plastic AAR truck with a metal knuckle and silver pin.
1959:	Introduction of the arch bar truck that was developed for the General set, and the inexpensive Advance Catalogue and uncatalogued sets.
Mid-1961–1962:	Same as 1959, but a plastic knuckle replaced the metal knuckle.
Late 1962–1963:	Same as mid-1961 to 1962, but with a plastic, self-contained Delrin knuckle that eliminated the need for a knuckle pin. Earliest examples had an integral copper metal spring that was soon replaced by a less-expensive plastic spring.
Late 1963–1969:	Introduction of the late AAR truck with the axle ends visible when viewed from the bottom, and with a self-contained Delrin knuckle.

For more detailed information on trucks, please refer to *Greenberg's Guide to Lionel Trains, 1945-1969, Volume 1, seventh edition.*

Two versions of the staple-end truck are shown On the left are side and bottom views of a 1946-1947 era truck with a late coil coupler, activated through a sliding shoe by a 1019 or an RCS. . On the right are side and bottom views of the last (1950-1951) version of the staple-end truck. Note the hole in the activator flap and the rivet with its flared end down.

Two versions of the bar-end truck are shown. On the left are side and bottom views showing the 1955 changes that eliminated the pivot stud and added an extended tab to facilitate uncoupling. This truck was fastened to the car by means of a truck mounting clip. On the right are side and bottom views of the first edition of the bar-end truck introduced in 1952. This truck was mounted with a pivot stud and horseshoe washer. Notice the rivet passing through the activator plate has its round end down. The example shown here was attached first to a metal plate and then the plate was fastened to a car, as in the 6511 pipe car.

Chart V

A Quick Reference Guide to Dating O Gauge Outfit Boxes

1945   Conventional tan with paste-on label.

1946   Same as 1945

1947   Same as 1945.

1948   Same as 1945.

1949   Conventional tan with orange and blue printing directly on the box.

1950   Conventional tan with an orange field framed in blue with blue printing and most with the retail price.

1951   Conventional tan with blue frame only and blue printing, either with or without the OPS price stamping.

1952   Same as 1951.

1953   Conventional tan with red frame, blue printing, a large circled-L, and the retail price.

1954   Same as 1953.

1955   Same as 1953, but without the retail price and the phrase "1955 Outfit" either within or outside of the blue frame on box end.

1956   A dramatic change — the introduction of the tan-gray basket weave look.

1957   Same as 1956.

1958–1963   No production.

1964   Conventional tan with black rubber-stamped number, and the early release of the 1965-style box.

1965   Conventional type, solid white with orange lettering, except outfit 12800 which was packed in a Type D display-style box.

1966   Same as 1965.

1967–1969   No production.

Chart VI

A Quick Reference Guide to Dating O27 Gauge Outfit Boxes

(O27 and O outfit boxes were the same for all years 1946 through 1957.)

1958   Tan-gray basket weave look that originated in 1956.

1959   Introduction of the attached perforated-lid Type A, B, and C display boxes on a yellow background for the low and moderate outfits. Better outfits were packaged in a conventional-type box (also on a yellow background) while the Advance Catalogue sets came in a unique Type A display-style box on a white background.

1960   A combination year that included some outfits with Type A, B, and C yellow background display-style boxes the same as in 1959, and others with new half-orange, half-white graphics that included a sketch of a 4-6-2 Pacific steam engine on the upper portion of the lid.

1961   Low and moderate the same as 1960 with the half-orange, half-white graphics in Type A or B only, while the better sets were packaged in a conventional-type solid orange box. The Advance Catalogue sets came in a Type A display-style box on a white background with deep red print and graphics that were later adopted for the 1963 line.

1962   Same as 1961.

1963   Low and moderate outfits in a Type A display style with *new* orange and white graphics. The box lid pictured a small Hudson-type steam engine and a Santa Fe F-3. The better sets were packaged in a conventional-type tan corrugated box.

1964   The same artwork as 1963, but now the top was completely unattached and lifted off. This is referred to as the Type D display box.

1965   Type D display-style box with Hillside logo and new graphics. A 2037 steam engine pulling a string of freight cars was now pictured on a white background.

1966   Same as 1965.

1967   No production.

1968   Type D display-style box with special Hagerstown graphics.

1969   Conventional two-tier type on white background with red and blue printing and a picture of the outfit pasted on one end.

Description Key for display-type boxes:

Type A — Perforated attached top with interior channels or cardboard dividers.
Type B — Perforated attached top with one-piece die-cut interior filler.
Type C — Perforated attached top with no interior channels but with component boxes.
Type D — Lift-off top with interior channels.

Chart VII

A Quick Reference Guide to Dating Super O Outfit Boxes

1957	Conventional-type, two-tier, tan-brown basket weave look with motive power scenes on all four sides.
1958	Same as 1957.
1959	Same motive power scenes as 1957, but on a solid yellow background.
1960	Same motive power scenes as 1957, but on a background of solid orange coated stock.
1961	Same coloration as 1960, but the motive power scenes were deleted from the four sides.
1962	Same as 1961.
1963	Same as 1961.
1964	Outfit 13150 only in a conventional tan box.
1965	Outfit 13150 only in a conventional tan box.
1966	Outfit 13150 only in a conventional tan box.
1967	No production.
1968	No production.
1969	No production.

Note: Occasionally a nondescript tan conventional-type outfit box surfaces with a regular production set number in years that it should not. One can assume that these may have been special packing requests by a customer, such as a company that did mail-order business, or the limited numbers packed did not warrant the special ordering or reordering of a standard outfit box.

Chart VIII

A Quick Reference Guide to Dating 6464 Series Boxcars

Type I	The original production body mold introduced in 1953 with a full complement of eight rows of exterior rivet detail.
Type II-A	A revised version of the Type I that appeared in 1954 in which some rivet detail was eliminated to facilitate heat stamping of the enlarged and increasing amount of graphics.
Type II-B	Similar to Type II-A with some faint roof lines visible. These lines were the result of a die modification, made in 1955, to accommodate the ice hatch of the 6352 Pacific Fruit Express reefer that was included with the 352 ice station accessory.
Type III	A major revision that in essence created a new body mold. It was introduced late in 1958, and was considerably lighter in weight, had interior roof ribs, and had rivet detail similar to Types II-A and II-B. The ice hatch lines also disappeared because production on the 6352 had ceased.
Type IV	Similar to Type III, but with additional rivet detail removed. It was introduced in 1960 and would become the dominant body mold for the remainder of the decade.

Note: The original single-block door was changed in 1955 to a five-block door in order to accommodate the graphics on the new -275 State of Maine boxcar. The older single-block doors surface on regular production as late as 1957 as Lionel continued to deplete dated inventory.

Chart IX

The Super O Operating Envelopes

39-5	The basic package from 1957-1958 @ $3.50 retail (column 1, bottom).
39-10	A special envelope from 1958 @ $6.95 retail (column 2, top).
39-15	The same as 39-20 @ $5.25 retail but with an extra remote-control blade (not pictured).
39-20	A special envelope from 1957-1958 @ $4.75 retail (column 1, top and middle). Notice the different size of type that was used on column 1, top envelope, in 1957 only.
39-25	The basic package from 1959 forward @ $3.95 retail (column 2, middle and bottom, and column 3, top and middle). Notice that the No. 61 and No. 62 have been replaced with a No. 43; No. 39-7 instruction sheet replaced No. 39-2; and power bus/blade connectors were eliminated after 1960 (column 3, top and middle).
39-35	The special envelope from 1959 forward @ $5.95 retail. Contents similar to 39-20, but with the new 1959 revisions (column 3, bottom).

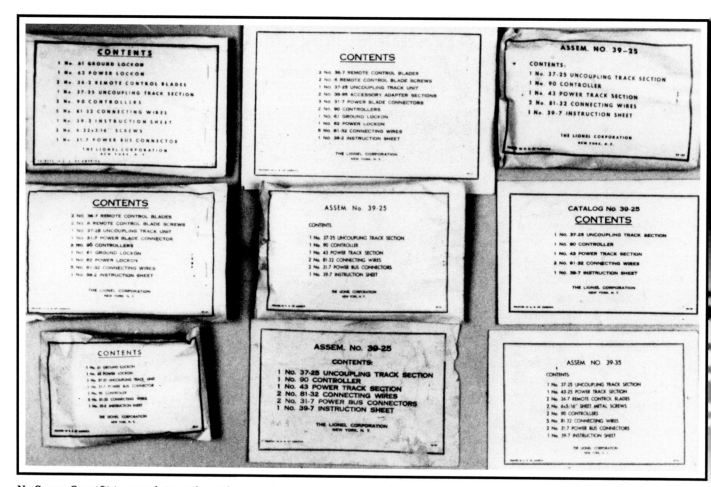

No Super O outfit is complete without the appropriate operating envelope. Reviewing these envelopes enables one to chronicle the history of Super O track. No. 61 and No. 62 power and ground lockons were soon replaced by an integral No. 43 power track section, and power bus/blade connectors were completely eliminated after 1960. Of particular interest is envelope 39-10 (column 2, top) from 1958 that contained No. 38 accessory adaptor tracks. They were included in only one set, outfit 2511W, and were essential to the operation of the 3424 Wabash brakeman. M. Sokol Collection.

1945

PRELUDE TO AN ERA

by Robert Swanson

World War II ended in August 1945 and Lionel returned to peacetime train production. During the fall of 1945 Lionel printed a four-page catalogue, actually a single, folded 11" x 17" sheet printed on both sides. This catalogue presented a single train set, number 463W, which would be available for Christmas 1945. As sometimes happened both before and after the war, there were discrepancies between what was listed and pictured in the catalogue and what was actually produced. Decisions about the numbering of cars were evidently made at the very last minute.

The big news for 1945 was the introduction of knuckle couplers and die-cast trucks with solid steel wheels. This reflected Lionel's strategic decision that postwar production would not contain two entirely separate lines of trains — inexpensive toys for boys, and expensive scale models for adults. Instead, production would be comprised of a single line

of trains, detailed and realistic, but with sets still priced in the $20 to $75 range.

The 463W set contained mostly prewar items which were now equipped with the new truck and coupler assembly. The single exception was the 2452 gondola. This car was entirely new with a highly detailed molded plastic body mounted on a stamped tinplate frame.

Packaging of the 463W set followed prewar practice. The set box was tan corrugated cardboard with the number "463W-2" printed directly on the box in black ink. An orange, blue, and white label was pasted on one side of the box which identified the set as an O Gauge freight set with built-in whistle.

Many times leftover prewar boxes, on which the correct item number was overstamped in black ink, were used for the

The 1945 catalogue showed set 463W in fine detail. However, the actual components differed in several notable ways from the listings.

1
9
4
5

engine and cars. Since the 2452 gondola was a totally new car, it always came in a new box with no overstamping.

Greenberg's Guide to Lionel Trains, 1945-1969, Volume II, second edition features an article entitled "The Real Beginnings of the Postwar Era: Lionel's Set 463W in 1945", and has additional photographs of the components of outfit 463W.

463W	O Gauge	$33.50 Retail

Contents: 224 steam locomotive with headlight; 2466W whistle tender; 2458 automobile car; 2452 gondola with barrels; 2555 Sunoco single-dome tank car; 2457 illuminated Pennsylvania N5 caboose; eight curved and three straight track; RCS uncoupling/operating section; and a 167 whistle controller.

Comments: The 224 locomotive was the same as prewar production except that it had black rather than shiny handrails and a long black drawbar. The drawbar had a very short turned-down section which was inserted directly into an oval slot in the tender floor. The 2466W tender (not 2224W as listed in the catalogue) had no mating drawbar in 1945. It had white heat-stamped lettering rather than the usual postwar silver lettering and, like the locomotive, it also had black handrail wires.

The tender and four freight cars were equipped with early flying shoe knuckle couplers and machined thick axles. The solid steel wheels were either whirly backed Type 1A trucks or deep dish Type 1B trucks. The regular postwar wheels, used on Type 1C (regular wheels, thick axles) and later trucks, were not introduced until 1946.

VG   LN

The new 2452 plastic-bodied gondola contained four 0209 barrels, which were the two-piece prewar variety that could be opened. The 2458 automobile car and 2555 tank car were both boxed with the numbers that appeared in the catalogue. However, the cars themselves were actually marked with the prewar numbers "2758" and "2755".

The 2457 caboose was marked and boxed as listed in the set contents, but not as pictured. The catalogue shows a stripped-down version of the Pennsylvania caboose with no window inserts, cupola end windows, smokestack, or rear coupler. The 2457 produced in 1945 was actually a premium caboose which included all of these deluxe features. Most cabooses were bright red with black window frames; however, a few used leftover prewar 2757 bodies that were brown with red window frames. Most of these brown cabooses have the Pennsylvania lettering offset about 1/4 inch to the left instead of being centered between the windows.

An instruction book was also included with each 463W set even though it was not listed in the catalogue. Again leftover prewar inventory was used. The instruction books observed to date were all marked with a 1940 copyright date and either a 1941 or 1942 reprint date. No instruction books have been found with 1945 dates.

The RCS remote-control track section was packed with its own instruction sheet. Most sets contained one which was dated 11-45 and described the new knuckle couplers. However, some early sets contained a prewar instruction sheet dated 2-41 that showed box type couplers. In these sets a 4" x 4-1/2" folded red tag with a red braided string was also included, which described the new knuckle couplers.

550   1100

1946

THE START OF SOMETHING GOOD

by Robert Swanson

In 1946 Lionel resumed production of a complete line of electric trains and related items, and twenty-three sets were available, ranging in price from $24.95 to $87.50. The only type of engine manufactured during this year was the steam engine. All rolling stock was designed to operate on O27 or O Gauge tubular track. Gone forever was the Lionel manufacture of OO Gauge, Standard Gauge, and solid T-rail track. 1946 production consisted of a single line of compatible equipment that was significantly more detailed and realistic than Lionel's prewar tinplate production.

Smoke and die-cast trucks with knuckle couplers were the two features most highly publicized in 1946. But there were many new items, probably more than in any single year in the production of Lionel trains. New steam power included the 726 Berkshire and the 2020 and 671 Pennsylvania steam turbines, all with smoke. The 221 was a new streamlined engine for the inexpensive end of the O27 line. On the other hand, two prewar-based locomotives pictured in the catalogue were not produced: the 703 Hudson and the 403 steam 0-6-0 switcher.

A number of new highly detailed cars with die-cast metal frames were introduced in 1946. These included the 2411 flatcar with pipes, the 2419 and 2420 work cabooses, and the 2460 crane car, whose earliest issues were the scarce gray cab variation. The 3451 operating log car and the 3459 operating ore car were also new issue. The new 2465 Sunoco two-dome tank car, 2454 boxcar, and 3454 operating merchandise car all had highly detailed molded plastic bodies mounted on stamped sheet metal frames, a design format that was introduced in 1945 with the 2452 gondola. The 1946 gondola was catalogued in two ways: 2452X came with neither brakewheels nor barrels while the 2452 had both of the aforementioned. The 3454 was catalogued in tuscan, and a few rare preproduction examples do exist. It was painted silver and lettered in blue as part of regular production, but a few red-lettered variations also exist. New six-wheel trucks with knuckle couplers and solid steel (sintered iron) wheels were used on the 2625 Irvington passenger cars, 2426 die-cast tenders and 2460 crane cars. All tenders, except the 221, were lettered "Lionel Lines".

In 1946, Lionel also introduced the ultimate in remote control — the 4109WS electronic set. Engine direction, whistle operation, and individual car couplers could be controlled anywhere on the layout by miniature radio frequency receivers mounted in the tender and in each car. While technically outstanding, this much publicized set did not sell well, either because of its high price ($75) or the public's perception that it was too complicated.

While the new items received most of the publicity in 1946, it must be recognized that much of the 1946 production consisted of prewar items, with little or no modification other than the new die-cast trucks and knuckle couplers. Since sets using these items required little or no new tooling, they represent most of the very early (spring) 1946 production. Tinplate cars, both freight and passenger, are the ones usually found with the early flying shoe coil couplers. They are usually found in sets headed by either a 1666 or 224 steam engine. By the time the new locomotives with smoke units were in production, the fragile flying shoe design had been replaced by the more rugged Type 3A truck and coil coupler. Consequently, sets containing locomotives with smoke units rarely contained cars with flying shoe couplers.

Several other "running changes" were made during the 1946 production year. Berkshire locomotive production started with the "large stack" motor and tender with white lettering. Production soon shifted to "short stack" motors (the number of field and armature laminations was reduced) and tenders with silver lettering. The 2454 Pennsylvania boxcar was phased out and replaced with the 2454 Baby Ruth boxcar. Early in the year, rare center-decal versions of the 2465 Sunoco tank car quickly gave way to the usual two-decal marking. Leftover 2758 and 2755 tank car bodies from 1945 (maybe even prewar) were quickly used up and replaced by correctly numbered 2458 and 2555 bodies. Even transformers were changed. Evidently the 60-watt 1041 was not up to the task of powering the 2020 turbine with its smoke bulb, so it was replaced by the more powerful 75-watt 1042 transformer.

Boxes and packaging in 1946 basically represented carry-overs of prewar practices. In fact, many items were shipped in overstamped prewar boxes; there were just too many other things to contend with in this year of reverting to full peacetime production. All things considered, it was a truly outstanding year for Lionel.

1400   **O27 Gauge**   **$30 Retail**

Contents: 221 steam locomotive with headlight; 221T New York Central non-whistle tinplate tender; two 2430 blue Pullmans; 2431 blue observation; eight curved and three straight track; 1019 uncoupling/operating section; and a 1037 40-watt transformer.

Comments: Though shown as green in the catalogue, the new 221 Empire State locomotive and tender were painted gray in 1946. Some early locomotives were shipped with aluminum-colored wheels rather than the usual blackened wheels. Tenders, either with or without whistle, always came with a Type 3A coupler truck. On the other hand, the 1946 blue and silver passenger cars always came with Type 1C trucks (early coil design, thick axles, and regular wheels). All

VG   LN

1 9 4 6

1946 tinplate passenger cars also had rubber-stamped silver lettering. Evidently the blue cars were manufactured early in 1946 along with the green and brown passenger cars, and then held until the tooling was complete for the new 221 locomotive later in the year (resulting in tenders with the later coil coupler design). Tenders with early coil couplers have not been observed to date.   **425   850**

1400W   **O27 Gauge**   **$35.95 Retail**

Contents: Same as 1400, but with a whistle tender and a 60-watt 1041 transformer.   **450   875**

1401   **O27 Gauge**   **$24.95 Retail**

Contents: 1654 steam locomotive with headlight; 1654T non-whistle tinplate tender; 2452X gondola; 2465 Sunoco two-dome tank car; 2472 non-illuminated Pennsylvania N5 caboose; eight curved and one straight track; 1019 uncoupling/operating section; and a 1037 40-watt transformer.

Comments: The 1654 locomotive and tinplate tender were prewar designs. Except for the drawbar and tender trucks, they could have been made from leftover parts. The 2465 was the only totally new-for-1946 car in the set. The 2452X gondola evolved from the 2452, introduced in 1945, from which the brakewheels and barrels were eliminated. The red 2472 caboose was derived from the brown prewar 2672.

This was the least expensive set Lionel sold in 1946, and evidently high demand required at least two different production runs. Early production sets came equipped with Type 2 flying shoe trucks, even on the tender. Later production sets had mostly Type 3A trucks with more recently designed coil couplers.   **75   125**

1401W   **O27 Gauge**   **$30.95 Retail**

Contents: Same as 1401, but with a whistle tender and a 1041 60-watt transformer.   **90   150**

1402   **O27 Gauge**   **$30 Retail**

Contents: 1666 steam locomotive with headlight; 2466T non-whistle tender; two 2440 illuminated Pullmans; 2441 illuminated observation; eight curved and three straight track; 1019 uncoupling/operating section; and a 1037 40-watt transformer.

Comments: The 1666 locomotive was a prewar carryover, except that the cab floor was extended with a curved section to create the illusion that it had closer spacing with the tender. All evidence to date indicates that green illuminated 2440 and 2441 passenger cars were always included in this set, and that the blue and silver cars were simply catalogue illustrations. Like the blue and silver cars in outfit 1400, the 1946 green passenger cars always had rubber-stamped silver lettering and Type 1C trucks (thick axles and regular wheels).   **325   650**

1402W   **O27 Gauge**   **$35.95 Retail**

Contents: Same as 1402, but with a whistle tender and a 1041 60-watt transformer.   **350   675**

1403   **O27 Gauge**   **$30 Retail**

Contents: 221 steam locomotive with headlight; 221T New York Central non-whistle tinplate tender; 2411 flatcar with pipes; 2465 Sunoco two-dome tank car; 2472 non-illuminated Pennsylvania N5 caboose; eight curved and three straight track; 1019 uncoupling/operating section; and a 1037 40-watt transformer.

Comments: The 221 Empire State locomotive was always painted gray, rather than green as pictured in the catalogue. In this set, the locomotive wheels were usually (if not always) black. The drivers had no stainless steel rims. The tender and cars were most often all equipped with Type 3A trucks, though occasionally a tank car surfaces with Type 2 trucks. This was the only O27 set to include the 2411 flatcar, which in 1946 carried a load of three metal pipes.   **250   450**

1403W   **O27 Gauge**   **$35.95 Retail**

Contents: Same as 1403, but with a whistle tender and a 1041 60-watt transformer.   **265   450**

1405   **O27 Gauge**   **$30 Retail**

Contents: 1666 steam locomotive with headlight; 2466T non-whistle tender; 2452X gondola; 2465 Sunoco two-dome tank car; 2472 non-illuminated Pennsylvania N5 caboose; eight curved and three straight track; 1019 uncoupling/operating section; and a 1037 40-watt transformer.

Comments: Except for the 1666 locomotive and 2466 tender, this set is identical to outfit 1401. Outfit 1405 was one of three O27 freight sets headed by the 1666 that was shown in the Spring 1946 catalogue. It is frequently found with components that have flying shoe couplers, indicating early 1946 production. A later production run, evidently much later in the year, resulted in sets with all Type 3A trucks (later type coil couplers).   **105   175**

1405W   **O27 Gauge**   **$35.95 Retail**

Contents: Same as 1405, but with a whistle tender and a 1041 60-watt transformer.   **120   200**

1407B   **O27 Gauge**   **$37.50 Retail**

Contents: 1665 steam switcher with headlight; 2403B slope-back bell-ringing tender; 2560 crane; 2452X gondola; 2419 work caboose; eight curved and five straight track; 1019 uncoupling/operating section; and a 1037 40-watt transformer.

VG   LN

Comments: The 1665 switcher was the number given to the prewar 1662 switcher which was now equipped with a knuckle coupler in front. The die-cast metal tender was also brought up to postwar standards to include both a knuckle coupler and die-cast trucks. Catalogue colors not withstanding, the 2560 crane car continued to be produced in prewar colors: yellow cab with red roof. The crane car is the only carry-over tinplate car which has not been observed with early flying shoe couplers. The explanation may be that it was always paired with the new 2419 work caboose, which probably was not ready for production until much later in the year.
                                              600   1000

1409   O27 Gauge $40 Retail

Contents: 1666 steam locomotive with headlight; 2466T non-whistle tender; 3559 operating coal car; 2465 Sunoco two-dome tank car; 3454 operating merchandise car; 2472 non-illuminated Pennsylvania N5 caboose; eight curved and five straight track; 1019 uncoupling/operating section; and a 1037 40-watt transformer.

Comments: This was an action-packed freight set containing two operating cars: the 3559 dump car and the 3454 merchandise car.

Apparently this set did not get into production as early as some other 1946 outfits. The evidence for this comes from the type of truck used on the 3454 merchandise car. Early 1946 production is usually evidenced by the inclusion of flying shoe trucks and couplers. 1946 versions of the merchandise car always have Type 3A trucks, indicating mid- to late 1946 production. When found intact, 1409 sets usually have a mixture of early and late coil coupler designs.   225   375

1409W   O27 Gauge $45.95 Retail

Contents: Same as 1409, but with a whistle tender and a 1041 60-watt transformer.   240   400

1411W   O27 Gauge $42.50 Retail

Contents: 1666 steam locomotive with headlight; 2466WX whistle tender; 2452X gondola; 2465 Sunoco two-dome tank car; 2454 boxcar; 2472 non-illuminated Pennsylvania N5 caboose; eight curved and three straight track; 1019 uncoupling/operating section; and a 1041 60-watt transformer.

Comments: This was the same as set 1405W except for the addition of a 2454 boxcar. Early production of this set came with Type 2 trucks on the tender and all cars. Outfits produced early in 1946 also included the scarce 2454 Pennsylvania boxcar with either orange or brown doors. Later production had rolling stock with Type 3A trucks and the common 2454 Baby Ruth boxcar. Some sets turn up with a mixture of Type 2 and Type 3 trucks, and usually contain the Baby Ruth boxcar.

	VG	LN
Pennsylvania	225	375
Baby Ruth	135	225

VG   LN

1413WS   O27 Gauge $55 Retail

Contents: 2020 steam turbine locomotive with headlight and smoke; 2466WX whistle tender; 2452X gondola; 2465 Sunoco two-dome tank car; 2454 boxcar; 2472 non-illuminated Pennsylvania N5 caboose; eight curved and three straight track; 1019 uncoupling/operating section; and a 1041 60-watt transformer.

Comments: Outfit 1413WS had exactly the same contents as 1411W except that the new 2020 steam turbine with smoke replaced the non-smoking 1666. When listed separately, the 2020 locomotive was priced only $9.75 more than the 1666. However, Lionel anticipated that the demand for sets with a smoking locomotive would be tremendous, and therefore priced this set $12.50 higher than 1411W.

Though pictured in the catalogue with an orange door Baby Ruth boxcar with a Lionel logo to the right of the door, this set usually came with the common brown door Baby Ruth boxcar with the Pennsylvania logo to the right. There is one known exception which reinforces the rule "Never say always." A 1413WS set has been reported that included a brown door 2454 Pennsylvania boxcar. What is even more unusual is that the tender and all of the cars contain early flying shoe type trucks, indicative of Spring 1946 production. Maybe a few "salesman sample" outfits were put together using preproduction sample 2020 engines and the rest of the components from the otherwise identical 1411W set.   275   475

1415WS   O27 Gauge $67.50 Retail

Contents: 2020 steam turbine locomotive with headlight and smoke; 2020W whistle tender; 3459 operating ore car; 3454 operating merchandise car; 2465 Sunoco two-dome tank car; 2472 non-illuminated Pennsylvania N5 caboose; ten curved and five straight track; 1019 uncoupling/operating section; pair 1121 remote-control switches; and a 1041 60-watt transformer.

Comments: This action-packed set included smoke, whistle, two operating cars, and a pair of remote-control switches. The 3454 merchandise car was painted silver instead of brown as illustrated, and the 3459 was the scarce silver variation. The result was a freight set with an all-silver consist except for the red caboose. The 3454 merchandise car always came with Type 3A couplers, which dates this set as late 1946 production.   575   975

1417WS   O27 Gauge $60 Retail

Contents: 2020 steam turbine locomotive with headlight and smoke; 2020W whistle tender; 2465 Sunoco two-dome tank car; 3451 operating log car; 2560 crane; 2419 work caboose; eight curved and five straight track; 1019 uncoupling/operating section; and a 1041 60-watt transformer.

Comments: A work train headed by a high speed steam turbine locomotive! This was certainly not a prototypical assignment for the real S-1, but Lionel frequently took some license in assembling sets. Since they had only one smoking

1
9
4
6

	VG	LN

locomotive for the O27 line in 1946, Lionel was determined to make as much use of it as they could.

Along with the new 2020 locomotive, this set included two new cars with die-cast frames, the 3451 operating log car and the 2419 work caboose. The 2560 crane car was not brown as illustrated, but had the conventional yellow cab and red roof. **350   575**

1419WS　　O27 Gauge　　$85 Retail

Contents: 2020 steam turbine locomotive with headlight and smoke; 2020W whistle tender; 3459 operating ore car; 2452X gondola; 2560 crane; 2419 work caboose; 97 remote-control operating coal elevator; ten curved and five straight track; 1019 uncoupling/operating section; pair 1121 remote-control switches; and a 1041 60-watt transformer.

Comments: This is one of two all-out premium O27 sets that Lionel offered in 1946. At $85, it was obvious that price was no object. Besides smoke, whistle, operating ore car, and a pair of switches, this set included a number 97 operating coal elevator. Along with a gondola, crane car, and work caboose, what more could a young engineer want in 1946?

Probably more straight track (the set included just six sections counting the remote-control track) and a larger transformer (a 75-watt 1042 transformer was usually substituted for the listed 60-watt 1041). **900   1500**

1421WS　　O27 Gauge　　$85 Retail

Contents: 2020 steam turbine locomotive with headlight and smoke; 2020W whistle tender; 3451 operating log car; 2465 Sunoco two-dome tank car; 3454 merchandise car; 2472 non-illuminated Pennsylvania N5 caboose; 164 remote-control log loader; ten curved and five straight track; 1019

Puffs SMOKE! — and whistles like a real train.

No. 1419WS

Brand New Lionel operating Dump Car — operated by electric remote control.

Two De Luxe LIONEL Freight Outfits powered by New Pennsylvania Steam Turbine Locomotives

These are outfits of exquisite beauty. An exceptional model railroad system with operating accessories. They are masterpieces of scale detailing. All cars are equipped with the New LIONEL exclusive electro magnetic remote control real R.R. Knuckle Couplers, solid steel wheels, and die cast trucks.

No. 1421WS

These sets are distinguished as the two most expensive O27 sets ever sold by Lionel ($85 each) and contain premium accessories and switches. Set 1419WS is shown with a silver dump — it sometimes came this way — and with a 2560 crane with a tuscan cab. The 2560 cab was actually painted light yellow with a red roof.

	VG	LN

uncoupling/operating section; pair 1121 remote-control switches; and a 1041 60-watt transformer.

Comments: Set 1421WS was the second premium O27 set priced at $85. Besides the smoking 2020 turbine locomotive, its most outstanding feature was a 164 operating log loader and a 3451 operating log dump car. A silver (not brown as pictured) 3454 operating merchandise car and a pair of remote-control switches added to the action. Lionel evidently made very few of these high-priced premium O27 sets and even fewer have survived intact. Once separated from the set, however, none of the individual items can be considered rare or unique. They were all available for separate sale and were also used in other sets. **725 1200**

2100	**O Gauge**	**$37.50 Retail**

Contents: 224 steam locomotive with headlight; 2466T non-whistle tender; two 2442 illuminated brown Pullmans; 2443 illuminated brown observation; eight curved and three straight track; and an RCS uncoupling/operating section.

Comments: There is ample evidence to confirm very early 1946 production of this outfit. The 224 locomotive frequently had black handrails, and a few sets have been observed with complete leftover 1945 locomotives and tenders

using the long drawbar which connected directly to the tender floor. The tenders were equipped with Type 1B trucks (dished wheels and thick axles).

The passenger cars contained in this set make an interesting study. The cars are listed as 2442 Pullmans and 2443 observation, but are clearly shown in the catalogue as green cars. Lionel made 2442 and 2443 cars in 1946, but they were always brown. They also made green passenger cars in 1946, but they were always numbered "2440" and "2441". 1946 tinplate passenger cars can always be identified (regardless of color) by silver rubber-stamped lettering and Type 1C trucks (thick axles and regular wheels). Based on the observations of several sets (including one boxed set) and the relative scarcity of brown cars compared to green cars, it is believed that Lionel took advantage of the confusion created in the catalogue and actually packaged two different versions of the 2100 set. One version had the brown cars (2442 and 2443) as listed in the catalogue. The other version had the green cars (2440 and 2441) as pictured. **350 700**

2100W	**O Gauge**	**$43.50 Retail**

Contents: Same as 2100, but with a whistle tender and a 167 whistle controller. **375 725**

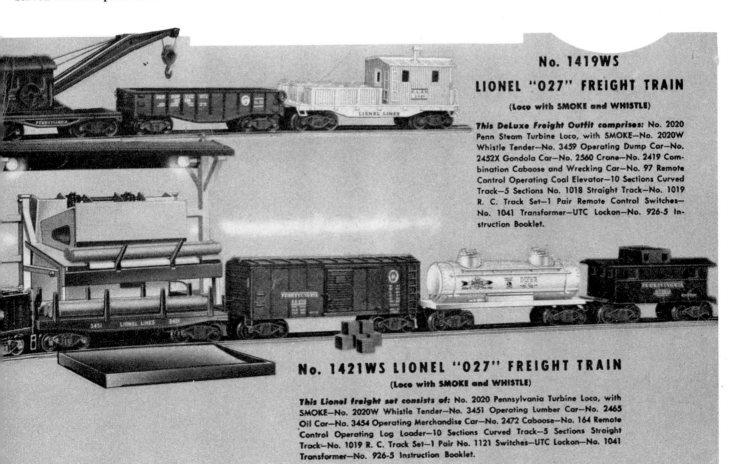

No. 1419WS
LIONEL "O27" FREIGHT TRAIN
(Loco with SMOKE and WHISTLE)

This DeLuxe Freight Outfit comprises: No. 2020 Penn Steam Turbine Loco, with SMOKE—No. 2020W Whistle Tender—No. 3459 Operating Dump Car—No. 2452X Gondola Car—No. 2560 Crane—No. 2419 Combination Caboose and Wrecking Car—No. 97 Remote Control Operating Coal Elevator—10 Sections Curved Track—5 Sections No. 1018 Straight Track—No. 1019 R. C. Track Set—1 Pair Remote Control Switches—No. 1041 Transformer—UTC Lockon—No. 926-5 Instruction Booklet.

No. 1421WS LIONEL "O27" FREIGHT TRAIN
(Loco with SMOKE and WHISTLE)

This Lionel freight set consists of: No. 2020 Pennsylvania Turbine Loco, with SMOKE—No. 2020W Whistle Tender—No. 3451 Operating Lumber Car—No. 2465 Oil Car—No. 3454 Operating Merchandise Car—No. 2472 Caboose—No. 164 Remote Control Operating Log Loader—10 Sections Curved Track—5 Sections Straight Track—No. 1019 R. C. Track Set—1 Pair No. 1121 Switches—UTC Lockon—No. 1041 Transformer—No. 926-5 Instruction Booklet.

	VG	LN

1946

2101   O Gauge $37.50 Retail

Contents: 224 steam locomotive with headlight; 2466T non-whistle tender; 2555 Sunoco single-dome tank car; 2452 gondola; 2457 illuminated Pennsylvania N5 caboose; eight curved and three straight track; and an RCS uncoupling/operating section.

Comments: At first glance, this outfit appears to be continued production of set 463W made in 1945, but with the 2458 automobile car removed. A study of the individual components shows this was generally not true. First, the 224 locomotive uses the postwar casting with the rounded back to the cab floor. The tender had a short drawbar for coupling to the engine and the Lionel Lines lettering was now in the usual postwar silver. Trucks were usually Type 1C (thick axle) or Type 2 (thin axle) though a few tenders show up with leftover Type 1B trucks.

The tank car was now correctly numbered "2555" and usually had either Type 1C or Type 2 trucks. The tank car frame had also been modified to strengthen it around the truck mounting point. 1946 gondola and caboose production are distinguished from 1945 by the use of either Type 1C or Type 2 trucks. The O Gauge gondolas now came with solid one-piece barrels and brakewheels, and cabooses generally had only one coupler in 1946.   **175**   **300**

2101W   O Gauge $43.50 Retail

Contents: Same as 2101, but with a whistle tender and a 167 whistle controller.   **195**   **325**

2103W   O Gauge $45 Retail

Contents: 224 steam locomotive with headlight; 2466W whistle tender; 2458 automobile car; 3559 operating coal car; 2555 Sunoco single-dome tank car; 2457 illuminated Pennsylvania N5 caboose; eight curved and three straight track; RCS uncoupling/operating section; and a 167 whistle controller.

Comments: While not shown in the Spring 1946 catalogue, this outfit was apparently produced during the same time period as the Spring 1946 sets. In fact, this set may have been a substitute for 1409W, which could not have been produced in the spring because the 3454 merchandise car was not available. 2103W sets equipped with Type 2 trucks, or mostly Type 2 with a sprinkling of Type 1C, are fairly easy to find. The linkage between the 2103W and the 1409W sets is the prewar-based 3559 dump car. Many examples of this car can be found today with Type 2 flying shoe trucks. This car was included in only two outfits catalogued in 1946 — 1409W and 2103W. With 3559 dump cars in production, but with 3454 merchandise cars delayed, Lionel probably realized they could not produce complete 1409W sets, but they did have all the components needed for 2103W set production.   **240**   **400**

	VG	LN

2105WS   O Gauge $50 Retail

Contents: 671 steam turbine locomotive with headlight and smoke; 2466W whistle tender; 2555 Sunoco single-dome tank car; 2454 Baby Ruth boxcar; 2457 illuminated Pennsylvania N5 caboose; eight curved and three straight track; RCS uncoupling/operating section; and a 167 whistle controller.

Comments: This was the least expensive but probably the most common O Gauge set with smoke that Lionel offered in 1946. The 671 Pennsylvania steam turbine was essentially the same as the 2020 except for the number. The tender and Baby Ruth boxcar were the same as those included in O27 outfits. A 2555 tank car and 2457 caboose with Type 3A couplers completed the set.   **325**   **550**

2110WS   O Gauge $75 Retail

Contents: 671 steam turbine locomotive with headlight and smoke; 2466W whistle tender; three 2625 Irvington Pullmans; eight curved and five straight track; RCS uncoupling/operating section; and a 167 whistle controller.

Comments: The prewar Irvington passenger cars returned, now equipped with knuckle couplers and pulled by a Pennsylvania steam turbine with smoke. All three passenger cars were identical. The Pennsylvania S-1 steam turbine locomotive was finally coupled to an appropriate consist. A truly realistic set, except for the tender which would be corrected in 1948.   **1400**   **2300**

2111WS   O Gauge $60 Retail

Contents: 671 steam turbine locomotive with headlight and smoke; 2466W whistle tender; 3459 operating ore car; 2411 flatcar with pipes; 2460 twelve-wheel crane; 2420 work caboose with searchlight; eight curved and five straight track; RCS uncoupling/operating section; and a 167 whistle controller.

Comments: Another work train headed (untypically) by a high speed steam turbine locomotive. But what a work train it was — four brand-new cars for 1946 all with highly detailed die-cast metal bases. This was the first outfit to contain the new twelve-wheel crane, whose earliest issues were the scarce gray cab variation. The 3459 automatic ore car was the scarce silver variation but not marked "B & O" as pictured in the catalogue. The rest of the illustrations seem to be accurate, much to Lionel's credit in a year when so many new items were being produced and changed.   **600**   **1000**

2113WS   O Gauge $67.50 Retail

Contents: 726 Berkshire steam locomotive with headlight and smoke; 2426W whistle tender; 2855 Sunoco single-dome tank car; 3854 operating merchandise car; 2857 illuminated caboose; eight curved and seven straight track; RCS uncoupling/operating section; and a 167 whistle controller.

VG   LN

VG   LN

Comments: Headed by the new smoking 2-8-4 Berkshire locomotive, this three-car freight set was quality all the way. The 3854 operating merchandise car was based on the prewar 1/4" scale boxcar with the operating merchandise mechanism and a roof hatch added. Production started with the car made essentially as pictured in the catalogue except the Pennsylvania logo was also brown, not black. The painted brown doors soon gave way to chemically-blackened doors. The blackened doors had much less friction against the painted car body and provided more reliable operation. The tank car was not the silver 2755 pictured, but the rare black 2855. Construction of the car was the same as 2755 and 2555 tank cars: die-cast frame, tinplate tank, and Bakelite dome. The black color and the 2855 number are what make this car so rare and desirable.

The caboose included in this set continues to cause considerable debate in train collecting circles. Considering all evidence, it seems that two different cabooses were shipped with set 2113W during 1946, but neither one was marked "2857" as listed in the catalogue. Mid-year production sets probably contained leftover 2957 prewar cabooses mounted on Type 3A coil coupler trucks. Once the supply of 2957 bodies was exhausted, which may have been very quickly, the rest of the 2113WS outfits were equipped with standard 2457 red illuminated cabooses.

With 2457	1200	2000
With 2957	1500	2500

2114WS O Gauge **$77.50 Retail**

Contents: 726 Berkshire steam locomotive with headlight and smoke; 2426W whistle tender; three 2625 Pullmans; eight curved and five straight track; RCS uncoupling/operating section; and a 167 controller.

Comments: Something old, something new; all good. Three prewar Irvington passenger cars, now equipped with knuckle couplers and numbered "2625", returned to the Lionel catalogue, and they were pulled by the powerful new Berkshire steam engine.

The 1946 edition of the 726 had double worm drive and machined stanchions to hold the handrails. Production started with the scarce large stack motor and a die-cast tender with white lettering. The number of iron laminations in the motor was soon reduced, resulting in the more common short stack motor. At about the same time the lettering on the tender changed from white to silver.

The passenger cars were essentially prewar frames and bodies equipped with new six-wheel trucks and knuckle couplers. Postwar cars show some subtle differences besides the truck and number change. The postwar cars were painted reddish-brown or maroon color, rather than the medium brown used on prewar cars. The "Lionel Lines" lettering was offset to the left in 1946, as pointed out in a recent article on the Madison cars by Tom Rollo (Volume II). Trucks on the 1946 cars can be further identified by the lack of four stake marks in the area where the knuckle coupler head is attached to the connecting support bar. These stake marks are present in all 1947 and later six-wheel trucks.   **1500   2500**

2115WS O Gauge **$87.50 Retail**

Contents: 726 Berkshire steam locomotive with headlight and smoke; 2426W whistle tender; 2458 automobile car; 3451 operating log car; 2460 twelve-wheel crane; 2420 work caboose with searchlight; eight curved and three straight track; RCS uncoupling/operating section; and a 167 whistle controller.

Comments: This was the final and most expensive set listed in the 1946 catalogue that was actually produced. It was one of two outfits to contain the new twelve-wheel crane. This work train set appears to be substantially over-priced, especially when compared to the other O Gauge work train, outfit 2111WS. The total value of the four cars listed in each set was exactly the same, $26.50. The price of the Berkshire when purchased separately was $37.50, only $2.50 more than the 671 steam turbine priced at $35. The 2115WS set was priced $27.50 higher than the 2111WS, but the customer received component items valued only $2.50 more. In fact, when priced separately all the items in set 2115WS add up to only $74.15. One wonders if the $87.50 price on the 1946 price sheet was a mistake. (Note that none of the items were unique to this set. They could all have been purchased separately or in other 1946 sets.)   **600   1000**

4109WS Electronic Set O Gauge
$75 Retail

Contents: 671R steam turbine locomotive with headlight and smoke; 4424W whistle tender; 4452 gondola; 4454 boxcar; 5459 automatic dump car; 4457 caboose; eight curved and four straight track; and an ECU-1 electronic control unit.

Comments: The electronic set 4109WS was the first outfit shown in the 1946 catalogue (page 2). It was a great technological advancement, but a marketing flop. Train buyers evidently did not think the play value of this set was commensurate with its complexity or price.

The items produced for the electronic set differed somewhat from those pictured in the 1946 catalogue. First, all rolling stock including the engine had a small circular Lionel logo decal affixed to each side which was color coded to match the colored buttons on the transmitter (Electronic Control Unit). These decals were not shown in the 1946 catalogue. In addition, the 5459 automatic dump car was pictured in silver, but was always made in black with white lettering. Furthermore, the 4454 boxcar was always painted orange and had Baby Ruth markings to the left of the door; it was not brown with Pennsylvania markings as shown. The gondola and caboose were made as shown except that most cabooses were equipped with two couplers, not just one.

In 1946, the 671R steam turbine differed from the standard 671 only in the addition of two black decals with a white "L", which were placed on the turbine on each side. The tender and cars differed from regular production by the inclusion of a miniature radio receiver in each car and two receivers in the tender (one for whistle operations and the second for control of the locomotive E-unit). The cars usually had special numbers stamped on them in the 4000 or 5000 series. However, boxcars with the standard 2454 number and gondolas with the

VG   LN

**1
9
4
6**

standard 2452 number have both been observed. Trucks in 1946 were typical of Type 3A production in that there were no stake marks where the knuckle was attached to the support plate, but they differed from standard production in several other respects. First, both trucks always had center-rail pickup rollers, but no sliding pickup shoes for uncoupler trucks. Second, the trucks were always equipped with grounding washers around the mounting stud to ensure a low-resis-

tance ground path to the car frame. Finally, the trucks were equipped with stainless steel axles to improve grounding.

Early 1946 electronic set production apparently started with unplated brass pickup rollers on all cars and the frequent use of blue or yellow insulated wire. As additional materials became available, pickup rollers were plated and less obtrusive black insulated wire was used. **500   1000**

1947

GOOD GETS BETTER

by Robert Swanson

At first glance, the 1947 consumer catalogue seems to show 1947 products as primarily 1946 carry-over items, enhanced by a couple of new engines and cars. Nothing could be further from the truth. What the catalogue does not tell is that a number of the new-for-1946 items had to be substantially redesigned and retooled. In fact, the only 1946 locomotive carried over to 1947 was the lowly 1654, the bottom-of-the-line steam engine used in only one O27 outfit.

The only totally new engine for 1947 was the 2332 Pennsylvania GG-1 electric. This was the single-motored version with the AC horn which would be produced through 1949. The 675 and 2025 steam engines with smoke that were introduced in 1947 actually evolved from the prewar 225. Although the 726 Berkshire and 671/2020 turbines appear to be 1946 carry-overs, they actually were substantially re-engineered with new smoke units, new single worm drive motors, vertical E-units, and different boiler details. The 221 Empire State locomotive not only changed from gray to black, but the body casting was modified to make the pilot stronger. The drive wheels on the 221 were also changed in 1947 to stainless steel rims like those on the more expensive locomotives. All tenders, except the 221, were still lettered "Lionel Lines".

Two new freight cars were introduced in the 1947 catalogue: the 3462 operating milk car and the 2461 transformer car. And like the engines, there were a number of changes in the carry-over items, even though they carried the same number. The tooling for the die-cast frame used for the 2411 flatcar and for the 2419 and 2420 work cabooses was modified to strengthen the underside of the frame around the die ejection pins. The extra welded steps were eliminated from the four corners of the 2457 caboose. Catwalk rivet detail was also deleted from the 2457 and 2472 cabooses.

Passenger cars also saw their share of changes in 1947, as tinplate cars switched from rubber-stamped silver lettering to heat-stamped white lettering. The result was a much clearer and more durable marking. The Irvington cars in 1947 carried three different names (Irvington, Manhattan, and Madison) even though they all had the same 2625 number. The 1947 Art Deco boxes provided a clue as to what was to come in 1948. Some 1947 boxes were overstamped on the ends with the numbers "2627" and "2628" in black ink.

Literally underneath all these rolling stock changes was another much needed change. The Type 3A truck and coupler assembly introduced in mid-1946 solved many of the problems associated with the early flying shoe design. However, it created another problem: a loose knuckle coupler which all too often became separated from its supporting steel plate. Lionel's solution to this problem was elegant in its simplicity: a staking operation was added after the knuckle was attached to its supporting plate. This change, which produced what are known as Type 3B trucks, caused an interlocking of the two parts at four additional points and resulted in a very strong joint. Type 3B trucks are believed to have been used on all items produced in 1947. Cars found in some 1947 sets containing Type 3A trucks probably represent leftover 1946 production.

Lionel introduced a new transformer in 1947, designated as the Type S, and included it in all O27 sets which contained a smoking locomotive. The catalogue identified the Type S as 75-watts but it was made and marked as an 80-watt transformer. The 167 whistle controller was another item changed in 1947. An internal automatic circuit breaker was added even though this was not mentioned in the catalogue. The change was documented in the 167C instruction sheet which was first published in April 1947. The simpler and less expensive CTC lockon also replaced the more complex UTC.

The outfit set boxes continued unchanged in 1947. The Art Deco component boxes also continued to be produced, but with the addition of the American Toy Manufacturers Association logo on one side.

Finally, there were two new cabooses manufactured in 1947 which were included in a number of sets even though they were never mentioned in the 1947 consumer catalogue: the 2257 and 2357 SP-type with plastic bodies. These cabooses were listed in the 1947 Advance Catalogue even though they were not pictured. With the introduction of other new items and the extensive design changes made to the steam engines, the development of new cabooses was evidently given a lower priority. Consequently it fell behind schedule to the point where production in 1947 seemed very doubtful. When the time came to print the consumer catalogue, Lionel decided to omit any reference to a new type of caboose. This decision must have been made at the last minute, because the O27 Gauge caboose listings are almost all incorrect. Most O27 Gauge freight sets were listed with the illuminated 2457 caboose, although in actual production the non-illuminated 2472 continued to be used.

Although delayed, development of the plastic caboose continued in 1947 and toward the end of the year some 2257 and 2357 cabooses found their way into 1947 sets. The boxes for these early SP-type cabooses were always the Art Deco style with complete cardboard liners. The boxes were correctly printed with the 2257 number for non-illuminated O27 cabooses and 2357 for illuminated O Gauge cabooses, but the contents themselves were not as consistent. The boxes sometimes yield some very surprising contents, such as a non-illuminated red 2357 with a red plastic smokestack in a 2257 box in an O27 set. Some other very unusual variations have been found in 1947 SP-type cabooses but at the present time these variations cannot be associated with specific sets.

	VG	LN

1431 — O27 Gauge — $22.50 Retail

Contents: 1654 steam locomotive with headlight; 1654T non-whistle tinplate tender; 2452X gondola; 2465 Sunoco two-dome tank car; 2472 non-illuminated Pennsylvania N5 caboose; eight curved and one straight track; 1019 uncoupling/operating section; and a 1035 60-watt transformer.

Comments: This set was virtually identical to outfit 1401 manufactured in 1946 except for the CTC lockon and 1035 transformer. Items in this set should have Type 3B trucks, instead of the Type 2 and 3A used in 1946. The instruction book included in this outfit could have been dated either 1946 or 1947, since leftover 1946 instruction books were used with early 1947 sets. **75 125**

1431W — O27 Gauge — $27.50 Retail

Contents: Same as 1431, but with a 1654W whistle tender and a 75-watt 1042 transformer. **90 150**

1432 — O27 Gauge — $27.50 Retail

Contents: 221 Empire State steam locomotive with headlight; 221T New York Central non-whistle tinplate tender; two 2430 blue Pullmans; 2431 blue observation; eight curved and three straight track; 1019 uncoupling/operating section; and a 1035 60-watt transformer.

Comments: This set was similar to outfit 1400 from 1946, but contained a black 221 locomotive and tender, and passenger cars with white heat-stamped lettering that was much clearer than the earlier silver rubber-stamped lettering. **375 750**

1432W — O27 Gauge — $33.50 Retail

Contents: Same as 1432, but with a 221W whistle tender and a 75-watt 1042 transformer. **400 775**

1433 — O27 Gauge — $27.50 Retail

Contents: 221 Empire State steam locomotive with headlight; 221T New York Central non-whistle tinplate tender; 2411 flatcar with logs; 2465 Sunoco two-dome tank car; 2457 illuminated Pennsylvania N5 caboose; eight curved and three straight track; 1019 uncoupling/operating section; and a 1035 60-watt transformer.

Comments: This set was similar to outfit 1403 from 1946, but contained a black 221 locomotive and tender. The 2411 flatcar used the reinforced die-cast frame and the load was switched from metal pipe to wooden logs. The rolling stock and tender were equipped with the new Type 3B trucks. Though the catalogue lists a 2457 caboose, the set is always found with the non-illuminated 2472 caboose. **175 300**

1433W — O27 Gauge — $33.50 Retail

Contents: Same as 1433, but with a 221W whistle tender and a 1042 75-watt transformer. **200 325**

1434WS — O27 Gauge — $42.50 Retail

Contents: 2025 steam locomotive with headlight and smoke; 2466WX whistle tender; two 2440 illuminated green Pullmans; 2441 illuminated green observation; eight curved and three straight track; 1019 uncoupling/operating section; and a Type S transformer.

Comments: This set was similar to outfit 1402 from 1946. The new 2025 steam engine replaced the 1666. The green passenger cars were now equipped with the more reliable Type 3B trucks and clearer white heat-stamped lettering. This set also included the new Type S transformer and CTC lockon. **475 800**

1435WS — O27 Gauge — $42.50 Retail

Contents: 2025 steam locomotive with headlight and smoke; 2466WX whistle tender; 2452X gondola; 2454 Baby Ruth boxcar; 2457 illuminated Pennsylvania N5 caboose; eight curved and three straight track; 1019 uncoupling/operating section; and a Type S transformer.

Comments: This set was similar to outfit 1405 from 1946. The new 2025 locomotive replaced the 1666 and the 2454 Baby Ruth boxcar replaced the 2465 tank car. The engine in this set had the plain pilot (no simulated coupler) and frequently was the aluminum smokestack variation. Examples of this set have been found with a 2472 metal caboose, a 2257 plastic SP-type caboose, or the rare non-illuminated red 2357 caboose mentioned earlier. Ironically, it has never been found with the listed 2457 caboose. As the least expensive freight set with smoke in 1947, it was probably made in large quantities over several production runs, which accounts for the numerous variations.

	VG	LN
With 2472 or 2257	150	250
With 2357	265	450

1437WS — O27 Gauge — $47.50 Retail

Contents: 2025 steam locomotive with headlight and smoke; 2466WX whistle tender; 2452X gondola; 2465 Sunoco two-dome tank car; 2454 Baby Ruth boxcar; 2472 non-illuminated Pennsylvania N5 caboose; eight curved and five straight track; 1019 uncoupling/operating section; and a Type S transformer.

Comments: This outfit was nearly identical to set 1435WS except for the addition of a 2465 tank car and two more sections of straight track. This set has been observed with engines having either a black or aluminum smokestack, and boiler fronts marked with the usual red and gold Pennsylvania keystone or the simple "2025" number heat-stamped in white. This set has also been observed with either a metal 2472 or plastic 2257 SP-type caboose. In fact there is at least

VG   LN

one report that this set came with a 2419 work caboose, possibly included during the transition period from metal to plastic cabooses. **175   300**

1439WS   O27 Gauge $52.50 Retail

Contents: 2025 steam locomotive with headlight and smoke; 2466WX whistle tender; 3559 operating coal car; 2465 Sunoco two-dome tank car; 3454 merchandise car; 2457 illuminated Pennsylvania N5 caboose; eight curved and five straight track; 1019 uncoupling/operating section; and a Type S transformer.

Comments: Similar to outfits 1409W and 1413WS from 1946, except for the 2025 locomotive and Type S transformer which replaced earlier items. The tender and cars were fitted with Type 3B trucks, common for 1947. The set is usually, if not always, found with the non-illuminated 2472 metal caboose, rather than the 2457 as listed in the catalogue. Late production may have also come with the plastic 2257 SP-type caboose, but this has not been confirmed to date.

225   375

1441WS   O27 Gauge $57.50 Retail

Contents: 2020 steam locomotive with headlight and smoke; 2020W whistle tender; 2560 crane; 2461 transformer car; 3451 operating log car; 2419 work caboose; eight curved and five straight track; 1019 uncoupling/operating section; and a Type S transformer.

Comments: This set was similar to set 1417WS produced in 1946, except that the new 2461 transformer car replaced the tank car and the Type S transformer replaced the 1042. The 2020 steam turbine in this set was the completely redesigned version with heater-type smoke unit, single worm drive motor, and vertical E-unit. The transformer on the 2461 car was red in 1947, not black as in later years.

375   625

1443WS   O27 Gauge $70 Retail

Contents: 2020 steam locomotive with headlight and smoke; 2020W whistle tender; 3459 operating ore car; 3462 operating milk car; 2465 Sunoco two-dome tank car; 2457 illuminated Pennsylvania N5 caboose; ten curved and five straight track; 1019 uncoupling/operating section; pair 1121 remote-control switches; and a Type S transformer.

Comments: This top-of-the-line O27 set was similar to set 1415WS produced in 1946, except that the merchandise car was replaced by the new operating milk car. The Type S transformer and CTC lockon also replaced earlier designs. The 2020 was the redesigned version with heater-type smoke unit and single worm drive motor. The caboose included in this set was the non-illuminated metal 2472, not the 2457 that was listed in the catalogue. Plastic 2257 SP-type cabooses have yet to be reported with this outfit. **325   550**

VG   LN

2120S   O Gauge $37.50 Retail

Contents: 675 steam locomotive with headlight and smoke; 2466T non-whistle tender; two 2442 illuminated brown Pullmans; 2443 illuminated brown observation; eight curved and three straight track; RCS uncoupling/operating section; and an 88 reversing controller.

Comments: This outfit was headed by the new 675 locomotive with smoke. The 675 had the early-style pilot without the simulated knuckle coupler and could have come with either a black or aluminum-colored smokestack. Some 675 locomotives manufactured in 1947 also had boiler fronts heat-stamped with the 675 number instead of the usual red and gold Pennsylvania herald. The 1947 catalogue correctly shows the 2442 and 2443 passenger cars as brown, not green. The passenger cars produced in 1947 came with white heat-stamped lettering and Type 3B trucks. **425   725**

2120WS   O Gauge $43.50 Retail

Contents: Same as outfit 2120S, but with a 2466WX whistle tender and a 167 whistle controller.

Comments: The 167 whistle controller included in this set was the new "C" version with a built-in circuit breaker, even though the box was still marked just "167".

450   750

2121S   O Gauge $35 Retail

Contents: 675 steam locomotive with headlight and smoke; 2466T non-whistle tender; 2555 Sunoco single-dome tank car; 2452 gondola with barrels; 2457 illuminated Pennsylvania N5 caboose; eight curved and three straight track; RCS uncoupling/operating section; and an 88 reversing controller.

Comments: The tender and cars were equipped with the improved Type 3B trucks, but were otherwise the same as in 1946. The 675 locomotive can be found in the same variations as described in set 2120S. **195   325**

2121WS   O Gauge $41 Retail

Contents: Same as outfit 2121S, but with a 2466WX whistle tender and a 167 whistle controller. **210   350**

2123WS   O Gauge $47.50 Retail

Contents: 675 steam locomotive with headlight and smoke; 2466WX whistle tender; 2458 automobile car; 3559 operating coal car; 2555 Sunoco single-dome tank car; 2457 illuminated Pennsylvania N5 caboose; eight curved and three straight track; RCS uncoupling/operating section; and a 167 whistle controller.

Comments: This was the third 675 outfit offered in 1947. The 675 locomotive can be found in several variations as described in outfit 2120S comments. The tender and cars came with the improved Type 3B trucks. The 2457 caboose produced in 1947 generally did not have the additional steps

33

1
9
4
7

	VG	LN

welded to the black frame. Rivet detail also disappeared from the catwalk stamping, as did the Eastern Division lettering which had appeared on earlier versions of this caboose.

250 425

2124W   O Gauge $62.50 Retail

Contents: 2332 Pennsylvania five-stripe GG-1; three 2625 Pullmans; eight curved and five straight track; RCS uncoupling/operating section; and a 167 horn controller.

Comments: This was the debut of the ever popular GG-1 electric locomotive. The catalogue pictured the Lionel prototype with the 4911 number and handrail detail leading to the two side doors. Production locomotives of course were all numbered 2332 in 1947. Some very early examples of this locomotive were the rare painted black variation instead of the normal production Brunswick green. There were also several keystone variations in 1947 as both rubber stamps and decals were utilized.

The passenger cars were similar to the Irvington cars produced in 1946, but with one very important difference. For the first time, each of the three cars had a different name: Irvington, Manhattan, and Madison. Oddly enough, in 1947 all three cars continued to carry the same "2625" number. Some component boxes were overstamped "2627" and "2628", indicating the numbering changes that were to come in 1948.

1650 2750

2125WS   O Gauge $50 Retail

Contents: 671 steam turbine locomotive with headlight and smoke; 671W whistle tender; 2411 flatcar with logs; 2454 Baby Ruth boxcar; 2452 gondola with barrels; 2457 illuminated Pennsylvania N5 caboose; eight curved and five

straight track; RCS uncoupling/operating section; and a 167 whistle controller.

Comments: This set was listed in the 1947 Advance Catalogue as a special Spring 1947 promotional set. This explains the two distinct versions of this set found today.

A significant number (but certainly not all) of the 2125WS sets are found with 1946 locomotives and tenders. The 671 turbine had the smoke bulb, double worm drive, and horizontal E-unit, all characteristic of 1946 production. The tender had Type 3A trucks, also characteristic of 1946. The boxes for the engine and tender did not have any American Toy Manufacturer's Association logo. The whistle controller was the special 167S version modified for use with smoke-bulb locomotives, as indicated by the overstamped "S" on the box. The cars in this set were all equipped with Type 3B trucks and the flatcar had a load of wooden logs, all indicative of 1947 production. Furthermore, the rolling stock boxes all had the American Toy Manufacturer's Association logo which first appeared in 1947. This was the special "Spring Promotion" version of the set, assembled to use up leftover 1946 versions of the 671 turbine locomotive.

The more common version of this set, however, came with the redesigned 671 and a tender with Type 3B trucks. These items both came in boxes with the American Toy Manufacturer's Association logo. The later version of the set also included the new 167C whistle controller, although the box is simply marked "167".

265 450

2126WS   O Gauge $65 Retail

Contents: 671 steam turbine locomotive with headlight and smoke; 671W whistle tender; three 2625 Pullmans;

In 1947 Lionel introduced the 2332 GG-1. The color illustration showed the Lionel prototype numbered "4911". The Lionel prototy̶ has survived. The number 4911 actually appeared on a real GG-1. Note that the front pantograph is up, counter to prototype pract̶ and that there are no wires to power the locomotive!

VG LN

eight curved and five straight track; RCS uncoupling/operating section; and a 167 whistle controller.

Comments: The contents of this outfit were the same as set 2110WS, made in 1946, except that all components were 1947 variations. The 671 turbine had the heater-type smoke unit and vertical E-unit. The tender had a Type 3B truck and the 2625 passenger cars came with three different names: Irvington, Manhattan, and Madison. The boxes all had the American Toy Manufacturer's Association logo printed in black ink on one side. **1250 2100**

2127WS   O Gauge $60 Retail

Contents: 671 steam locomotive with headlight and smoke; 671W whistle tender; 3459 operating ore car; 2461 transformer car; 2460 black cab twelve-wheel crane; 2420 work caboose with searchlight; eight curved and five straight track; RCS uncoupling/operating section; and a 167 whistle controller.

Comments: The components in set 2127WS were typical 1947 production, meaning a slant-motored 671 steam turbine and cars equipped with Type 3B trucks. This was a handsome work train with the best rolling stock Lionel had to offer. The 1947 edition of the 2461 came with a red transformer that was changed to black in subsequent years. **350 600**

2129WS   O Gauge $67.50 Retail

Contents: 726 Berkshire steam locomotive with headlight and smoke; 2426W whistle tender; 3854 scale merchandise car; 2411 flatcar with logs; 2855 Sunoco single-dome tank car; 2457 illuminated Pennsylvania N5 caboose; eight curved and seven straight track; RCS uncoupling/operating section; and a 167 whistle controller.

Comments: This outfit as produced differed substantially from what was pictured in the 1947 catalogue. It is one of the most collectable of all the Berkshire sets. The locomotive was the redesigned 726 Berkshire with a slant motor, vertical E-unit, and cotter pins attaching the handrails. The 3854 scale merchandise car had black doors, and the 2411 flatcar carried a load of three wooden logs instead of metal pipes. The 2855 tank car produced in 1947 was gray with the 2855 number stamped in white on the frame. And, more often than not, this set is found with the new plastic-bodied 2357 SP-type caboose. The 1947 versions of this caboose came with the brakewheels facing in towards the caboose platforms, which was prototypically correct. However, the inward facing brakewheels complicated assembly of the body on the frame so the orientation was soon changed.

Component boxes in this set are all marked with the American Toy Manufacturer's Association logo, and the cars were equipped with Type 3B trucks. **850 1400**

2131WS   O Gauge $75 Retail

Contents: 726 Berkshire steam locomotive with headlight and smoke; 2426W whistle tender; 3462 operating milk

VG LN

car; 3451 operating log car; 2460 black cab twelve-wheel crane; 2420 work caboose with searchlight; eight curved and seven straight track; RCS uncoupling/operating section; and a 167 whistle controller.

Comments: This was the top-of-the-line set for 1947. The locomotive was, of course, the redesigned version of the 726 Berkshire and the cars were typical 1947 production with Type 3B trucks, except for the crane car which had six-wheel trucks. All appeared in 1947 boxes with the American Toy Manufacturer's Association logo on one side.

At $75, this outfit was priced $12.50 lower than the similar 2115WS set from 1946. The $75 set price represents only a 5 percent discount over the total price of the component items, if they had all been purchased separately. However, this set was still no bargain compared to other O Gauge sets, which were priced 10 to 20 percent below component prices. Lionel expected the purchasers of top-of-the-line sets to be much less sensitive to price than purchasers of the more moderately priced sets. **550 900**

4109WS   Electronic Set $75 Retail

Contents: 671R steam Pennsylvania locomotive with headlight and smoke; 4671W whistle tender; 4452 gondola; 4454 boxcar; 5459 ore dump car; 4457 caboose; eight curved and six straight track; and an ECU-50 electronic control unit.

Comments: The 4109WS electronic set was the only 1946 outfit which carried its number over into 1947. This may have been because there were significant quantities of sets left over from 1946, and Lionel wanted to sell it in 1947 as new merchandise. There was also a transitional 1946/1947 version of this set which provides many more questions than answers.

The transition set basically had a 1946 smoke-bulb locomotive, but 1947 cars with Type 3B trucks. The 671R locomotive was distinctive in that it had a boiler front with prism-type headlight lens to match the smoke bulb, but it also had the number "671" heat stamped on the front instead of the usual red and gold keystone decal. The tender was 1946 production with a Type 3A coupler (no stake marks). The caboose in the transition set appears to be 1947 production because of the absence of foot steps and catwalk rivet detail.

Other 1947 sets have been observed with 1947 locomotives and tenders. The locomotives had heater-type smoke units, vertical E-units with lever protruding through the top of the boiler, and all eight drivers with bright stainless steel rims. The tenders with these locomotives had Type 3B couplers.

The transition sets were probably assembled early in 1947, before the redesigned steam turbine was ready for production, as a convenient way of using up existing inventory. There was an advantage to this in the electronic sets, because the 1946 version of the 671 could be used in electronic sets without modification, except for the addition of two small decals. The 1947 turbine required a motor using the 1946 brushplate in order to obtain the jack necessary for the connection to the tender. **500 1000**

1948

BETTER GETS BETTER YET

Some noteworthy box changes occurred in 1948 as the *Early Classic* style of paper boxes was introduced. This new component box with smaller letters and scaled-down graphics was introduced for the O27 line, while carry-over 2400 and 3000 series coil coupler cars still came in Art Deco boxes. The 2625 Irvington Art Deco passenger car box was amended to include two new numbers: the 2627 Madison and the 2628 Manhattan.

Three box anomalies can be seen in the new style 3559 box and in the 6257 and 6419 Art Deco boxes. It is interesting to hypothesize reasons for their issue. It is widely believed that there was no 3559 production in 1948. Perhaps Lionel was left with some finished but unboxed 3559 inventory from 1947, and in order to deplete supplies, decided to reorder boxes in the new style. This allowed Lionel to update the look of an antiquated item and to complement the new component boxes that were used in O27 outfit 1445WS. Lionel achieved consistency in packaging the 6419 work caboose and the 6257 SP-type caboose by approaching the problem in the opposite way. Since the 6419 was included only in outfit 1477WS, whose other components were all 1947 items packaged in the Art Deco boxes, the work caboose was similarly packaged. The same premise probably holds true for the 6257 which was included in two 1948 outfits. Such changes seemed to make good business sense, and for whatever the reasons, the boxes do exist and are extremely scarce. Surprisingly, there is even a scarce and collectable 6257 caboose. It was a very early issue, possibly late 1947, and included a plastic smokestack that was painted the same color as the caboose.

Component packaging was also revised in 1948 — liners were eliminated from most new boxes in favor of an integral coupler protection flap. The new 2400, 2401, and 2402 green streamlined passenger cars were still packed with full wrap-around liners as were all the engines and the better tenders. The outfit boxes remained the same as in 1947.

New motive power was introduced by means of the 2333 series Santa Fe and New York Central F-3 units, the 1656 steam switcher with the 2403B/6403B tender, and the 2026 steam locomotive. The 1655 was issued to replace the 1654 and the 1001 Scout engine was presented with two outfits. It was with the new AA F-3 units that Lionel instituted the policy of referring to them with the alpha letters "P" and "T". This policy was later used for Alcos when they were reintroduced in 1957. The powered unit always had a "P" as part of the box and catalogue stock number while the non-powered, dummy unit or trailer utilized a "T". e.g., 2333P/2333T, 2373P/2373T, etc. When the F-3 B unit was introduced in 1950, it was given a "C" as part of both the catalogue and box numbers, e.g., 2343C, 2356C, etc. Depending on the terminology used, a three-unit F-3 combination can be referred to as either an "ABA" or "PCT".

An important new tender was introduced in the form of the streamlined twelve-wheel, Pennsylvania-lettered 2671W. Earliest issues of this tender were the scarce variation with backup lights, but buyer beware as many 2671W tenders have been retrofitted with reproduction light assemblies. The 2456/6456 hopper was a new design, and the 6454 series boxcar also debuted in three markings exclusive to the O27 line; they were the Baby Ruth, Santa Fe, and New York Central.

The 6019 uncoupling/operating section was new issue, replacing the 1019, and the 480-25 magnetic coupler and 1033 transformer were introduced for the O27 line. All O Gauge outfits still contained an RCS; the UCS was still in the developmental stage. It is for this reason that the new Lehigh Valley hopper car had to be issued under two numbers.

Many early production O27 sets came with some or all of the cars equipped with Type 3B coil couplers, even though the cars and boxes were numbered in the 6000 series. Evidently the new magnetic coupler experienced last minute production problems, and coil couplers were used out of necessity to maintain O27 set production schedules.

1111   **O27 Gauge**   **$15.95 Retail**

Contents: 1001 Scout steam locomotive with headlight; 1001T Lionel Scout tinplate tender; 1002 black gondola; 1005 Sunoco tank car; 1007 red SP-type caboose; eight curved and one straight track; 1009 Manumatic uncoupling section; and a 1011 25-watt transformer.

Comments: The introduction of the Scout series in 1948 was Lionel's effort to reach a still lower end price point customer. At $15.95, this set cost 25 percent less than the $22.50 introductory 1430 outfit from 1947. The 1001 had a plastic boiler molding with a problem motor. The other components all came with the newly designed Scout truck and coupler that made integration with other regular production items impossible. A special metal *Manumatic* device was engineered as an inexpensive means by which to uncouple the cars; it simply clipped over a piece of track and was operated manually. The outfit box was standard issue for the period. The engine, protected by a liner, and the balance of the components all came in new Early Classic boxes. The Scout endeavor was a marketing mistake, minor though it may have been, since it allowed no room for growth because of the

VG   LN

restrictive coupling method. Lionel was still depleting Scout truck inventory in 1953.   **90   150**

1112   O27 Gauge $18.95 Retail

Contents: 1001 Scout steam locomotive with headlight; 1001T Lionel Scout tinplate tender; 1002 black gondola; 1004 orange Baby Ruth boxcar; 1005 Sunoco tank car; 1007 red SP-type caboose; eight curved and one straight track; 1009 Manumatic uncoupling section; and a 1011 25-watt transformer.

Comments: This was the second Scout set offered in 1948. It included a 1004 boxcar as an additional piece of rolling stock, and was the first freight set in the postwar era to have an even number. Please refer to comments on outfit 1111 for additional information.   **105   175**

1423W   O27 Gauge $29.95 Retail

Contents: 1655 steam locomotive with headlight; 6654W Lionel Lines tinplate tender with whistle; 6452 gondola; 6465 Sunoco two-dome tank car; 6257 SP-type caboose; eight curved and three straight track; 6019 uncoupling/operating section; and a 1042 75-watt transformer.

Comments: The 1655 was a small steam engine that was simply a revised 1654. The outfit box was standard issue for the period. The engine, protected by a liner, and all the other components came in a mixture of paper boxes, either new issue or overstamped Art Deco types from 1947. This set may even have contained the scarce 6257 Art Deco box. Note that the 1948 edition of the 6452 gondola often has an incorrect "6462" stamped on the side.   **90   150**

1425B   O27 Gauge $35.95 Retail

Contents: 1656 steam switcher with headlight; 2403B slope-back bell-ringing tender; 6456 black Lehigh Valley hopper; 6465 Sunoco two-dome tank car; 6257X SP-type caboose; eight curved and three straight track; 6019 uncoupling/operating section; and a 1034 75-watt transformer.

Comments: The 1656 switcher was a version of the 1665 that was last catalogued in 1946. The outfit box was standard issue for the period. The engine and tender, protected by liners, and the balance of the components came in new Early Classic boxes. The tender was still the old coil-coupler ed 2403B. The new Lehigh Valley hopper was offered as 6456 with magnetic couplers for the O27 line and as 2456 with coil couplers in O Gauge. The caboose box was unique to this set — the "X" suffix meant that the caboose itself had a magnetic coupler at *both* ends, allowing additional play value with the 1656 which had an operating front coupler. This is the most desirable of all the 1948 steam/freight outfits.   **550   900**

VG   LN

1426WS   O27 Gauge $42.75 Retail

Contents: 2026 steam locomotive with headlight and smoke; 6466WX Lionel Lines whistle tender; two 6440 green Pullmans; 6441 green observation; eight curved and three straight track; 6019 uncoupling/operating section; and a 1032 75-watt transformer.

Comments: This set was very similar to outfit 1434WS from 1947. The 2026 was a new medium-sized addition to the O27 steam roster. It was paired with the 6466WX whistle tender which had a magnetic coupler. The artist's rendering in the catalogue erroneously shows the tinplate passenger cars as 2440 series; evidently the catalogue artwork was done prior to the renumbering of the cars. Early issues of this outfit may even have contained 2440 series cars in Art Deco boxes since Lionel was in a transitional phase, changing from coil to magnetic couplers. The engine and tender, protected by liners, and the passenger cars usually came in newly released Early Classic boxes. The outfit box was standard issue for the period.   **475   800**

1427WS   O27 Gauge $39.75 Retail

Contents: 2026 steam locomotive with headlight and smoke; 6466WX Lionel Lines whistle tender; 6454 boxcar; 6465 Sunoco two-dome tank car; 6257 SP-type caboose; eight curved and three straight track; 6019 uncoupling/operating section; and a 1032 75-watt transformer.

Comments: This was one of three sets to be catalogued in 1948 with the new 2026 engine. It was a medium-sized addition to the O27 steam roster and was paired with an updated 2466WX tender that was now designated as 6466WX, which had a magnetic coupler. The outfit box was standard issue for the period. The engine and tender, protected by liners, and all of the other components came in new Early Classic boxes. The 6454 boxcar could have come in any of three road names since their inclusion in 1948 sets was done rather randomly.   **150   250**

1429WS   O27 Gauge $47.95 Retail

Contents: 2026 steam locomotive with headlight and smoke; 6466WX Lionel Lines whistle tender; 3451 operating log car; 6454 boxcar; 6465 Sunoco two-dome tank car; 6357 illuminated SP-type caboose; eight curved and five straight track; 6019 uncoupling/operating section; and a 1033 90-watt transformer.

Comments: The 2026 was a new medium-sized addition to the O27 steam roster. It was paired with an updated 2466WX tender that was now designated as 6466WX and had a magnetic coupler. The outfit box was standard issue for the period. The 3451 was a carry-over item from 1947 and came in an Art Deco box. The new 6454 boxcar could have come in any of three road names because their inclusion in 1948 sets was done rather randomly. The engine and tender, protected by liners, and the 6454 came in Early Classic boxes, while the tank car and the caboose could have come in either newly issued boxes or overstamped Art Deco types.   **175   300**

VG LN   VG LN

1
9
4
8

twelve-wheel crane; 2420 work caboose with searchlight; eight curved and five straight track; and an RCS uncoupling/operating section.

Comments: This was the third 671 set offered for the year, and it was a close duplication of outfit 2127WS from 1947 that now included the new twelve-wheel 2671W Pennsylvania tender at the same $60 price. The only other difference was that the transformer on the 2461 was black rather than red. The tender came with a protective liner in a new Early Classic box with a large "2671W" printed on the end flaps and on the four sides, dating this box to 1948 only. Earliest editions of the tender were the scarce variation with backup lights. The rolling stock came in 1947-style Art Deco boxes while the engine box could have been either Art Deco or Early Classic. The outfit box was standard issue for the period.

375 625

Comments: This outfit was a close copy of set 2124W from 1947, with the Madison and Manhattan Pullmans finally being given their own number. The outfit box was standard issue for the period. The 2332 came in a corrugated carton with a liner while the passenger cars, also protected by liners, usually came in individually numbered, 1947-style Art Deco boxes. This box type was a bit unusual in that the passenger cars, being newly renumbered, should have been issued in new Early Classic boxes. The best explanation for this inequity is that Lionel was more concerned with the conversion of the O27 line and simply reran the existing style of box instead of immediately doing additional artwork. It is quite possible for the Pullmans to have surfaced in correct 1948-style boxes late during the product year. 1650 2750

2144W   O Gauge $67.50 Retail

Contents: 2332 single-motored green Pennsylvania five-stripe GG-1; 2625 Irvington Pullman; 2627 Madison Pullman; 2628 Manhattan Pullman; eight curved and five straight track; and an RCS uncoupling/operating section.

2145WS   O Gauge $67.50 Retail

Contents: 726 Berkshire steam locomotive with headlight and smoke; 2426W Lionel Lines whistle tender; 3462 operating milk car; 2411 flatcar with logs; 2460 black cab twelve-wheel crane; 2357 illuminated SP-type caboose; eight

The Electronic Set came in two major versions. The 1946-1947 set had a 4457 N-5 Pennsylvania metal caboose, and the 1948-1949 set came with the 4357 SP caboose. The 1948-1949 set is shown above. Although the engine was designated 671R by Lionel in its catalogue, with the "R" standing for remote, the locomotive was actually marked "671". H. Holden Collection.

VG   LN   VG   LN

curved and seven straight track; and an RCS uncoupling/operating section.

Comments: This set was a near repeat of outfit 2131WS from 1947, with a non-operating 2411 flatcar replacing the operating 3451 and an SP-type caboose being substituted for the 2420 work caboose. The outfit box was standard issue for the period. The 1948 edition of the 726 had a simulated coupler not present on most 1947 production. It came in a corrugated carton slightly wider than the 1947 version, with an appropriately fitted full wraparound liner. The balance of the component boxes were the 1947 Art Deco type although it was possible for the 2426W to surface in a new Early Classic box. This was one of very few instances in the postwar era in which a work caboose was not included with an outfit that contained a crane. It would seem that Lionel was merely trying to deplete inventory on 2357 coil coupler cabooses, in anticipation of the conversion to magnetic couplers.

450   775

2146WS   O Gauge $75 Retail

Contents: 726 Berkshire steam locomotive with headlight and smoke; 2426W Lionel Lines whistle tender; 2625 Irvington Pullman; 2627 Madison Pullman; 2628 Manhattan Pullman; eight curved and seven straight track; and an RCS uncoupling/operating section.

Comments: The Berkshire was again at the head of an Irvington passenger set after an absence during the previous year. The outfit box was standard issue for the period. The 1948 edition of the 726 had a simulated front coupler that was not present on most 1947 production. It came in a corrugated carton slightly wider than the 1947 version, with an appropriately fitted full wraparound liner. The 2627 Madison and 2628 Manhattan Pullmans were finally given their own number. The tender and the individually numbered passenger cars came with protective liners in 1947-style Art Deco boxes. This box type was a bit unusual in that the passenger cars, being newly renumbered, should have been issued in new Early Classic boxes. The best explanation for this inequity is that Lionel was more concerned with the conversion of the O27 line

and simply reran the existing style of box in lieu of immediately doing additional artwork. It is quite possible for the tender and Pullmans to have surfaced in correct 1948-style boxes late during the product year.   **1400   2300**

4110WS   Electronic Set $199.95 Retail

Contents: 671R steam turbine locomotive with headlight and smoke; 4671W Lionel Lines whistle tender; 4452 black gondola with barrels, 4454 orange Baby Ruth boxcar; 5459 ore dump car; 4357 illuminated SP-type caboose; ten curved, eighteen straight, and two half-straight track; pair 022 remote-control switches; 151 semaphore; 97 operating coal elevator; ECU-1 electronic control unit; and a VW 150-watt transformer.

Comments: This set was the successor to outfit 4109WS. The set number 4110WS again broke Lionel's long-standing tradition of using even numbers for passenger sets. As you can readily see, the $199.95 price tag was staggering. To say that this set was overpriced in an understatement. Lionel added contents valued at $67.25 above what was included with outfit 4109WS from 1947 yet raised the price $124.95. One must wonder whether Lionel catalogued this outfit not to make money, but for the bragging rights of having the most expensive and technologically advanced toy train set ever produced. This set offered the new-design SP-type caboose that replaced the tinplate 4457. The bodies for the first year of 4357 caboose production were molded in red plastic and then painted brown. They came in an early version of the Die 3 mold which had ladder slots and an unusual extra board molded in the catwalk near the front of the caboose. This same body mold sometimes surfaces as a red unpainted caboose in Scout sets. The engine, tender, and other rolling stock were essentially unchanged from the previous issue but now came in new Early Classic boxes. This set is extremely difficult to obtain complete and boxed in collector condition. Some versions of this set came packaged in two separate boxes! This two-box variation is exceptionally rare.   **1000   2000**

1949

STATUS QUO

The only new piece of motive power introduced in 1949 was the bell-ringing GM diesel switcher. It made its debut with Santa Fe markings as "6220" for the O27 line and as "622" in O Gauge. Lionel's first attempt at Magnetraction was made without fanfare on these Santa Fe switchers.

The 6462 gondola with steps and brakewheels was a new item for 1949, as were the 6520 searchlight car, the 3464 operating boxcar, the 3656 operating cattle car, and the 6457 caboose. Earliest issues of the new fully trimmed magnetic coupler SP-type caboose came with a painted plastic stack. 1949 production of the cattle car included an Armour paper-like sticker, and the very earliest examples came with the scarce black lettering. This was also the year in which the scarce green generator came with an early production run of the 6520 searchlight car.

The development of the new UCS uncoupling/operating section for O Gauge was now complete. Therefore, most of the O Gauge product line was equipped with No. 480-25 magnetic couplers that were introduced on the O27 line in 1948.

The outfit boxes remained basically the same as in previous years, except that the paste-on identification label was eliminated in favor of a carton to which the printing was applied by the manufacturer. This process eliminated Lionel's task of marking outfit boxes, and thus was a cost-saving measure.

Lionel repeated a goodly portion of the 1948 outfits; therefore the outfit boxes could have been either carry-over from 1948 or the new 1949 issue. All engines and better tenders continued to be packed with box liners. The Early Classic boxes remained essentially unchanged except that the name "San Francisco" was eliminated sometime during the product year. This is proven by the fact that only first-run boxes for the revised 3472 milk car have "San Francisco" listed in the border. (This newer box, without "San Francisco", will be termed *Middle Classic* in this text.) Because of this change, O27 component boxes were usually a mixture of both the 1948 and 1949 types. Meanwhile, the O Gauge group of boxes was a real hodgepodge as both Early and Middle Classic were utilized along with overstamped Art Deco boxes that were carry-overs from the 1948 O Gauge line.

Lionel instituted a new packaging policy in 1949 for their 3461 log dump and 3469 ore dump cars. As set components, these two cars usually came in boxes with an "X" as part of the stock number. The "X" suffix means that the unloading bin was placed loose inside the outfit box instead of being packed with the car itself. This was the norm for sets, and the policy was continued with the issuance of the 3361 in 1955. Packaging in this manner allowed Lionel to use a smaller box, avoiding the additional cost of providing a cardboard liner to hold the bin in place. On the other hand, items designated for separate sale came in a larger box with a liner, but without the "X" suffix, that included the unloading bin.

	VG	LN

1115   O27 Gauge $15.95 Retail

Contents: 1110 Scout steam locomotive with headlight; 1001T Lionel Scout tinplate tender; 1002 black gondola; 1005 tank car; 1007 red SP-type caboose; eight curved and one straight track; 1009 Manumatic uncoupling section; and a 1011 25-watt transformer.

Comments: This was a close duplication of outfit 1111 from 1948, except that the new die-cast 1110 replaced the 1001. The outfit box was standard 1949 issue and all of the components, including the engine, protected by a liner, came in either Early or Middle Classic boxes. Please refer to outfit 1111 in **1948** for more information.   **90**   **150**

1117   O27 Gauge $18.95 Retail

Contents: 1110 Scout steam locomotive with headlight; 1001T Lionel Scout tinplate tender; 1002 black gondola; 1005 tank car; 1004 orange Baby Ruth boxcar; 1007 red SP-type caboose; eight curved and one straight track; 1009 Manumatic uncoupling section; and a 1011 25-watt transformer.

Comments: This was a close duplication of outfit 1112 from 1948, with the new die-cast 1110 replacing the 1001. The outfit box was standard 1949 issue and all of the components, including the engine which was protected by a liner, came in either Early or Middle Classic boxes. Please refer to outfit 1111 in **1948** for more information.   **105**   **175**

1423W   O27 Gauge $29.95 Retail

Comments: A repeat of the 1948 outfit with the 6452 gondola catalogued as having barrels. As a repeat, the outfit box could have been either a 1948 carry-over or the new 1949 issue. Please refer to **1948** for more detailed information.   **90**   **150**

1425B   O27 Gauge $35.95 Retail

Comments: A repeat of the 1948 outfit, often with a tender which was renumbered "6403B" on the underframe and came in a 6403B box, but still with coil couplers. The caboose was catalogued as only "6257", rather than "6257X",

VG   LN   VG   LN

which had magnetic couplers at both ends. As a repeat, the outfit box could have been either a 1948 carry-over or the new 1949 issue. Please see **1948** for more detailed information.

550   900

1426WS   O27 Gauge $42.75 Retail

Comments: A repeat of the 1948 outfit with the green tinplate passenger cars properly numbered as 6400 series in the artist's rendering. As a repeat, the outfit box could have been either a carry-over from 1948 or the new 1949 issue. Please refer to **1948** for more specific information.

475   800

1430WS   O27 Gauge $59.75 Retail

Comments: An exact duplication of the 1948 outfit with the green 2400 series passenger cars. As a repeat, the outfit box could have been either a carry-over from 1948 or the new 1949 issue. Please refer to **1948** for more information.

800   1400

1447WS   O27 Gauge $59.50 Retail

Comments: A repeat of the 1948 outfit, but with a 6461 transformer car replacing the 2461 and a 3461 log dump car replacing the 3451. The outfit box could have been either a carry-over from 1948 or the new 1949 issue. Please refer to **1948** for more complete information.

375   625

1451WS   O27 Gauge $39.75 Retail

Contents: 2026 steam locomotive with headlight and smoke; 6466WX Lionel Lines whistle tender; 6462 black gondola with barrels; 3464 operating boxcar; 6257 SP-type caboose; eight curved and three straight track; 6019 uncoupling/operating section; and a 1033 90-watt transformer.

Comments: The outfit box was standard 1949 issue. The engine and tender, protected by liners, and the balance of the components all came in a mixture of Early and Middle Classic boxes. The 6462 gondola with steps and brakewheels and the operating boxcar, which came with either New York Central or Santa Fe markings, were new items in the product line.

135   275

1453WS   O27 Gauge $47.95 Retail

Contents: 2026 steam locomotive with headlight and smoke; 6466WX Lionel Lines whistle tender; 3464 operating boxcar; 6465 Sunoco two-dome tank car; 3461 operating log car; 6357 illuminated SP-type caboose; eight curved and five straight track; 6019 uncoupling/operating section; and a 1033 90-watt transformer.

Comments: This set was a near duplication of outfit 1429WS from 1948, with only a new 3464 operating boxcar replacing a non-operating 6454 boxcar. The 3464 came with either New York Central of Santa Fe markings. The outfit box

VG   LN

was standard 1949 issue. The engine and tender, protected by liners, and the balance of the components came in either Early or Middle Classic boxes.   195   325

1455WS   O27 Gauge $52.50 Retail

Contents: 2025 steam locomotive with headlight and smoke; 6466WX Lionel Lines whistle tender; 6462 black gondola with barrels; 6465 Sunoco two-dome tank car; 3472 operating milk car; 6357 illuminated SP-type caboose; eight curved and five straight track; 6019 uncoupling/operating section; and a 1033 90-watt transformer.

Comments: This was the only 2025 freight set offered in 1949. The outfit box was standard issue. The engine and tender, which were protected by liners, and the balance of the components came in either Early or Middle Classic boxes. The 1949 edition of the 3472 operating milk car usually had the aluminum doors that were common to the discontinued 3462. The 6462 gondola with steps and brakewheels was a new item.

225   375

1457B   O27 Gauge $49.50 Retail

Contents: 6220 Santa Fe bell-ringing diesel switcher; 3464 operating boxcar; 6462 black gondola with barrels; 6520 searchlight car; 6419 work caboose; eight curved and five straight track; 6019 uncoupling/operating section; and a 1034 75-watt transformer.

Comments: The GM diesel switcher was the only new piece of motive power in the 1949 product line. It was catalogued with Lionel logo but came only with Santa Fe markings as part of regular production. This switcher was identical to the O Gauge 622 but carried the four-digit "6220" designation because it was also catalogued as part of the O27 line. The rolling stock was all new for 1949 and came with magnetic couplers. The operating boxcar came with either NYC or Santa Fe markings. The gondola came with both steps and brakewheels, and the searchlight car occasionally surfaces with the scarce green generator variation. The outfit box was standard 1949 issue and the engine, packaged with a full wraparound liner, and the other components all came in Early or Middle Classic boxes.   500   850

1459WS   O27 Gauge $67.50 Retail

Contents: 2020 steam turbine locomotive with headlight and smoke; 6020W Lionel Lines whistle tender; 6411 flatcar with logs; 3656 operating cattle car; 6465 Sunoco two-dome tank car; 3469 operating ore car; 6357 illuminated SP-type caboose; eight curved and eleven straight track; 6019 uncoupling/operating section; and a 1033 90-watt transformer.

Comments: This was the top-of-the-line O27 set for 1949. The outfit box was standard issue. The engine and tender, protected by liners, and the balance of the components all came in a combination of Early and Middle Classic boxes. The cattle car was a new item for 1949 and all of the 1949 production included the Armour sticker, while the very earli-

VG   LN   VG   LN

1949

est examples came with the scarce black lettering. The 1949 edition of the cattle car platform was also unique to this year. It came with orange gates; the binding posts were on the opposite side of the ramp; the platform did not lift out; and the very earliest issues included a chain that went across the top of the ramp. The 3469 ore dump car was the magnetic coupler replacement for the discontinued 3459.   **390   650**

2135WS   O Gauge $37.50 Retail

Contents: 675 steam locomotive with headlight and smoke; 6466WX Lionel Lines whistle tender; 6456 black Lehigh Valley hopper; 6411 flatcar with logs; 6457 illuminated SP-type caboose; eight curved and three straight track; and a UCS uncoupling/operating section.

Comments: A near duplication of the 1948 outfit with some minor changes, and the price reduced from $39.95. The tender and the balance of the components were now fitted with magnetic couplers and became 6400 series cars as the development of the new UCS was completed. The engine and tender, protected by liners, and all of the rolling stock came in both Early and Middle Classic boxes. As a repeat, the outfit box could have been either a 1948 carry-over or the new 1949 issue.   **210   350**

2136WS   O Gauge $39.95 Retail

Contents: 675 steam locomotive with headlight and smoke; 6466WX Lionel Lines whistle tender; two 6442 brown Pullmans; 6443 brown observation; eight curved and three straight track; and a UCS uncoupling/operating section.

Comments: A repeat of the 1948 outfit with some minor changes and the price reduced from $42.50. The tender and the passenger cars were now fitted with magnetic couplers and became 6400 series cars as the development of the new UCS was completed. The engine and tender, protected by liners, and the passenger cars all came in Middle Classic boxes. As a repeat, the outfit box could have been either a 1948 carry-over or the new 1949 issue.   **500   850**

2139W   O Gauge $57.50 Retail

Contents: 2332 single-motored green Pennsylvania five-stripe GG-1, 6456 black Lehigh Valley hopper; 3464 operating boxcar; 3461 operating log car; 6457 illuminated SP-type caboose; eight curved and five straight track; and a UCS uncoupling/operating section.

Comments: A near duplication of the 1948 outfit with some minor changes. A new operating 3464 boxcar with either Santa Fe or NYC markings replaced the 2458 automobile boxcar, yet the price remained the same. The hopper, log dump, and caboose now became 6456, 3461, and 6457 respectively, with magnetic couplers, as the development of the new UCS was completed. The outfit box was usually standard 1949 issue. The engine came boxed in a corrugated carton with a protective liner, while the balance of the components came in Early and Middle Classic boxes.   **775   1300**

2140WS   O Gauge $57.75 Retail

Comments: An almost identical repeat of the 1948 outfit, with the new UCS replacing the RCS. As a repeat, the outfit box could have been either a carry-over from 1948 or the new 1949 issue. Please see **1948** for further information.   **800   1400**

2141WS   O Gauge $57.50 Retail

Contents: 671 steam turbine locomotive with headlight and smoke; 2671W Pennsylvania whistle tender; 3472 operating milk car; 6456 black Lehigh Valley hopper; 3461 operating log car; 6457 illuminated SP-type caboose; eight curved and five straight track; and a UCS uncoupling/operating section.

Comments: A repeat of the 1948 outfit with some minor changes and the price reduced from $58.75. The rolling stock and caboose were now fitted with magnetic couplers and underwent the appropriate number changes as the development of the new UCS was completed. The 1949 edition of the 3472 operating milk car usually had the aluminum doors that were common to the discontinued 3462. The engine and tender, protected by liners, and the balance of the components all came in a mixture of Early and Middle Classic boxes. As a repeat, the outfit box could have been either a carry-over from 1948 or the new 1949 issue.   **315   525**

2144W   O Gauge $67.50 Retail

Comments: An almost identical repeat of the 1948 outfit, except that the new UCS replaced the RCS. As a repeat, the outfit box could have been either a 1948 carry-over or the new 1949 issue, but the passenger car boxes were usually Early Classic with "San Francisco" listed in the border. Please refer to **1948** for more detailed information.   **1650   2750**

2146WS   O Gauge $75 Retail

Comments: A nearly identical repeat of the 1948 outfit, except that the new UCS replaced the RCS. As a repeat, the outfit box could have been either a 1948 carry-over or the new 1949 issue, but the passenger car boxes and the tender box were usually Early Classic with "San Francisco" listed in the border. Please refer to **1948** for more detailed information.   **1400   2300**

2147WS   O Gauge $50 Retail

Contents: 675 steam locomotive with headlight and smoke; 6466WX Lionel Lines whistle tender; 3472 operating milk car; 6465 Sunoco two-dome tank car; 3469 operating ore car; 6457 illuminated SP-type caboose; eight curved and three straight track; and a UCS uncoupling/operating section.

Comments: The outfit box was standard 1949 issue. The engine and tender, protected by liners, and all of the other components came in a combination of Early and Middle Classic boxes. The tender, caboose, and rolling stock were fitted

VG   LN

with magnetic couplers and underwent the appropriate number changes as the development of the new UCS was now complete. The 1949 edition of the operating milk car usually had the aluminum doors that were common to the discontinued 3462.   **275   450**

2149B   O Gauge $52.50 Retail

Contents: 622 Santa Fe bell-ringing diesel switcher; 6520 searchlight car; 3469 operating ore car; 2460 black cab twelve-wheel crane; 6419 work caboose; eight curved and five straight track; and a UCS uncoupling/operating section.

Comments: The diesel switcher was a new item in the 1949 product line. It was catalogued with the Lionel logo, but came only with Santa Fe markings as part of regular production. This switcher was identical to the O27 Gauge 6220, but it carried the three-digit "622" designation because it was also catalogued as part of the O Gauge line. The outfit box was standard 1949 issue. The engine came with full wraparound liner in a Middle Classic box, while the balance of the components came in boxes of various types. The work crane was a carry-over item and still came in the original issue Art Deco box while the other items usually came in Middle Classic boxes. The new searchlight car occasionally surfaces with the scarce green generator variation, while the 3469 ore dump car with magnetic couplers replaced the discontinued 3459.   **500   850**

2151W   O Gauge $67.50 Retail

Contents: 2333P/2333T Santa Fe or New York Central AA F-3 units; 3464 operating boxcar; 6555 Sunoco single-dome tank car; 3469 operating ore car; 6520 searchlight car; 6457 illuminated SP-type caboose; eight curved and nine straight track; and a UCS uncoupling/operating section.

Comments: This was the second and last of the 2333 sets to be catalogued. The 1949 editions of the extremely popular F-3 sets replaced the 2458 automobile boxcar with either the new Santa Fe or New York Central operating boxcar, and included the new operating searchlight car which was not part of the 1948 outfits. The rolling stock and caboose were fitted with magnetic couplers as the development of the new UCS was completed. The outfit box was standard 1949 issue. The powered unit came in a corrugated box with a protective liner, while the T unit, also packaged with a liner, and all the other components came in both Early and Middle Classic boxes. The searchlight car was sometimes the scarce green generator variation, but was usually the very common orange. It would be nice to think that Lionel always packed a New York Central operating boxcar with the New York Central outfit and a Santa Fe with the Santa Fe outfit, but such was not the case — either road name could have appeared with either set.

	VG	LN
NYC	**1075**	**1800**
Santa Fe	**1025**	**1700**

VG   LN

2153WS   O Gauge $60 Retail

Contents: 671 steam turbine locomotive with headlight and smoke; 2671W Pennsylvania whistle tender; 3469 operating ore car; 6520 searchlight car; 2460 black cab twelve-wheel crane; 6419 work caboose; eight curved and five straight track; and a UCS uncoupling/operating section.

Comments: This set was similar to outfit 2143WS from 1948. The outfit box was standard 1949 issue. The rolling stock, except for the crane, came with magnetic couplers. The new searchlight car occasionally surfaces with the scarce green generator variation, and the 3469 with magnetic couplers replaced the discontinued 3459. The work crane was a carry-over item and still came in the original issue Art Deco box, while the other components, including the engine and tender, protected by liners, came in Early and Middle Classic boxes.   **325   550**

2155WS   O Gauge $67.50 Retail

Contents: 726 Berkshire steam locomotive with headlight and smoke; 2426W Lionel Lines whistle tender; 6411 flatcar with logs; 3656 operating cattle car; 2460 black cab twelve-wheel crane; 6457 illuminated SP-type caboose; eight curved and seven straight track; and a UCS uncoupling/operating section.

Comments: The outfit box was standard 1949 issue. The engine came in a corrugated carton with a protective liner, while the extremely desirable 2426W tender also came with a liner in either an Early or Middle Classic box. The work crane was a carry-over item and still came in the original issue Art Deco box while the balance of the components usually came in Middle Classic boxes.

The log car and caboose were fitted with magnetic couplers and underwent the appropriate number changes as the development of the new UCS was now complete. The cattle car was a new item. All of 1949 production included the Armour sticker while the very earliest examples came with the scarce black lettering. The 1949 edition of the cattle car platform was also unique to this year. It came with orange gates; the binding posts were on the opposite side of the ramp; the platform did not lift out; and the very earliest issues included a chain that went across the top of the ramp. This was the second consecutive year in which a Berkshire freight set included a crane but not a work caboose.   **525   875**

4110WS   Electronic Set $199.95 Retail

Comments: Sales on the Electronic Set were undoubtedly slow. Lionel simply recatalogued this outfit to move existing inventory. Please refer to **1948** for more information.   **1000   2000**

1950

A TRULY GOLDEN YEAR

Quality, not variety, prevailed in 1950, and the rolling stock selection was fair at best. Virtually the entire motive power product line was revamped as Magnetraction made its full impact. Three "premier" pieces of equipment made their debut in the form of the 773 Hudson, the 2023 UP Alco units, and the twin-motored 2330 GG-1; some of their sets, namely 2148WS, 1464W, and 2159W, are near the top of any collector's list. Even some of the low-end and moderately priced sets are extremely scarce. They have one-year-only engines in one-year-only outfits, but because of their close resemblance to other items of this era, they have not aroused much collector interest.

The outfit box had a new style of print in 1950. It was a conventional corrugated type with an orange panel printed on the ends, and then reprinted with a blue frame and blue lettering and usually included the retail price. All individual pieces, even the transformer and the components of the low-end sets, were still individually boxed inside the outfit box. This was the year in which Lionel began to include uncut billboard sheets as part of outfit packaging. Lionel still persisted in using paper boxes with protective liners for their smaller- and medium-sized steam engines, while the larger engines were packed, also with liners, in corrugated cartons. A new packaging concept was developed for the 2023. The engines were packed in a corrugated master carton without component boxes. Such packaging would become standard procedure for all of the early Alco pairs through 1954.

Component boxes were a combination of the Early Classic style that included "San Francisco" and the newer version from which "San Francisco" was deleted. There was no rhyme nor reason as to how the O Gauge outfit numbers were assigned — they do not follow the normal sequential numbering pattern by price points.

Steps on the rolling stock all but disappeared in 1950 as did the Armour decals on the 3656 and 6656. Any steps that did appear were actually 1949 product year items and came boxed as such in elongated boxes with coupler protection flaps. The road names on the 3464 and 6454 series boxcars again appear to have been chosen randomly for inclusion in sets, and the "X" suffix used on the 3461 and 3469 boxes again meant that the unloading bin was placed loose inside the outfit box. This would continue as the norm for sets; packaging in this fashion allowed Lionel to use a smaller box and avoided the additional cost of providing a cardboard liner to hold the bin in place.

Also gone were the protective liners from the 2400 series passenger cars. The new Middle Classic boxes were downsized and elongated, and now included a coupler protection flap. The Santa Fe and New York Central F-3 units were finally given their own numbers but still retained the larger

GM decals. This was the year in which F-3 B units were introduced. Strange though it may seem, the new B units always had a "C" as part of their catalogue number, i.e., 2343C, 2344C, etc. The 2046W tender was also new issue. It was an important item whose usage was continuous, whether as 2046W, 2046WX, 736W, or 773W, for nearly two decades.

The Scout series outfits that were introduced in 1948 failed to meet sales projections, and Lionel took a step to help alleviate the problem — the company began to catalogue *semi-Scout* outfits. An explanation of Scout phraseology is as follows: Lionel catalogued a total of six true Scout sets, that is, sets that included a "Lionel Scout" tender and components with both Scout trucks and couplers. The engines in these true Scout sets were 1001, 1110, and 1120. The words *Scout-like* and *Scout-type* have been adapted through the years to include *all* small inexpensive engines with an 0-4-0 or 2-4-2 wheel alignment. The term *semi-Scout* is used in this text to define rolling stock and the 6001T and 6066T tenders that have the combination of Scout trucks with magnetic couplers. They were assembled in this manner *only* to move surplus inventory on Scout trucks. The word *Scout*, because of its negative connotation, became anathema and was dropped from the catalogue in 1953.

	VG	LN

1113   **O27 Gauge**   **$14.95 Retail**

Contents: 1120 Scout steam locomotive with Magnetraction; 1001T Lionel Scout tinplate tender; 1002 black gondola; 1005 Sunoco tank car; 1007 SP-type caboose; eight curved and one straight track; 1009 Manumatic uncoupling section; and a 1011 25-watt transformer.

Comments: The outfit box was the new standard 1950 issue, and the 1120 was a new Scout engine with Magnetraction. The engine, protected by a liner, and the other components all came in Middle Classic paper boxes. The Manumatic track section was the only means by which to uncouple Scout cars. For additional Scout set comments, please refer to outfit 1111 in **1948**.   **105**   **175**

1457B   **O27 Gauge**   **$39.95 Retail**

Contents: 6220 Santa Fe bell-ringing diesel switcher; 6520 searchlight car; 3464 operating boxcar; 6462 black gondola with barrels; 6419 work caboose; eight curved and five

VG   LN

straight track; 6019 uncoupling/operating section; and a 1034 75-watt transformer.

Comments: This is a repeat of a 1949 set but the outfit box was the new standard 1950 issue, and the price was reduced from $49.50. The 6220 was the O27 Gauge number for the bell-ringing switcher, and although it was catalogued as New York Central, it exists as such only in prototype form. Either maroon or orange generators appeared on the searchlight car, and the operating boxcar came with either NYC or Santa Fe markings. The engine and the caboose, protected by liners, and the other components all came in Middle Classic boxes.   500   850

An end view of two 1950 set boxes. Outfit 1457B included the price of $39.95, which was standard procedure while outfit 2175W had no price printed on the box. B. Myles Collection.

1461S   O27 Gauge $19.95 Retail

Contents: 6110 steam locomotive with smoke and Magnetraction; 6001T Lionel Lines non-whistle tender; 6002 black gondola; 6004 orange Baby Ruth boxcar; 6007 SP-type caboose; eight curved and three straight track; 6019 uncoupling/operating section; and a 1012 35-watt transformer.

Comments: This can be called a "semi-Scout" set because all of the trucks, including those on the tender, were Scout-type but had magnetic couplers. The outfit box was the standard 1950 style, and the 6110 was a new issue engine. The 6004 was catalogued in yellow but is not known to exist in that color. The engine, protected by a liner, and the other components all came in Middle Classic boxes. This is a scarce set that included one-year-only components, but has not stirred much collector interest.   165   275

VG   LN

1463W   O27 Gauge $29.95 Retail

Contents: 2036 steam locomotive with headlight and Magnetraction; 6466W Lionel Lines whistle tender; 6462 black gondola; 6465 Sunoco two-dome tank car; 6257 SP-type caboose; eight curved and three straight track; 6019 uncoupling/operating section; and a 1033 90-watt transformer.

Comments: The 2036 was a new engine for the 1950 product line. The set was bland and unexciting but did come with a 1033 transformer which, even by today's standards, is a quality piece of equipment. Also note that as a cost-saving measure Lionel refrained from putting barrels in the gondolas of their lower-priced sets. The outfit box was standard issue, and the engine and tender, protected by liners, as well as the other components all came in Middle Classic boxes.   165   275

1464W   O27 Gauge $55 Retail

Contents: 2023 UP Alco AA units; 2481 Plainfield Pullman, 2482 Westfield Pullman, and 2483 Livingston observation in yellow and gray "Anniversary" colors; eight curved and five straight track; 6019 uncoupling/operating section; and a 1033 90-watt transformer.

Comments: This outfit is commonly called "the Anniversary set" by collectors and is a postwar "prize." The engine was catalogued with a gray nose and gray side-frame trucks, but it cannot be confirmed whether or not any of these "rare" gray-nosed variations were shipped as set components. The 2023 was a piece of engineering excellence; this new engine was the forerunner of future Alcos that were produced continuously, except in 1955 and 1956, through 1969. The engines came unboxed inside a corrugated master carton while the passenger cars came in Middle Classic boxes with coupler protection flaps.   1500   2500

1467W   O27 Gauge $47.50 Retail

Contents: 2023 UP Alco AA units; 6656 stock car; 6465 Sunoco two-dome tank car; 6456 black or maroon Lehigh Valley hopper; 6357 illuminated SP-type caboose; eight curved and five straight track; 6019 uncoupling/operating section; and a 1033 90-watt transformer.

Comments: This was the freight version of the Anniversary set. The outfit box was the standard 1950 issue while the rolling stock was normal run-of-the-mill items. The 6656 was catalogued in brown but is not known to exist in this color as part of regular production. The engines came unboxed inside a corrugated master carton while the balance of the components came in Middle Classic boxes.   360   600

1469WS   O27 Gauge $39.95 Retail

Contents: 2035 steam locomotive with headlight, smoke, and Magnetraction; 6466W Lionel Lines whistle tender; 6462 black gondola; 6465 Sunoco two-dome tank car; 6456 black or maroon Lehigh Valley hopper; 6257 SP-type caboose;

VG   LN   VG   LN

eight curved and three straight track; 6019 uncoupling/operating section; and a 1033 90-watt transformer.

Comments: This outfit box could have been either a 1949 type or the new issue for 1950. Some production took place in late 1949 as evidenced by the outfit box, but 1950 was the first year in which this set was catalogued. The 2035 was a revamped 2025 steam engine while the rolling stock was standard run-of-the-mill equipment. The engine and tender, protected by liners, and the other components all came in Middle Classic boxes.   150   250

1471WS   O27 Gauge $57.50 Retail

Contents: 2035 steam locomotive with headlight, smoke, and Magnetraction; 6466W Lionel Lines whistle tender; 3469 operating ore car; 6465 Sunoco two-dome tank car; 6454 boxcar; 3461 operating log car; 6357 illuminated SP-type caboose; eight curved and seven straight track; 6019 uncoupling/operating section; and a 1033 90-watt transformer.

Comments: This was the second 2035 set offered for the year, and the outfit box was standard 1950 issue. The 6454 was catalogued with the SP logo but could possibly have been an Erie or a Pennsylvania — Lionel appears to have randomly chosen any road name 6454 boxcar for inclusion in sets. The engine and tender, protected by liners, and the other components all came in Middle Classic boxes.   250   400

1473WS   O27 Gauge $49.95 Retail

Contents: 2046 steam locomotive with headlight, smoke, and Magnetraction; 2046W Lionel Lines whistle tender; 3464 operating boxcar; 6465 Sunoco two-dome tank car; 6520 searchlight car; 6357 illuminated SP-type caboose; eight curved and five straight track; 6019 uncoupling/operating section; and a 1033 90-watt transformer.

Comments: The outfit box was the new 1950 type and the 2046 was another new high-quality engine. The 2046W was the new streamlined tender that was developed to complement medium-sized engines. It, along with the yet to be released 6026 body style, would become the backbone of Lionel's whistle tender production for the remainder of the decade. The operating boxcar was catalogued as a Santa Fe but an equal number of boxcars with the NYC road name appeared throughout the year. It is believed that Lionel randomly chose either road name for inclusion in outfits. The engine was packed in a corrugated carton with liner while the tender, also protected by a liner, and the other components all came in Middle Classic boxes.   300   500

1475WS   O27 Gauge $67.50 Retail

Contents: 2046 steam locomotive with headlight, smoke, and Magnetraction; 2046W Lionel Lines whistle tender; 3656 operating cattle car; 3461 operating log car; 6472 refrigerator car; 3469 operating ore car; 6419 work caboose; eight curved and seven straight track; 6019 uncoupling/operating section; and a 1033 90-watt transformer.

Comments: This was the top-of-the-line O27 set for the year, and was the second outfit this year headed by the new 2046. At $67.50, it was more expensive than eight O Gauge sets and equal in price to two others. This outfit had three quality operating cars as well as the new 2046W tender, and was only one of two O27 sets ever to include the 3656 cattle car. The engine was packed in a corrugated carton with liner while the tender, also protected by a liner, and the other components all came in Middle Classic boxes.   350   600

2148WS   O Gauge $85 Retail

Contents: 773 Hudson steam locomotive with headlight, smoke, and Magnetraction; 2426W Lionel Lines whistle tender; 2625 Irvington, 2627 Madison, and 2628 Manhattan Pullman cars with silhouettes; eight curved and seven straight track; and a UCS uncoupling/operating section.

Comments: This is one of the most coveted of the postwar sets, and at $85 was a considerable amount of money for the time. This less detailed reissue of the prewar scale Hudson came in a corrugated carton with full wraparound liner and with the very desirable 2426W Lionel Lines tender. The tender was catalogued with New York Central markings but did not come as such as part of regular production. To avoid confusion with the 1964 reissue, notice that the proper engine box was made by the Star Company and lettered in black. 1950 was the last year that the Madison cars were catalogued and it was the only year in which they were manufactured with silhouettes. In order to be absolutely correct the passenger cars and the 2426W tender, also protected by liners, *must* be in the proper boxes, those which are the Middle Classic style with the city names "New York" and "Chicago," not "San Francisco". It is of interest to note that the liner dimensions for the passenger car boxes were still ever-so-slightly oversized, making their use difficult. This is one of the reasons that Madison car boxes are usually found in less than desirable condition.

The preferred outfit box was the standard 1950 issue with blue printing on an orange field, but another correct,

An end view of a set box variation of the 1950 Hudson passenger outfit 2148WS. This box had a printed paste-on label that was last used in 1948! Why this was done is a minor mystery, but it is evident that it was a new-issue box because of the presence of the number "2148WS" on both sides. B. Myles Collection.

VG   LN

VG   LN

although less desirable outfit box was made. It was a new issue 2148WS box, but it had a printed paste-on label that was last used as a means of identification in 1948! Why this was done is a minor mystery. Please refer to page 48 for a picture of this set box variation.   **3600   6000**

2150WS   O Gauge $55 Retail

Contents: 681 steam turbine locomotive with headlight, smoke, and Magnetraction; 2671W Pennsylvania whistle tender; 2421 Maplewood Pullman, 2422 Chatham Pullman, and 2423 Hillside observation in new silver and gray colors; eight curved and five straight track; and a UCS uncoupling/operating section.

Comments: The outfit box was the standard 1950 type and this was one of three 681 sets to be offered in the product line. The silver/gray passenger cars were the third different color combination produced for the 2400 series cars. All of the components came in Middle Classic paper boxes — the engine and tender, protected by liners, and the passenger cars in elongated types with coupler protection flaps. In terms of collectibility, this is a rare set. It is far more difficult to obtain with the outfit box than the more notable 1464W Anniversary set.   **650   1200**

2159W   O Gauge $52.50 Retail

Contents: 2330 green Pennsylvania five-stripe GG-1; 3464 operating boxcar; 6462 black gondola with barrels; 3461 operating log car; 6456 black Lehigh Valley hopper; 6457 illuminated SP-type caboose; eight curved and seven straight track; and a UCS uncoupling/operating section.

Comments: The 2330 was the twin-engine Magnetraction replacement for the 2332; it is an undervalued item and much harder to obtain in collector condition that the 2340 and 2360 five-stripers from the 1955-1956 era. The rolling stock was all very common 1950 issue. The outfit box was standard issue and strangely enough, the catalogue made no mention of the fact that the 2330 had twin motors. The engine came in a corrugated carton with a protective liner while the other components came in Middle Classic boxes. The price of this set was $5 less than the 1949 GG-1, yet the 2330 was a superior engine and this outfit included an extra freight car!   **1500   2500**

2161W   O Gauge $67.50 Retail

Contents: 2343P/2343T Santa Fe AA F-3 units; 3469 operating ore car; 3464 operating boxcar; 3461 operating log car; 6520 searchlight car; 6457 illuminated SP-type caboose; eight curved and seven straight track; and a UCS uncoupling/operating section.

Comments: The 2343 with Magnetraction was the successor to the 2333, and Lionel finally decided to give both the Santa Fe and New York Central their own stock numbers. The porthole lens was also revised for the 2343 and 2344. It was now a flatter celluloid type that resembled a contact lens.

With four operating cars, the 2161W was the higher-priced alternative set to 2175W. The outfit box was the new 1950 issue. The 6520 came with either an orange or maroon generator while the 3464 could have been either a NYC or Santa Fe road name. The powered unit was packed in a corrugated carton with a liner while the dummy T unit, also protected by a liner, and the balance of the rolling stock came in Middle Classic boxes.   **700   1400**

2163WS   O Gauge $49.95 Retail

Contents: 736 Berkshire steam locomotive with headlight, smoke, and Magnetraction; 2671WX Lionel Lines whistle tender; 6472 refrigerator car; 6462 black gondola with barrels; 6555 Sunoco single-dome tank car; 6457 illuminated SP-type caboose; eight curved and seven straight track; and a UCS uncoupling/operating section.

Comments: This was one of two Berkshire sets to be catalogued this year. The outfit box was standard issue for 1950. The rolling stock was commonplace, yet the 6555 was a quality tank car. The "WX" suffix applied to the twelve-wheel tender box meant that the lettering was "Lionel Lines" instead of the more common "Pennsylvania". The Lionel Lines markings were widely spaced and rubber stamped in either silver or white; this is a scarce variation of the streamlined tender. The engine was packed in a corrugated carton with a liner while the tender, also protected by a liner, and the other components came in Middle Classic boxes.   **375   625**

2165WS   O Gauge $57.50 Retail

Contents: 736 Berkshire steam locomotive with headlight, smoke, and Magnetraction; 2671WX Lionel Lines whistle tender; 3472 operating milk car; 6456 black Lehigh Valley hopper; 3461 operating log car; 6457 illuminated SP-type caboose; eight curved and seven straight track; and a UCS uncoupling/operating section.

Comments: This was the second Berkshire set offered in 1950, and the outfit box was the standard new issue. The WX tender with Lionel Lines markings is scarce. The lettering was widely spaced and rubber stamped in either silver or white. The engine was packed in a corrugated carton with a liner while the tender, also protected by a liner, and the other commonplace items came in Middle Classic boxes.   **400   650**

2167WS   O Gauge $39.95 Retail

Contents: 681 steam turbine locomotive with headlight, smoke, and Magnetraction; 2671W Pennsylvania whistle tender; 6462 black gondola with barrels; 3464 operating boxcar; 6457 illuminated SP-type caboose; eight curved and five straight track; and a UCS uncoupling/operating section.

Comments: The outfit box was standard issue for 1950, and the new 681 was the upgraded Magnetraction version of the 671. The 2671W was a Pennsylvania-lettered twelve-wheel tender; as a point of reference, all 1950 O Gauge steam outfits had twelve-wheel tenders. The 6457 was the upgraded

1950

	VG	LN

version of the 6357 with a full complement of trim. The engine and tender, protected by liners, and the other components all came in Middle Classic boxes. This was one of three 681 sets to be offered in the product line. **300   500**

2169WS   O Gauge $79.50 Retail

Contents: 773 Hudson steam locomotive with headlight, smoke, and Magnetraction; 2426W Lionel Lines whistle tender; 3656 operating cattle car; 6456 black or maroon Lehigh Valley hopper; 3469 operating ore car; 6411 flatcar with logs; 6457 illuminated SP-type caboose; eight curved and seven straight track; and a UCS uncoupling/operating section.

Comments: The outfit box was standard issue for 1950, and the 773 was the less detailed postwar reissue of the scale Hudson. The 2426W is the most desirable of all postwar tenders; it was catalogued with New York Central markings but was manufactured and shipped in sets with Lionel Lines. The rolling stock was the standard mix of items from the 1950 product line. The engine was packed in a corrugated carton with a liner while the tender, also protected by a liner, and the other components came in Middle Classic boxes. In order to avoid confusion with the 1964 reissue, note that the proper engine box was made by the Star Company and lettered in black. What a disappointment that the mighty Hudson had a roster of cars that was used so prevalently throughout the product line. **1800   3000**

2171W   O Gauge $67.50 Retail

Contents: The components were the same as outfit 2161W except that the 2344 New York Central was substituted for the 2343 Santa Fe.

Comments: The New York Central, even though an East Coast railroad, was not nearly as good a seller as the brightly colored Santa Fe. The less colorful paint scheme was no doubt the primary cause for the slower sales.

725   1200

2173WS   O Gauge $52.50 Retail

Contents: 681 steam turbine locomotive with headlight, smoke, and Magnetraction; 2671W Pennsylvania whis-

	VG	LN

tle tender; 3472 operating milk car; 6555 Sunoco single-dome tank car; 3469 operating ore car; 6457 illuminated SP-type caboose; eight curved and seven straight track; and a UCS uncoupling/operating section.

Comments: This was one of three 681 outfits catalogued in 1950. There is nothing of major importance about this set except that it offered two quality operating cars. The engine and tender, protected by liners, and the other components all came in Middle Classic boxes. **325   500**

2175W   O Gauge $57.50 Retail

Contents: 2343P/2343T Santa Fe AA F-3 units; 6456 maroon Lehigh Valley hopper; 3464 operating boxcar; 6555 Sunoco single-dome tank car; 6462 black gondola with barrels; 6457 illuminated SP-type caboose; eight curved and seven straight track; and a UCS uncoupling/operating section.

Comments: The 2343 with Magnetraction was the successor to the 2333, and Lionel finally decided to give both the Santa Fe and the New York Central their own stock numbers. The porthole lens was also revised for the 2343 and 2344. It was now a flatter, celluloid type that resembled a contact lens. The rolling stock was run-of-the-mill, while the outfit box was the new 1950 type, but without the retail price. The 3464 surfaces with either Santa Fe or NYC markings. The powered unit was packed in a corrugated carton with a protective liner while the dummy T unit, also with a liner, and the balance of the rolling stock came in Middle Classic boxes. Please refer to page 47 for a picture of the outfit box. **750   1500**

2185W   O Gauge $57.50 Retail

Contents: The components were identical to outfit 2175W except that the 2344 New York Central replaced the Santa Fe.

Comments: The New York Central, even though an East Coast railroad, was not nearly as good a seller as the brightly colored Santa Fe. **775   1300**

1951

A TOUGH ACT TO FOLLOW

The full impact of the Korean War was being felt at Lionel, causing the company to come to a virtual standstill. Inflation was rampant and prices escalated in excess of 20 percent. In order to stem this tide of inflation the United States Economic Stabilization Agency, Office of Price Stabilization (OPS), began to issue stringent pricing guidelines. The OPS stamps and stickers began to appear on boxes late in the product year.

The consumer catalogue offerings were a watered-down version of the 1950 line. Only five O Gauge sets were catalogued and they were *all* repeats from 1950. The quality 6555 tank car was replaced in each set previously offered by the commonplace 6465. This exchange saved Lionel an additional dollar (in 1950 prices) in component cost. There were no new

items of consequence, only renumbered versions of existing body molds, such as the 6012 gondola, the 6014 boxcar, and the 6017 caboose. Sometime during the product year the porthole lens on the F-3 units was changed to a snap-in type. The only other innovation was the recoloring of the 2023 UP Alco in silver and gray.

The component boxes were the same as those used in 1950, and all individual pieces, even the transformer and the components of the low-end sets, were still individually boxed inside the outfit box. The outfit box underwent a slight change — the orange panel and the retail price were deleted from the printing process. Any use of unaltered carry-over boxes, because of the price inequity, would have been business suicide. The outfit prices of leftover inventory was simply amended by

The contents of Lionel Scout outfit 1119. Although this set was not catalogued until 1951, it came in a 1950-style outfit box. Notice the OPS sticker, prominently placed on the end of the outfit box, that gave the ceiling price of $17.75. Even the transformers in low-end sets were component boxed during this era. Also notice that the engine came in a paper box rather than a corrugated type. This practice proved to be unwise as the weight of the engine, in this outfit and others, has often caused irreparable damage to the box. R. LaVoie Collection.

1951

VG   LN

pasting a new OPS sticker over the old price. Please refer to page 53 for a picture of outfit box 2173WS that was amended in this manner.

1119   O27 Gauge $17.75 Retail

Contents: 1110 Scout steam locomotive with headlight; 1001T Lionel Scout tinplate tender; 1002 black gondola; 1004 orange Baby Ruth boxcar; 1007 red SP-type caboose; eight curved and one straight track; 1009 Manumatic uncoupling section; and a 1011 25-watt transformer.

Comments: The outfit box was either a 1950 type, even though it was not catalogued that year, or the new 1951 issue. The 1110, which was last catalogued in 1949, was reissued to replace the 1120. The Manumatic track section was the only means by which to uncouple Scout cars. The engine, protected by a liner, and the other components all came in Middle Classic boxes. For additional Scout comments, please see outfit 1111 in **1948**.   90   150

1463WS   O27 Gauge $35.75 Retail

Contents: 2026 steam locomotive with headlight and smoke; 6466W Lionel Lines whistle tender; 6462 black gondola with barrels; 6465 Sunoco two-dome tank car; 6257 SP-type caboose; eight curved and three straight track; 6019 uncoupling/operating section; and a 1033 90-watt transformer.

Comments: This set came in the new 1951-type outfit box and was very similar to 1463W that was catalogued in 1950. The 2026 without Magnetraction was used as a replacement for the 2036 of the previous year. The engine and tender, protected by liners, and the other components all came in Middle Classic boxes.   135   225

1464W   O27 Gauge $66.50 Retail

Contents: 2023 silver and gray UP Alco AA units; 2421 Maplewood Pullman, 2422 Chatham Pullman, and 2423 Hillside observation in the silver and gray paint scheme; eight curved and five straight track; 6019 uncoupling/operating section; and a 1033 90-watt transformer.

Comments: The outfit box was the new 1951 type, and the components were the same as the 1950 1464W, although numbered and/or colored differently, with the price increased from $55. This particular set is scarce and difficult to find in collector condition. Why did Lionel choose such a dreary color combination? Maybe it was a means by which to move unsold, finished inventory on the 2421, 2422, and 2423 that were introduced in 1950. What better means to move stock than to repeat a version of a success story, namely the Anniversary set. In Hollywood jargon, this was the sequel.

The engines came without component boxes in the usual Alco corrugated master carton inside the outfit box. The passenger cars came in Middle Classic boxes with coupler protection flaps.   600   1200

VG   LN

1467W   O27 Gauge $57.50 Retail

Comments: A near repeat of the 1950 set in a 1951 outfit box with the price increased from $47.50. The 2023 UP Alco was recolored — yellow and gray became a silver and gray combination. Please see **1950** for more information.   360   600

1469WS   O27 Gauge $48.50 Retail

Comments: A near repeat of the 1950 set in a 1951 outfit box with the price increased from $39.95. A maroon Lehigh Valley hopper was substituted for the black, and the 6462 gondola was shown in the catalogue as having barrels. Ironically, this nondescript set can be found in three different outfit boxes. Please refer to **1950** for additional information.   150   250

1471WS   O27 Gauge $70 Retail

Comments: A repeat of the 1950 set in a 1951 outfit box with the price increased from $57.50. For more information, please see **1950**.   250   400

1477S   O27 Gauge $29.95 Retail

Contents: 2026 steam locomotive with headlight and smoke; 6466T Lionel Lines non-whistle tender; 6012 black gondola; 6014 white Baby Ruth boxcar; 6017 SP-type caboose; eight curved and three straight track; 6019 uncoupling/operating section; and a 1034 75-watt transformer.

Comments: The outfit box was the new 1951 type, and the 2026 without Magnetraction was resurrected to replace the 2036 with Magnetraction (which was the earlier replacement for the 2026 in 1950)! This 2026 differs from the 1948-1949 version. Refer to *Greenberg's Guide to Lionel Trains, 1945-1969, Volume I* for more detailed information. The engine, protected by a liner, and the other components all came in Middle Classic boxes.   120   200

1481WS   O27 Gauge $70 Retail

Contents: 2035 steam locomotive with headlight, smoke, and Magnetraction; 6466W Lionel Lines whistle tender; 3464 operating boxcar; 3472 operating milk car; 6465 Sunoco two-dome tank car; 6462 black gondola with barrels; 6357 illuminated SP-type caboose; eight curved and seven straight track; 6019 uncoupling/operating section; and a 1033 90-watt transformer.

Comments: The outfit box was the standard 1951 type with blue printing inside of a blue frame. What appeared to be a new outfit was nothing more than a reshuffled deck using up inventory on existing rolling stock. It seems unwise for Lionel to have offered two 2035 sets, the 1481WS and the 1471WS, on the same page of the catalogue at the same price that look so much alike. The engine and tender, protected by liners, as well as the other components all came in Middle Classic boxes.   250   400

		VG	LN

2163WS   O Gauge $60 Retail

Comments: A repeat of the 1950 set in a 1951 outfit box with the price increased from $49.95, and with a 6465 Sunoco two-dome tank car replacing the 6555. Please see **1950** for further information.   375   625

2167WS   O Gauge $47.75 Retail

Comments: A repeat of the 1950 set in a 1951 outfit box with the price increased from $39.95. **1950** contains additional information.   300   500

2173WS   O Gauge $62.50 Retail

Comments: A repeat of the 1950 set in a 1951 outfit box with the price increased from $52.50, and with a 6465 Sunoco

two-dome tank car replacing the 6555. Please refer to **1950** for detailed information.   325   550

2175W   O Gauge $70 Retail

Comments: A repeat of the 1950 Santa Fe set in a 1951 outfit box with the price increased from $57.50, and with a 6465 Sunoco two-dome tank car replacing the 6555. See **1950** for more information.   750   1500

2185W   O Gauge $70 Retail

Comments: A repeat of the 1950 New York Central set in a 1951 outfit box with the price increased from $57.50, and with a 6465 Sunoco two-dome tank car replacing the 6555. Refer to **1950** for other information.   775   1300

An end view of outfit box 2173WS from 1951. This was a carry-over outfit from 1950 that had the 1950 price of $52.50 changed to $62.50 by the use of an OPS sticker. Inflation was rampant in 1951 and prices escalated in excess of 20 percent. M. Sokol Collection.

An end view of the NYC freight outfit 2185W in the new 1951 style outfit box. This set was a repeat and also exists in the 1950 style outfit box with an orange field along with the blue printing. B. Myles Collection.

1952

RUNNING IN PLACE

The Korean War again took its toll on Lionel production — Magnetraction was not available on any steam engine because of the acute shortage of the Alnico magnetic material required for magnetizing axles. The war even affected Lionel's production of O27 and O Gauge track. Standard steel was temporarily replaced with a dull flat gray alloy. The outfit boxes were the same as in 1951, with blue printing inside of a blue frame, but most new issues now included the OPS stamp. The component boxes also remained the same, except for the addition of the OPS stamp as part of the manufacturing process, and all items, even the transformer and the components of low-end sets, were still individually boxed. The Middle Classic box was still being used for the turbine and some of the O27 steam engines. Bar-end trucks made their debut late in 1951, so the composition of 1952 sets was often a mixture of new and old, the old being the staple-end truck.

The 2031 Rock Island, although never included in a set, and the 2032 Erie were new in 1952, as were the highly coveted 2345 Western Pacific, the 623 Santa Fe, and 624 C & O switchers, none of which were included in sets. The only new pieces of rolling stock that were introduced were the 6460 eight-wheel crane, the 3474 Western Pacific operating boxcar, and the 3520 searchlight car with remote-controlled on/off mechanism. The most noted innovation of the year was the introduction of the extruded-aluminum 2500 series passenger cars that were copied in principle from the product of a competitor, American Model Toy Company (AMT).

	VG	LN

1119   O27 Gauge $17.75 Retail

Comments: An exact repeat and/or carry-over of the 1951 set. The sale of Scout sets was suffering, and the 1119 outfit was the last true Scout set to be catalogued. For additional Scout comments, please refer to outfit 1111 in **1948**.

90   150

1464W   O27 Gauge $66.50 Retail

Contents: 2033 Union Pacific Alco AA units; 2421 Maplewood Pullman, 2422 Chatham Pullman, and 2423 Hillside observation in the new silver-with-silver-roof color scheme; eight curved and five straight track; 6019 uncoupling/operating section; and a 1033 90-watt transformer.

Comments: This outfit was Part III of the Union Pacific trilogy. The engine and the cars were recolored in a silver-with-silver combination and black lettering. The passenger cars retained the same numbers as in 1951 but the

	VG	LN

engines were now listed as "2033". The outfit box was the standard 1951-1952 issue. The engines came in the usual Alco corrugated master carton without component boxes, and they were placed as such inside the outfit box. The passenger cars came in OPS Classic boxes with coupler protection flaps.

600   1200

1465   O27 Gauge $22.50 Retail

Contents: 2034 steam locomotive with headlight; 6066T Lionel Lines non-whistle tender; 6032 black gondola; 6035 Sunoco single-dome tank car; 6037 SP-type caboose; eight curved and three straight track; 6019 uncoupling/operating section; and a 1012 35-watt transformer.

Comments: This was another of the semi-Scout sets with Scout trucks and magnetic couplers. The 2034 was a new die-cast engine and came with a protective liner in a Middle Classic box. The tender and nondescript rolling stock also came in Middle Classic boxes. The outfit box itself was an anachronism as it is a 1950 type with an orange panel, blue lettering, and the retail price, along with an OPS stamp. Could this have been a planned 1950 outfit that was not released? Chances are that it was, as even the outfit number fits perfectly into the 1950 series between 1464W and 1467W.

120   200

An end view of outfit 1465 from 1952. The set box itself was an anachronism. It is a 1950 type with an orange panel, blue lettering, and the retail price, but it also includes an OPS stamp. This was probably an outfit planned for 1950 that for one reason or another was not released. Even the outfit number fits perfectly into the 1950 series between 1464W and 1467W. B. Myles Collection.

	VG	LN

1467W   O27 Gauge $57.50 Retail

Contents: 2032 Erie Alco AA units; 6656 stock car; 6456 black or maroon Lehigh Valley hopper; 6465 Sunoco two-dome tank car; 6357 illuminated SP-type caboose; eight curved and five straight track; 6019 uncoupling/operating section; and a 1033 90-watt transformer.

Comments: The rolling stock was all common run-of-the-mill equipment. This was the third consecutive year that the 1467W had been catalogued, but this time the new 2032 Erie was the motive power. The outfit box was standard 1951-1952 issue and all of the freight components came in OPS Classic boxes, while the engines came unboxed in their own corrugated master carton, separated and held in place by cardboard fillers.   **325   500**

1477S   O27 Gauge $29.95 Retail

Comments: An exact repeat and/or carry-over of the 1951 set. Please see **1951** for more detailed information.   **120   200**

1479WS   O27 Gauge $49.95 Retail

Contents: 2056 steam locomotive with headlight and smoke; 2046W Lionel Lines whistle tender; 6462 black gondola with barrels; 6465 Sunoco two-dome tank car; 6456 black or maroon Lehigh Valley hopper; 6257 SP-type caboose; eight curved and three straight track; 6019 uncoupling/operating section; and a 1033 90-watt transformer.

Comments: The 2056 was for all intents the Korean War issue of the 2046, less Magnetraction. Lionel had the good sense to box this piece in a corrugated carton with a protective liner while the other common nondescript pieces of rolling stock came in OPS Classic boxes. The outfit box was the standard issue for the year. The 2056 is somewhat scarce as it was a one-year-only engine.   **300   500**

1483WS   O27 Gauge $65 Retail

Contents: 2056 steam locomotive with headlight and smoke; 2046W Lionel Lines whistle tender; 3472 operating milk car; 6462 black gondola with barrels; 6465 Sunoco two-dome tank car; 3474 operating Western Pacific boxcar; 6357 illuminated SP-type caboose; eight curved and seven straight track; 6019 uncoupling/operating section; and a 1033 90-watt transformer.

Comments: This was the second of the three 2056 sets that were catalogued in 1952. The engine was boxed in a corrugated carton with a protective liner, while the tender, also protected by a liner, and the remainder of the components came in OPS Classic boxes. The 3474 was a new item for 1952, and this was one of only two sets in which it was ever included. The outfit box was the standard 1951-1952 issue.

425   700

1484WS   O27 Gauge $70 Retail

Contents: 2056 steam locomotive with headlight and smoke; 2046W Lionel Lines whistle tender; 2421 Maplewood Pullman, 2422 Chatham Pullman, 2423 Hillside observation, and 2429 Livingston Pullman in the new silver-with-silver roof color scheme; eight curved and seven straight track; 6019 uncoupling/operating section; and a 1033 90-watt transformer.

Comments: This was the top-of-the-line O27 set for 1952, and it was equal in price to the Santa Fe and New York Central F-3 O Gauge freight sets. The outfit box was the standard 1951-1952 issue. The engine was boxed in a corrugated container with a protective liner, while the tender, also protected by a liner, and the passenger cars with coupler protection flaps came in OPS Classic boxes. This is a scarce set and it is the only one of the three that contained the silver-with-silver-roof passenger cars to include the 2429 Livingston Pullman.   **650   1200**

1485WS   O27 Gauge $39.95 Retail

Contents: 2025 steam locomotive with headlight and smoke; 6466W Lionel Lines whistle tender; 6462 black gondola with barrels; 6465 Sunoco two-dome tank car; 6257 SP-type caboose; eight curved and three straight track; 6019 uncoupling/operating section; and a 1033 90-watt transformer.

Comments: This O27 version of the 675, with a 2-6-4 wheel arrangement and spoked drivers, was last catalogued in 1949, and was reintroduced because of the shortage of Alnico material required for Magnetraction. The outfit box was standard issue for 1951-1952 and all the components, including the engine and tender, protected by liners, came in OPS Classic boxes. This set, because of its outfit number and lower price, appears to have been a late addition to the product line.   **165   275**

1489WS   O27 Gauge $45 Retail

Contents: 2025 steam locomotive with headlight and smoke; 6466W Lionel Lines whistle tender; 6456 black or maroon Lehigh Valley hopper; 6656 stock car; 6257 SP-type caboose; eight curved and three straight track; 6019 uncoupling/operating section; and a 1033 90-watt transformer.

Comments: This outfit was nothing more than a run-of-the-mill 2025 set, but at least it included a whistle tender. The outfit box was standard 1952 issue. The engine and tender, packaged with protective liners, and the balance of the components came in OPS Classic boxes.   **165   275**

2177WS   O Gauge $39.95 Retail

Contents: 675 steam locomotive with headlight and smoke; 2046W Lionel Lines whistle tender; 6462 black gondola with barrels; 6465 Sunoco two-dome tank car; 6457 illuminated SP-type caboose; eight curved and five straight track; and a UCS uncoupling/operating section.

1952

	VG	LN

Comments: The 675 was similar to the 1949 version but had a 2-6-4 wheel alignment and spoked drivers. It was brought back because of the shortage of Alnico magnetic material required for Magnetraction. All of the components, including the engine and tender which were protected by liners, came in the OPS Classic boxes, while the outfit box was standard 1951-1952 issue. **210   350**

2179WS   O Gauge $47.75 Retail

Contents: 671 steam turbine locomotive with headlight and smoke; 2046WX Pennsylvania whistle tender; 3464 operating boxcar; 6465 Sunoco two-dome tank car; 6462 black gondola with barrels; 6457 illuminated SP-type caboose; eight curved and five straight track; and a UCS uncoupling/operating section.

Comments: This was another engine reissued because of the Alnico magnetic material shortage. This engine sometimes surfaces with an "RR" below the "671" on the cab and as such is the most desirable variation for collectors; it came in a Middle Classic or OPS Classic box with a protective liner that differs from the pre-1950 version in that "San Francisco" is not part of the logo. The tender also came with a liner in a box with "2046WX" stamped on the end flap. This was Lionel's designation for an eight-wheel tender lettered "Pennsylvania" as opposed to "Lionel Lines". The outfit box was standard 1951-1952 issue, and the rolling stock, all commonplace, came in OPS Classic boxes. The 3464 came with either Santa Fe or NYC markings. **250   425**

2183WS   O Gauge $54.50 Retail

Contents: 726 Berkshire steam locomotive with headlight and smoke; 2046W Lionel Lines whistle tender; 3464 operating boxcar; 6462 black gondola with barrels; 6465 Sunoco two-dome tank car; 6457 illuminated SP-type caboose; eight curved and seven straight track; and a UCS uncoupling/operating section.

Comments: This was yet another reissued number, necessitated by the shortage of Alnico magnetic material, of a 1949 engine. The outfit box was standard 1951-1952 issue. The 726 usually had an "RR" below the number on the cab. It came in a corrugated carton with a protective liner, "726" stamped on the end flaps, and dated "1952" below the box manufacturer's seal; that 1952 date eliminates any confusion about the proper box for the 726 RR. The commonplace rolling stock came in OPS Classic boxes and was identical in composition to the previously listed 2179WS outfit. The 3464 came with either Santa Fe or NYC markings. **325   525**

2187WS   O Gauge $62.50 Retail

Contents: 671 steam turbine locomotive with headlight and smoke; 2046WX Pennsylvania whistle tender; 6462 black gondola with barrels; 3472 operating milk car; 3469 operating ore car; 6456 maroon Lehigh Valley hopper; 6457 illuminated SP-type caboose; eight curved and seven straight track; and a UCS uncoupling/operating section.

	VG	LN

Comments: The engine and tender information for this set is the same as for outfit 2179WS. The outfit box was standard issue, and all of the rolling stock came in OPS Classic boxes. The components were all common but at least this set offered two operating cars. **275   475**

2189WS   O Gauge $69.50 Retail

Contents: 726 Berkshire steam locomotive with headlight and smoke; 2046W Lionel Lines whistle tender; 3520 searchlight car; 3656 operating cattle car; 6462 black gondola with barrels; 3461 operating log car; 6457 illuminated SP-type caboose; eight curved and seven straight track; and a UCS uncoupling/operating section.

Comments: The engine and tender information is the same as for outfit 2183WS. This was the best steam set that Lionel offered in 1952, and it included three operating cars. The outfit box was standard issue and all of the rolling stock came in OPS Classic boxes. The 3520 with remote-controlled on/off was a new item. **350   575**

2190W   O Gauge $89.50 Retail

Contents: 2343P/2343T Santa Fe AA F-3 units; 2531 Silver Dawn observation, 2532 Silver Range Vista Dome, 2533 Silver Cloud Pullman, and 2534 Silver Bluff Pullman extruded-aluminum passenger cars; eight curved and nine straight track; and a UCS uncoupling/operating section.

Comments: The outfit box for this "Super Speedliner" set was standard issue for 1951-1952, except that it came stamped with the $89.50 retail price. The 2343P was boxed in a corrugated carton with a liner while the T unit came in either a Middle Classic or OPS Classic box and was also protected by a liner. The 2500 series passenger cars were new in 1952, and they were a sight to behold. The packaging of these cars was outstanding; each came wrapped with Lionel paper in an individually numbered paper box with a properly fitting cardboard liner. Most 1952 rolling stock boxes included the OPS stamp as part of the manufacturing process; it would be ideal to obtain this outfit with a matched set of boxes.

It is also rather difficult to obtain a matched set of passenger cars since the earliest examples had the light socket

Outfit 2190W contained the 2343 Santa Fe passenger set with the newly released 2500 series extruded-aluminum cars. Note that outfit 2190W also included a printed price which was not the norm for 1952. B. Myles Collection.

VG   LN

assembly wired directly to the contact roller, and Lionel seemed to be experimenting with both rivets and glue as a means of attaching the nameplates. It is believed by some experienced collectors that, because of the complexity of the procedure, hex heads were the earliest method of attaching nameplates. The 1952 edition of the Santa Fe is definitely datable because the corrugated carton for the powered unit is stamped "1952" below the box manufacturer's seal and each of the AA units had the snap-in porthole lens. The large red GM decal was also replaced by a much smaller black decal.

1650   2750

2191W   O Gauge $70 Retail

Contents: 2343P/2343C/2343T Santa Fe ABA F-3 units; 6462 black gondola with barrels; 6656 stock car; 6456 maroon Lehigh Valley hopper; 6457 illuminated SP-type caboose; eight curved and seven straight track; and a UCS uncoupling/operating section.

Comments: The outfit box was the standard 1951-1952 type. This was the first F-3 set to include a B unit as part of the outfit package, and although the ABA combination had an

VG   LN

awesome look, its massiveness dwarfed the common nondescript rolling stock. Most 1952 paper boxes included the OPS stamp as part of the manufacturing process. The 2343P was boxed in a corrugated carton with a protective liner while the C and the T units, also packaged with liners, came in either Middle Classic or OPS Classic boxes. The 1952 edition of the Santa Fe is definitely datable because the corrugated carton for the powered unit is stamped "1952" below the box manufacturer's seal and each of the ABA units had the snap-in porthole lens. The large red GM decal was also replaced by a much smaller black decal.   900   1800

2193W   O Gauge $70 Retail

Comments: This outfit contained the same components as in outfit 2191W, except that the 2344 NYC ABA combination was substituted for the Santa Fe units. The 1952 edition of the NYC underwent the same changes as did the Santa Fe, including the elimination of the large black GM decal in favor or a much smaller one.   950   1600

1952

1953

Innovations Continue

The outfit box was restyled in 1953 with new graphics and logo; except for carry-forward 1952 types, all were conventional two-tier boxes with blue printing inside a red frame with the retail price on the ends, and a large circled-L on the sides. The engine and rolling stock boxes remained essentially unchanged as the OPS stamps disappeared.

1953 was a very good year because Magnetraction returned. The Alnico magnetic material that was essential to Magnetraction was no longer in limited supply as pressures brought on by the Korean conflict began to ease. The 2046, 681, and 736 steam engines were back again while the new issue steam power were the 1130, 2037, 2055, and 685. But why did Lionel still persist in boxing some of their steam engines in paper boxes? Although these engines were always packed with a protective liner, the sheer weight of the die-cast engine has almost always done damage to the ears and end flaps of the box. It is extremely difficult to find paper engine boxes intact and in collectable condition. Regrettably, the highly detailed 2343, 2344, and 2345 F-3 units were discontinued in favor of less detailed engines with the same road names: the 2353, 2354, and 2355 series.

New rolling stock consisted of the 6417 porthole caboose, the 6511 pipe car with die-cast mounting bracket that was the forerunner to an entire series of flatcars, 6415 Sunoco tank car, 6468 double-door automobile car, and the 3484 operating Pennsylvania boxcar. Lastly, the legendary 6464 series boxcars were introduced in four road names: they were the -1 Western Pacific, -25 Great Northern, -50 M St. L, and the -75 Rock Island. A new tender design was also introduced in the square freight-type 6026 body. One other important although inexpensive item was introduced — the 6009 uncoupling section. In previous years Lionel included the more expensive 6019 that both uncoupled and controlled operating cars in all the O27 (except true Scout) outfits. Lionel justly reasoned that there was no need to include such an expensive item in low-end sets; hence, the development of the 6009 which would evolve to become the 6029, then the 6139, and finally the 6149. Can you imagine how many hundreds of thousands of dollars these modest pieces of equipment saved The Lionel Corporation through the years?

	VG	LN

1464W   O27 Gauge $66.50 Retail

Comments: An exact repeat of the 1952 2033 Union Pacific silver-with-silver Alco AA passenger set. The outfit box could have been either a 1952 type with the $66.50 price stamped on the ends, or the new 1953 circled-L box. Please see **1952** for additional information.   **600**   **1200**

	VG	LN

1467W   O27 Gauge $57.50 Retail

Comments: An exact repeat of the 1952 2032 Erie Alco AA freight set. The outfit box could have been either a 1952 type with the $57.50 price stamped on the ends, or the new 1953 circled-L box. **1952** contains further information.   **325**   **550**

1500   O27 Gauge $19.95 Retail

Contents: 1130 steam locomotive with headlight; 6066T Lionel Lines non-whistle tender; 6032 black gondola; 6034 orange Baby Ruth boxcar; 6037 SP-type caboose; eight curved and one straight track; 6009 uncoupling section; and a 1012 35-watt transformer.

Comments: This was another of the semi-Scout sets whose tender and rolling stock were equipped with Scout trucks and magnetic couplers. The caboose was usually catalogued in red but is known to exist only in shades of tuscan. Lionel must have been inundated with Scout trucks as they catalogued three sets in 1953 to rid themselves of inventory. All of the components, even the engine which was protected by a liner, came in Middle Classic boxes while the outfit box was the new circled-L type. Earliest versions of this set have been known to contain a die-cast 1130 that was created from previously unstamped leftover 2034 castings.   **105**   **175**

1501S   O27 Gauge $24.95 Retail

Contents: 2026 steam locomotive with headlight and smoke; 6066T Lionel Lines non-whistle tender; 6032 black gondola; 6035 Sunoco tank car; 6037 SP-type caboose; eight curved and three straight track; 6009 uncoupling section; and a 1043 50-watt transformer.

Comments: This was the eighth and last of the 2026 sets that originated in 1948. It was another of the semi-Scout sets with a tender and rolling stock that had the strange combination of Scout trucks with magnetic couplers. All of the components, even the engine which was protected by a liner, came in Middle Classic boxes while the outfit box was the new circled-L type.   **90**   **150**

1502WS   O27 Gauge $57.50 Retail

Contents: 2055 steam locomotive with headlight, smoke, and Magnetraction; 2046W Lionel Lines whistle ten-

VG LN

der; 2421 Maplewood Pullman, 2422 Chatham Pullman, and 2423 Hillside observation in silver-with-silver-roof color scheme; eight curved and five straight track; 6019 uncoupling/operating section; and a 1033 90-watt transformer.

Comments: The outfit box was the new circled-L type and all of the components, including the engine and tender, protected by liners, came in Middle Classic boxes. The 2055 was new for 1953, while the passenger cars continued to show the 1952 color scheme. This is an underrated and scarce set. Although this was the last issue of the 2420 series passenger cars, none of the individual items are difficult to obtain when separated from the outfit. **550 1000**

1503WS   O27 Gauge $39.95 Retail

Contents: 2055 steam locomotive with headlight, smoke and Magnetraction; 6026W Lionel Lines whistle tender; 6462 black gondola with barrels; 6465 Sunoco two-dome tank car; 6456 black Lehigh Valley hopper; 6257 SP-type caboose; eight curved and three straight track; 6019 uncoupling/operating section; and a 1033 90-watt transformer.

Comments: The outfit box was the new circled-L type and all of the components, including the engine, which was protected by a liner, came in Middle Classic boxes. The 2055 was new for 1953 as was the 6026 freight-type tender, which being a better tender, was also packed with a cardboard liner. The run-of-the-mill rolling stock is quite datable, as opposed to what was produced in 1952, because it should all have bar-end trucks. **265 450**

1505WS   O27 Gauge $49.95 Retail

Contents: 2046 steam locomotive with headlight, smoke, and Magnetraction; 2046W Lionel Lines whistle tender; 6462 black gondola with barrels; 6464-1 Western Pacific boxcar; 6415 Sunoco three-dome tank car; 6357 illuminated SP-type caboose; eight curved and five straight track; 6019 uncoupling/operating section; and a 1033 90-watt transformer.

Comments: This outfit has the prestige of being the first to include a 6464 series boxcar and the highly detailed three-dome Sunoco tank car, even though it was an O27 set. Earliest issues of the tank car do not have the number "6415" rubber stamped on the tank. This set has been known to contain both the rare 6464 Western Pacific with interior roof ribs and the red-lettered variation. The 2046 with Magnetraction was reintroduced after missing the 1952 product year, and the outfit box was the new 1953 circled-L type. The tender, protected by a liner, and rolling stock came in Middle Classic boxes while the engine was boxed with a liner in a corrugated carton. **350 600**

1507WS   O27 Gauge $65 Retail

Contents: 2046 steam locomotive with headlight, smoke, and Magnetraction; 2046W Lionel Lines whistle tender; 6415 Sunoco three-dome tank car; 6462 black gondola with barrels; 3472 operating milk car; 6468 B & O double-door

VG LN

automobile car; 6357 illuminated SP-type caboose; eight curved and five straight track; 6019 uncoupling/operating section; and a 1033 90-watt transformer.

Comments: This was the second 2046 set offered in 1953. The engine with Magnetraction was reintroduced, replacing the Korean War issue 2056. The outfit box was the new circled-L type. The tender, protected by a liner, and rolling stock came in Middle Classic boxes while the 2046 was boxed with a liner in a corrugated carton. This O27 set had two new-design top-of-the-line cars, namely the highly detailed 6415 tank car and the blue double-door automobile car included as components. **350 575**

1509WS   O27 Gauge $70 Retail

Contents: 2046 steam locomotive with headlight, smoke, and Magnetraction; 2046W Lionel Lines whistle tender; 6456 maroon Lehigh Valley hopper; 3520 searchlight car; 3469 operating ore car; 6460 black cab crane; 6419 work caboose; eight curved and five straight track; 6019 uncoupling/operating section; and a 1033 90-watt transformer.

Comments: This was the premium O27 set for the product year and was the third to be headed by a 2046. The engine with Magnetraction was reintroduced and replaced the Korean War issue 2056. The outfit box was the new circled-L type. The engine was packed in a corrugated carton with a protective liner while the tender, also protected by a liner, and the rolling stock came in Middle Classic boxes. This was a very handsome set with its full complement of "work" cars, and was nearly identical in content to the 736 O Gauge outfit 2213WS. **350 600**

1511S   O27 Gauge $32.95 Retail

Contents: 2037 steam locomotive with headlight, smoke and Magnetraction; 6066T Lionel Lines non-whistle tender; 6032 black gondola; 3474 operating Western Pacific boxcar; 6035 Sunoco tank car; 6037 SP-type caboose; eight curved and three straight track; 6019 uncoupling/operating section; and a 1043 50-watt transformer.

Comments: This was the first of sixteen postwar 2037 sets to be catalogued, and it was a real hodgepodge. The tender, gondola, tank car, and caboose were semi-Scout pieces with Scout trucks and magnetic couplers, while the 2037 was a new number, high quality die-cast engine, and the 3474 was an operating boxcar with bar-end trucks. This outfit was probably a late addition to the product line, as the price and the 1511 number imply, simply to move Scout inventory. The engine, protected by a liner, and the other contents all came in Middle Classic boxes while the outfit box was the new circled-L type.

The early 1953 issues of the 2037 were rubber stamped; later versions were heat stamped. This was not an uncommon practice at Lionel since other examples of this practice, such as with the 646 steam engine, are a matter of record. Lionel was often remiss in preparing their heat-stamp tooling to coincide with production schedules. **225 375**

1
9
5
3

	VG	LN

	VG	LN

1953

2190W   O Gauge $89.50 Retail

Contents: 2353P/2353T Santa Fe AA F-3 units; 2531 Silver Dawn observation, 2532 Silver Range Vista Dome, 2533 Silver Cloud Pullman, and 2534 Silver Bluff Pullman extruded-aluminum passenger cars; eight curved and nine straight track; and a UCS uncoupling/operating section.

Comments: This was practically a repeat of the 1952 set as the less detailed 2353 replaced the highly detailed 2343. This no doubt saved Lionel money, yet the price of both the outfit and the separate-sale engines remained the same as in 1952. The outfit box could have been either a carry-over 1952 type with "$89.50" stamped on the ends, or the new 1953 circled-L box. It is difficult to determine whether any of the 1952 series boxes were unsold inventory and still contained the 2343, or if they were simply unused and newly packed with the 2353. The powered unit came in a corrugated carton with a protective liner while the T unit and the passenger cars also came with liners but in Middle Classic boxes. Again, it is difficult to obtain a matched set of these passenger cars as Lionel still seemed to be experimenting with both glue and with large and small round-head rivets as a means of attaching the nameplates. Hex heads also could have been used. Regardless of the type, a matched set of passenger cars is always preferred.   **1650   2750**

2201WS   O Gauge $39.95 Retail

Contents: 685 steam locomotive with headlight, smoke, and Magnetraction; 6026W Lionel Lines whistle tender; 6464-50 M St. L boxcar; 6465 Sunoco two-dome tank car; 6462 black gondola with barrels; 6357 illuminated SP-type caboose; eight curved and five straight track; and a UCS uncoupling/operating section.

Comments: The outfit box was the new circled-L type. The 685 and the 6026W freight type tender were new for 1953, and because it was a one-year production item, the 685 appeared in this set only. All of the components, including the engine and tender, protected by liners, came in Middle Classic boxes. The -50 M St. L boxcar was catalogued in green but does not exist as such in regular production. Note that the less expensive 6465 tank car was included with this introductory O Gauge outfit.   **400   650**

2203WS   O Gauge $49.95 Retail

Contents: 681 steam turbine locomotive with headlight, smoke, and Magnetraction; 2046WX Pennsylvania whistle tender; 6415 Sunoco three-dome tank car; 3520 searchlight car; 6464-25 Great Northern boxcar; 6417 Pennsylvania porthole caboose; eight curved and five straight track; and a UCS uncoupling/operating section.

Comments: The 681 turbine was reintroduced, replacing the non-Magnetraction Korean War issue 671. The tender may have come in a box with either "2046WX" or "2046W P.R.R." stamped on the end flaps — both were Lionel's designation for an eight-wheel tender lettered "Pennsylvania". This set had three new-for-1953 cars, namely the tank car,

porthole caboose, and -25 boxcar. This was one of only two sets to contain the -25 Great Northern boxcar. This car sometimes appears with a water-soluble Great Northern decal, but this variation is in all probability a post-factory addition. Earliest editions of the highly detailed, three-dome Sunoco tank car do not have the number "6415" rubber stamped on the car. The outfit box was the new circled-L type and all of the components, including the engine and tender which were protected by liners, came in the Middle Classic boxes.   **325   550**

2205WS   O Gauge $59.75 Retail

Contents: 736 Berkshire steam locomotive with headlight, smoke, and Magnetraction; 2046W Lionel Lines whistle tender; 3484 operating Pennsylvania boxcar; 6415 Sunoco three-dome tank car; 6468 B & O double-door automobile car; 6456 black Lehigh Valley hopper; 6417 Pennsylvania porthole caboose; eight curved and seven straight track; and a UCS uncoupling/operating section.

Comments: The 736 with Magnetraction was reintroduced to the product line, replacing the 726RR, and it would become the backbone of O Gauge steam power all the way through 1968. All of the rolling stock, except the 6456 hopper, was new for 1953, and this was one of the few postwar sets to include two items from the eleven-inch boxcar series, namely the 6468 and the 3484. The outfit box was the new circled-L type. The tender, protected by a liner, and rolling stock came in Middle Classic boxes while the engine was packed with a liner in a corrugated carton.   **425   725**

2207W   O Gauge $70 Retail

Contents: 2353P/2353C/2353T Santa Fe ABA F-3 units; 6462 black gondola with barrels; 3484 operating Pennsylvania boxcar; 6415 Sunoco three-dome tank car; 6417 Pennsylvania porthole caboose; eight curved and seven straight track; and a UCS uncoupling/operating section.

Comments: The outfit box was the new circled-L type. The 2353 series was the less detailed replacement for the 1950-1952 era 2343 units. The 2353P was boxed in a corrugated carton with a protective liner while the C and T units, also protected by liners, and the balance of the rolling stock came in Middle Classic boxes. The massiveness of the ABA combination again appeared to dwarf the rolling stock. This set had three new-for-1953 cars, namely the 3484, 6415, and 6417 porthole caboose. Earliest editions of the three-dome Sunoco tank do not have the number "6415" rubber stamped on the car.

Can you believe that the Santa Fe was pulling a Pennsylvania caboose? This outfit and outfit 2209W would have been ideal sets in which to introduce matching road name cabooses. Evidently someone at Lionel at least pondered the idea at some point since the porthole caboose was pictured with Santa Fe markings on page 42 of the 1960 catalogue!   **1000   2000**

	VG	LN

2209W   O Gauge $70 Retail

Comments: This set contained the same components as outfit 2207W except that the 2354 NYC ABA combination was substituted for the Santa Fe units.   **1050   1750**

2211WS   O Gauge $62.50 Retail

Contents: 681 steam turbine locomotive with headlight, smoke, and Magnetraction; 2046WX Pennsylvania whistle tender; 3656 operating cattle car; 6464-75 Rock Island boxcar; 3461 operating log car; 6417 Pennsylvania porthole caboose; eight curved and five straight track; and a UCS uncoupling/operating section.

Comments: This was the second 681 set catalogued in 1953. The engine was reintroduced, replacing the 671, now that the Alnico magnetic material required for Magnetraction was no longer in short supply. The outfit box was the new circled-L type, and all of the components, including the engine and tender, protected by liners, came in Middle Classic boxes. The tender may have come in a box with either "2046WX" or "2046W P.R.R." stamped on the end flaps, since both were

	VG	LN

Lionel's designation for an eight-wheel tender lettered "Pennsylvania" as opposed to "Lionel Lines". This was also the only set to ever include the -75 green Rock Island boxcar.   **350   575**

2213WS   O Gauge $70 Retail

Contents: 736 Berkshire steam locomotive with headlight, smoke, and Magnetraction; 2046W Lionel Lines whistle tender; 3461 operating log car; 3520 searchlight car; 3469 operating ore car; 6460 black cab crane; 6419 work caboose; eight curved and seven straight track; and a UCS uncoupling/operating section.

Comments: The 736 Berkshire was reintroduced, replacing the Korean War issue 726RR, because the Alnico magnetic material required for Magnetraction was no longer in limited supply. The outfit box was the new circled-L type. The rolling stock and tender, protected by a liner, came in Middle Classic boxes while the engine was boxed with a liner in a corrugated carton. This was the top-of-the-line O Gauge steam set for 1953, and it was quite reminiscent of the quality work trains catalogued in the late 1940s. The green example of the 3461 operating log car was a sometime component in this outfit.   **400   675**

1 9 5 3

1954

THE PINNACLE

As the title implies, this was about as good as it would get. The year 1954 brought a greater variety of rolling stock in colorations that made the outfits visually more appealing, and therefore more saleable. New motive power was introduced via the 646, 665, 682, and 2065 steam engines, and in the 2245, 2321, 2356 Southern, and 6250 Seaboard diesels. The 2245 Texas Special was a single-motored F-3 that was issued in an AB combination and, at $39.95 for separate sale, was priced the same as the AA Alco units. The 2321 Lackawanna speaks for itself. It was a piece of design and engineering excellence, except for the slightly loose-fitting cab that most often led to those accursed screw hole cracks.

Seven new 6464 series cars were presented in 1954: the -100 Western Pacific blue feather, -100 Western Pacific yellow feather, -125 Pacemaker, -150 Missouri Pacific, -175 silver Rock Island, -200 Pennsylvania, and the -225 Southern Pacific. New rolling stock were the 6446 cement car, 6356 stock car, 6672 reefer, and the 3562 operating barrel car in black and gray. An important new tender, the 1130T, was also introduced in 1954. It was a scaled-down version of the streamlined 2046 body style whose life span in various forms would stretch into the mid-1960s. The -25 gray operating barrel car was always catalogued with red letters, but the car itself is too common and the red-lettered variation too rare to positively say of which, if any, set it was a regular component. Lionel also began to deplete inventory on the larger unstained barrels, replacing them in gondolas with smaller stained barrels that were developed for the 3562.

The O Gauge 2530 baggage car was another innovation in 1954, and the 2400 series passenger cars were slightly recolored and now appeared as the red-lettered 2430 series. In the midst of all this newness the outfit boxes and the component boxes remained essentially unchanged from 1953; the only minor change occurred in the 6462 gondola boxes. An elongated box, similar to the 1949-1950 issue, reappeared with coupler protection flaps, and the outfit box continued as the circled-L type with blue printing and the retail price inside of a red frame.

1500   O27 Gauge $19.95 Retail

Contents: A repeat of the 1953 outfit number with the new 1130T tender with bar-end trucks replacing the 6066T semi-Scout tender.

Comments: This was the last of the semi-Scout sets in which rolling stock was equipped with Scout trucks and magnetic couplers. Finally the catalogue illustrated the rolling stock with Scout trucks! The 1130T tender, an important piece

	VG	LN

whose life span would run into the 1960s, was introduced with this set. Please see **1953** for further information.

	120	200

1503WS   O27 Gauge $39.95 Retail

Comments: This was a repeat of the 1953 outfit, except that a maroon 6456 was substituted for the black hopper, and a green 6462 gondola was substituted for the black. The gondola often came in a restamped box with the "-25" suffix added to designate green. The larger unstained barrels were usually replaced by the smaller stained barrels that were developed for the 3562 operating barrel car. Please refer to **1953** for additional information.   275   475

1513S   O27 Gauge $29.95 Retail

Contents: 2037 steam locomotive with headlight, smoke, and Magnetraction; 6026T Lionel Lines non-whistle tender; 6012 black gondola; 6014 red Baby Ruth boxcar; 6015 yellow Sunoco single-dome tank car; 6017 SP-type caboose; eight curved and three straight track; 6009 uncoupling section; and a 1043 50-watt transformer.

Comments: The outfit box was standard circled-L issue, and all of the components, including the engine and tender, which were protected by liners, came in Middle Classic boxes. Although this was a very unassuming set with run-of-the-mill equipment, the 6015 is a hard car to find boxed. The earliest examples of the 6015 are the scarce yellow-painted gray body molds that were undoubtedly excess inventory on 6035 shells.   150   250

1515WS   O27 Gauge $49.95 Retail

Contents: 2065 steam locomotive with headlight, smoke, and Magnetraction; 2046W Lionel Lines whistle tender; 6462 black gondola with barrels; 6415 Sunoco three-dome tank car; 6464-25 Great Northern boxcar; 6456-25 gray Lehigh Valley hopper; 6357 illuminated SP-type caboose; eight curved and three straight track; 6019 uncoupling/operating section; and a 1033 90-watt transformer.

Comments: The outfit box was standard 1953-1954 issue, and all of the components, including the engine and tender, which were protected by liners, came in Middle Classic

VG   LN

boxes. This was only one of two outfits to include the Great Northern boxcar. The -25 gray hopper was newly recolored for 1954.   **350   600**

VG   LN

on the lower right side. The 6427 caboose has Lionel Lines markings while the "-25X" suffix applied to the log dump car box meant that it was green, not black, and that the unloading bin was placed loose inside the outfit box rather than being packed with the car itself.   **400   650**

1516WS   O27 Gauge $59.95 Retail

Contents: 2065 steam locomotive with headlight, smoke, and Magnetraction; 2046W Lionel Lines whistle tender; 2432 Clifton Vista Dome, 2434 Newark Pullman, and 2436 Summit observation in the new silver-with-red-letter color scheme; eight curved and five straight track; 6019 uncoupling/operating section; and a 1033 90-watt transformer.

Comments: This was the first of ten outfits to include the 2430 series passenger cars. The outfit box was the standard circled-L type, and all of the components, including the engine and tender, which were protected by liners, came in Middle Classic boxes. Component boxes for 1954 sets *must* have the stock number shown on all four sides. These 2430 series passenger car boxes were printed in this manner and are a bit longer and a shade narrower than their 1955 counterparts. The components in this set are readily available, yet the outfit box itself is very scarce.   **450   800**

1517W   O27 Gauge $59.95 Retail

Contents: 2245P/2245C Texas Special AB F-3 units; 6464-225 Southern Pacific boxcar, 6561 depressed-center flatcar with cable reels, 6462-25 green gondola with barrels; 6427 Lionel Lines porthole caboose; eight curved and five straight track; 6019 uncoupling/operating section; and a 1033 90-watt transformer.

Comments: The 2245 was the first edition of a single-motored F-3 unit, and the first F-3 to be offered in an AB combination. The powered unit was packed in a corrugated carton with a protective liner while the B unit, also with a liner, came in a Middle Classic box. The remainder of the rolling stock also came in Middle Classic boxes, while the outfit box was the 1953-1954 circled-L type. The -225 boxcar was common only to this set. The 6427 Lionel Lines porthole caboose was new issue as were both the cable car and the green gondola. The gondola often came in a restamped box with the "-25" suffix added to designate green.   **900   1500**

1519WS   O27 Gauge $65 Retail

Contents: 2065 steam locomotive with headlight, smoke, and Magnetraction; 6026W Lionel Lines whistle tender; 6356 stock car; 6462-75 red-painted gondola with barrels; 3482 operating milk car; 3461-25 green operating log car; 6427 Lionel Lines porthole caboose; eight curved and five straight track; 6019 uncoupling/operating section; and a 1033 90-watt transformer.

Comments: The outfit box was the 1953-1954 circled-L type, and all of the components, including the engine and tender which were protected by liners, came in Middle Classic boxes. The 6356 stock car was a new 1954 item and the -75 gondola, which was painted in a shade of true red, was most common to 1954. The 3482 was the revised edition of the 3472, and the earliest issues of this car came with "3472" stamped

1520W   O27 Gauge $69.50 Retail

Contents: 2245P/2245C Texas Special AB F-3 units; 2432 Clifton Vista Dome, 2435 Elizabeth Pullman, and 2436 Summit observation in the new silver-with-red-letter color scheme; eight curved and five straight track; 6019 uncoupling/operating section; and a 1033 90-watt transformer.

Comments: The 2245 was the first edition of the single-motored F-3 units, and the first F-3 to be offered in an AB combination. The powered unit was packed in a corrugated carton with a protective liner while the B unit also came with a liner but in a Middle Classic box. This was the second of ten outfits to include the 2430 series passenger cars, and only one of two to include the 2435 Elizabeth Pullman. The Middle Classic passenger car boxes with coupler protection flaps are a bit longer and a shade narrower than their 1955 counterparts. Please refer to page 67 for an end view of the outfit box.   **1050   1750**

1521WS   O27 Gauge $69.50 Retail

Contents: 2065 steam locomotive with headlight, smoke, and Magnetraction; 2046W Lionel Lines whistle tender; 3620 searchlight car; 6561 depressed-center flatcar with cable reels, 6460 black cab crane; 3562 black operating barrel car; 6419-25 work caboose; eight curved and five straight track; 6019 uncoupling/operating section; and a 1033 90-watt transformer.

Comments: This was the fourth 2065 set catalogued for the year. The outfit box was the 1953-1954 circled-L type, and all of the components, including the engine and tender, protected by liners, came in Middle Classic boxes. The cable car and the operating barrel car were new items for 1954. This was one of two sets to include the scarce black operating barrel car. The proper box for this item has only "3562" on the end flaps. The work caboose, with only one coupler, usually came in a box with a "-25" suffix and marked "For O27 track" on the end flaps.   **425   700**

1523   O27 Gauge $49.95 Retail

Contents: 6250 Seaboard NW-2 switcher; 6511 brick red-painted pipe car; 6456-25 gray Lehigh Valley hopper; 6460-25 red cab crane; 6419-25 work caboose; eight curved and five straight track; 6019 uncoupling/operating section; and a 1034 75-watt transformer.

Comments: The outfit box was the standard 1953-1954 circled-L type. Every component in this set is worthy of a comment. First, the 6250 was a new road name and it would be the last of the "quality" switchers. It was the decaled version and was packed in the standard Middle Classic box with a full wraparound liner. Secondly, the work caboose with

1954

VG LN

only one coupler usually came in a box with a "-25" suffix and marked "For O27 track" on the end flaps. The gray hopper also had a "-25" suffix designation as part of the component box. Furthermore, the red 6460 crane was common only to this set and also came in a box with a "-25" suffix. Finally, this was the first outfit to include the 6511 pipe car with cast-metal underplate that was introduced for the 1953 product line.

650 1100

2201WS   O Gauge $39.95 Retail

Comments: A repeat of the 1953 outfit except that the new 665 with feedwater heater replaced the 685. This was the first of nine 665 outfits to be catalogued through the years. Please refer to **1953** for more detailed information.

275 475

2217WS   O Gauge $49.95 Retail

Contents: 682 steam turbine locomotive with headlight, smoke, Magnetraction, and lubricator linkage; 2046WX Pennsylvania whistle tender; 6464-175 Rock Island boxcar; 3562-25 gray operating barrel car; 6356 stock car; 6417 Pennsylvania porthole caboose; eight curved and five straight track; and a UCS uncoupling/operating section.

Comments: The outfit box was the standard 1953-1954 circled-L type. All of the components, including the engine and tender, which were protected by liners, came in Middle Classic boxes. The 682 was a slightly revamped 681 with lubricator linkage and the addition of a narrow white stripe along the running board. The tender came in a box with "2046W P.R.R." stamped on the end flaps as this was Lionel's designation for an eight-wheel tender lettered "Pennsylvania". Most tenders were rubber-stamped "2046-50" on the underframe near the water scoop. The rolling stock, except for the caboose, was all new issue.

The -175 Rock Island was common to only this set, and earliest editions have been known to come with the rare black-lettered variation. The component box for the Rock Island was usually a 6464-50 M St. L box that had been overstamped with the word "silver". The scarce box for this item is the one with a "-175" suffix that was used predominately for separate sale. This was one of three sets to include the new gray barrel car, which was always catalogued with red letters. The gray car itself is too common and the red-lettered variation too rare to positively say of which, if any, set that it was a regular component.

600 1000

2219W   O Gauge $59.95 Retail

Contents: 2321 Lackawanna F-M, 6456-25 gray Lehigh Valley hopper; 6464-50 M St. L boxcar; 6462-25 green gondola with barrels; 6415 Sunoco three-dome tank car; 6417 Pennsylvania porthole caboose; eight curved and five straight track; and a UCS uncoupling/operating section.

Comments: This was the introductory set for the Fairbanks-Morse diesel. The engine was catalogued with a gray roof, but earliest editions of this set may have contained the more desirable maroon roof variation. The outfit box was the 1953-1954 circled-L type, and the engine was packed in a

VG LN

corrugated carton with a protective liner while the remainder of the components came in Middle Classic boxes. The gray Lehigh Valley hopper came in a box with a "-25" suffix as did the green 6462 gondola. This was the third outfit to include the -50 M St. L boxcar.

1200 2000

2221WS   O Gauge $59.95 Retail

Contents: 646 steam locomotive with headlight, smoke, and Magnetraction; 2046W Lionel Lines whistle tender; 6468 B & O double-door automobile car; 3620 searchlight car; 3469 operating ore car; 6456-25 gray Lehigh Valley hopper; 6417-25 Lionel Lines porthole caboose; eight curved and seven straight track; and a UCS uncoupling/operating section.

Comments: The outfit box was the standard 1953-1954 circled-L type. The engine was packed with a protective liner in a corrugated carton that often had blue printing, while the tender, also packed with a liner, and the remainder of the components came in Middle Classic boxes. The 1954 edition of the 646 usually came with a rubber-stamped number and a die-cast trailing truck. The "-25" suffix applied to the caboose box meant that it had two couplers and "Lionel Lines" lettering instead of "Pennsylvania", while the "-25" suffix on the end flaps of the hopper box indicated that it was gray. The searchlight car was catalogued with an orange hood and may have come as such with the outfit. The orange hood 3620 is a known variation, but more often than not the searchlight hood was orange plastic painted gray. The gray paint is easily removed, and often done so, to create the more appealing orange-with-orange combination.

350 600

2222WS   O Gauge $65 Retail

Contents: 646 steam locomotive with headlight, smoke, and Magnetraction; 2046W Lionel Lines whistle tender; 2530 Railway Express baggage car; 2531 Silver Dawn observation and 2532 Silver Range Vista Dome extruded-aluminum passenger cars; eight curved and seven straight track; and a UCS uncoupling/operating section.

Contents: The outfit box was the standard 1953-1954 circled-L type. The engine came protected by a liner in a corrugated carton that often had blue printing, while the tender and the aluminum cars were also packed with liners but in Middle Classic boxes. The 1954 edition of the 646 usually came with a rubber-stamped number and a die-cast trailing truck. The baggage car was new for 1954 and for the first time was offered in a set. This was also the first time that aluminum cars were pulled by a steam engine. This set usually contained the extremely scarce large-door variation of the 2530 baggage car. For collectors the most desirable way to own this outfit would be with the large door baggage car and glued plates on the 2531 and 2532; rivets and even hex heads could also be viable options, but regardless of type, a matched set of passenger cars is always preferred.

With large door baggage car   1200 2000

The contents of 2321 Lackawanna outfit 2223W. 1954 was the introductory year for the Fairbanks-Morse twin-engine diesel. It was an awesome puller whose only shortcoming was a slightly loose-fitting cab that most often led to cracks in the screw holes. This set surfaces with a number of very interesting variations that are explained in the text. This outfit contained the scarce maroon roof variation of the Lackawanna and the -100 blue feather boxcar. Note that the Western Pacific boxcar came in a box with a -250 suffix. P. Sigrist Collection.

VG LN

2223W O Gauge $67.50 Retail

Contents: 2321 Lackawanna F-M; 6464-100 Western Pacific blue or yellow feather, 3461-25 green operating log car; 3482 operating milk car; 6462-125 red unpainted gondola with barrels; 6417-50 gray Lehigh Valley porthole caboose; eight curved and seven straight track; and a UCS uncoupling/operating section.

Comments: This was the second Fairbanks-Morse set catalogued in 1954. The engine was catalogued with a gray roof, but the early editions of this set came with the scarce maroon roof variation. The outfit box was the standard 1953-1954 circled-L type, and the engine was packed in a corrugated carton with a protective liner while the remainder of the components came in the Middle Classic boxes. The -125 gondola was unpainted red plastic with small stained barrels, and the log dump car came in a box with a "-25X" suffix. This was also the only set to include the scarce gray Lehigh Valley caboose which came in a box with a "-50" suffix, and the -100 Western Pacific boxcar.

It is with the boxcar that matters get a bit confusing: the -100 may have been the rare blue feather variation in a box with a "-250" suffix, or it may have come in a box with a "-100" suffix. The boxcar could also have been the -100 yellow feather in a "-100" box. Needless to say, the most desirable boxcar would be the -100 blue feather in a -250 box. The blue feather Western Pacific was reissued in 1966, and finally appeared with the numerically correct "-250" stamping. The original issue was usually a Type II body mold and can be considered an error car. It should have been stamped "-250" since that would have been the next number in the 6464 sequence following the -225 Southern Pacific. Evidently the purchasing department ordered a limited supply of the correct -250 boxes, but the production department mistakenly used the heat stamp that was developed for the -100 yellow feather.

	VG	LN
Maroon roof with -100 blue	2100	3500
Gray roof with -100 blue	1850	3100
Maroon roof with -100 yellow	1675	2800
Gray roof with -100 yellow	1450	2400

The contents of Berkshire steam outfit 2225WS. This is one of fifteen 736 sets that Lionel actually shipped during the postwar era but the only one offered in 1954. This outfit contained the scarce black 3562 barrel car. Note that the ramp of the barrel car was painted an uncomplimentary shade of yellow. This yellow was the same as what was used on the corral that came with the 3656 cattle car, and is a prime example of depletion of old inventory — paint in this instance. P. Sigrist Collection.

	VG	LN

2225WS   O Gauge $69.50 Retail

Contents: 736 Berkshire steam locomotive with headlight, smoke, and Magnetraction; 2046W Lionel Lines whistle tender; 3461-25 green operating log car; 3562 black operating barrel car; 3620 searchlight car; 6460 black cab crane; 6419 work caboose; eight curved and seven straight track; and a UCS uncoupling/operating section.

Comments: This was the only Berkshire set offered for the year and it was very similar to the 1953 work train outfit 2213WS. The outfit box was the standard 1953-1954 circled-L type. The engine was packed in a corrugated carton with a protective liner while the tender, also packed with a liner, and the balance of the components came in Middle Classic boxes. This was one of two sets to include the scarce black barrel car. Note that every item in this set, except the log dump car, contained some type of cardboard insert.   **500   825**

2227W   O Gauge $69.50 Retail

Contents: 2353P/2353T Santa Fe AA F-3 units; 3562-25 gray operating barrel car; 6356 stock car; 6456-75 enameled red Lehigh Valley hopper; 6468 B & O double-door automobile car; 6417-25 Lionel Lines porthole caboose; eight curved and seven straight track; and a UCS uncoupling/operating section.

Comments: This was a visually appealing set with an abundance of colors. The outfit box was the standard 1953-

	VG	LN

1954 circled-L type. The powered unit was boxed in a corrugated carton with a protective liner while the T unit came protected by a liner in a Middle Classic box. The remainder of the rolling stock also came in Middle Classic boxes. Lionel justly reasoned that it might be considered strange for a Santa Fe to again be pulling a Pennsylvania caboose, so the -25 Lionel Lines with operating couplers at both ends was included with this outfit, and with 2229W and 2231W that follow. The 3562 and the 6356 were new additions to the rolling stock roster while the scarce -75 hopper with enameled red paint and yellow lettering was common to only this and the 2229W NYC set. The proper hopper box must come with a "-75" suffix on the end flaps; in addition, the earliest examples of this set may contain the rare white-lettered variation of this hopper.   **800   1600**

2229W   O Gauge $69.50 Retail

Comments: This set had the same components as outfit 2227W except that the 2354 NYC was substituted for the Santa Fe units.   **900   1500**

2231W   O Gauge $79.50 Retail

Contents: 2356P/2356C/2356T Southern ABA F-3 units; 6511 brick red-painted pipe car; 6561 depressed-center

VG   LN

flatcar with cable reels; 3482 operating milk car; 6415 Sunoco three-dome tank car; 6417-25 Lionel Lines caboose; eight curved and seven straight track; and a UCS uncoupling/operating section.

Comments: This was a *most* attractive set headed by the colorful new Southern, the third catalogued road name to be offered in a twin-motored F-3 series outfit. The outfit box was the standard 1953-1954 circled-L type. The powered unit was packed in a corrugated carton with a liner, while the C and T units, also protected by liners, and the balance of the components came in Middle Classic boxes. The 6417-25 caboose with operating couplers at both ends was lettered "Lionel Lines" rather than "Pennsylvania". One of Lionel's shortcomings in the 1950s was their failure to produce more road name cabooses, but at least the Southern was not pulling a Pennsylvania caboose. The balance of the rolling stock was all standard for 1954, except for the possibility that the 3482 may have "3472" stamped on the lower right side.

                                      1950   3250

| **2234W** | **O Gauge** | **$89.50 Retail** |

Contents: 2353P/2353T Santa Fe AA F-3 units; 2530 Railway Express baggage car; 2531 Silver Dawn observation, 2532 Silver Range Vista Dome, and 2533 Silver Cloud Pullman extruded-aluminum passenger cars; eight curved and nine straight track; and a UCS uncoupling/operating section.

Comments: This was the third and last installment of the Santa Fe passenger series that originated in 1952. The powered unit was packed with a liner in a corrugated carton while the T unit and passenger cars also came with liners, but in Middle Classic boxes. The 2530 baggage car was new to the Santa Fe series, replacing the 2534 Silver Bluff Pullman of previous sets. The outfit box was the standard 1953-1954 circled-L type, but the printing on the ends was unique to this outfit in that the colors were reversed; the ends were printed in red surrounded by a blue frame. It is extremely difficult to

An end view of two 1954 set boxes. Pay particular attention to the reversed color printing on the box that was used solely for the top-of-the-line Santa Fe passenger outfit 2234W, and notice that the retail price was encircled on the lower left of both rectangular frames. M. Sokol Collection.

VG   LN

obtain a matched set of passenger cars because this outfit has been known to contain both rivets and glued plates, and even a hex head variation on occasion. The most acceptable way to own this set would be to have a matched set of glued plates. Regardless of the type, a matched set of passenger cars is always preferred by collectors.   **1500   3000**

1955

THE PENDULUM REVERSES

This was a pivotal year in Lionel history and is one of the most difficult of all to analyze. From the beginning of the postwar era, Lionel's marketing and production strategy had been to make the item better; in 1955, however, Lionel began to forsake quality for cost reductions. Less intricately-detailed F-3 units were introduced as were the inferior versions of the NW-2 switcher. The GP-7 was a new item that replaced the high quality and extremely reliable Alco units. Less expensive rolling stock was introduced in the form of the 6111 flatcar and the 6119 work caboose; gone was the die-cast chassis of the work crane.

Packaging also took a dramatic turn downwards. Gone were the protective box liners from the powered F-3 units, the steam engines, the tenders, the switchers, the work cabooses, the cranes, and the aluminum passenger cars. In some cases the liners were replaced by smaller cardboard inserts that made replacing the item properly in the box extremely difficult and often hazardous to the box itself. The corrugated carton for diesel and steam engines was newly designed. It now had flaps on the top and bottom that were folded and tucked into the middle section of the ends. The print color on the boxes was either black or blue, or in some rare instances, red. This was also the year in which Lionel broke with postwar tradition and experimented with packaging an unusual combination of both boxed and unboxed contents, in sets 1001 and 1525.

At least metal trucks were still the norm, as Lionel did not get around to cheapening them until 1957, but they were now attached with a push pin rather than a horseshoe clip, and an extended tab was added to facilitate uncoupling.

Amidst all this gloom and doom, however, several important items made their debut: namely the 60 trolley, the 41 Army motorized unit, the 3359 twin-bin dump car, the 3361 operating lumber car, the 3662 milk car, the 6517 bay window caboose, and the 6414 Evans auto loader. Mint examples of the new auto loader came with the vehicles packaged in gray cardboard sheaths. Autos were packed two to a sheath with white usually paired with aqua, and red paired with yellow. This method of packaging autos would be carried forward to the 6424 flatcar that was introduced in 1956. The 3361 lumber car was a new design that utilized only plastic as the body mold material. The car itself was stamped "336155" — the "55" denoted the year of issue. It was usually included in sets in a box stamped "3361X" that did not include an unloading bin as part of component packaging. Separate-sale examples came in a larger box that included an unloading bin, with only "3361" stamped on the end flaps. The new 3361 was a predecessor to other flatcars such as the 6362 and the 6361. Two new 6464 series boxcars were introduced in State of Maine and Rutland markings. The GG-1 reappeared after last being catalogued in 1950. Lastly, the 2500 series passenger

car body underwent a minor change as some of the ribbing was removed from the sides in order to accommodate the striping required for the 2540 series Congressional cars.

Another dilemma arose with regard to the outfit boxes. In order to hide retail pricing disparities, Lionel attempted to confuse and mislead retail customers by issuing two different but corresponding series of outfit numbers. The traditional four-number outfit boxes were reserved for the wholesale jobber or distributor to resell to their small independent dealers; the three-number outfit coding was relegated to department stores and chains. Lionel even issued unnumbered outfit boxes to some distributors and urged them to make up their own sets and to include accessories! The only constant when discussing 1955 set boxes is that they were the conventional circled-L type and that the phrase "1955 outfit" appeared somewhere on the carton itself. It is known to have appeared above, below, or inside the red frame on the box end.

Remember that this was a year of major transition, and therefore the outfits themselves most often contained a mix-

An end view of three 1955 outfit boxes: (Top) Special value 2016 steam freight outfit 1000W; (Middle) 2251W Virginian F-M freight set; (Bottom) 2247W Wabash F-3 freight set. B. Myles Collection.

VG   LN   VG   LN

ture of old and new types of engine and tender boxes, rolling stock boxes, passenger car bodies, truck attachment, couplers, etc. All 1955 Classic boxes still had the stock number printed on all four sides. This is most important since many of the items introduced in 1955 were also carried forward and are more apt to surface in the revised 1956 box, in which the stock number was deleted from the four sides.

1000W or 506   O27 Gauge $39.95 Retail

Contents: 2016 steam locomotive with headlight; 6026W Lionel Lines whistle tender; 6014 red Baby Ruth boxcar; 6012 black gondola; 6017 SP-type caboose; eight curved and three straight track; 6029 uncoupling section; and a 1033 90-watt transformer.

Comments: This outfit, along with 1001, was numbered differently from the normal sequence. Lionel touted this and the 1001 outfit in their promotional material as exceptional value sets. The outfit box was the standard two-tier 1955 issue. The engine was boxed in the new corrugated carton without a protective liner, while the tender, now without a liner, and rolling stock came in Middle Classic boxes. This was the only outfit ever to include the 2016 and that fact alone makes it collectable. See page 68 for an end view of the outfit box.   **300**   **500**

1001 or 501   O27 Gauge $22.50 Retail

Contents: 610 Erie NW-2 switcher; 6012 black gondola; 6014 red Baby Ruth boxcar; 6015 yellow Sunoco single-dome tank car; 6017 SP-type caboose; eight curved and one straight track; 6029 uncoupling section; and a 1014 40-watt transformer.

Comments: This was one of two sets that offered the significantly inferior version of the NW-2 diesel switcher. The outfit box was the standard 1955 issue, but had only a single tier. The engine with two small cardboard inserts came in a Middle Classic box while the other components were unboxed. This outfit and outfit 1525 or 500 were the two 1955 sets that had unusual combinations of boxed and unboxed contents. Furthermore, outfit 1001, along with 1000W, was numbered differently from the normal sequence. Lionel touted this and the 1000W outfit in their promotional material as exceptional value sets and most probably took a stronger manufacturing stance on them. This set has minimal collector interest as catalogued; the outfit box is far more scarce than the items it contained.   **210**   **350**

1513S or 504   O27 Gauge $35 Retail

Contents: This was a repeat or more probably a carry-forward of unsold 1954 outfits. The existence of a 1955-style outfit box is questionable. Please refer to **1954** for more information.   **150**   **250**

1525 or 500   O27 Gauge $19.95 Retail

Contents: 600 MKT NW-2 switcher; 6111 yellow flatcar with logs; 6014 red Baby Ruth boxcar; 6017 SP-type caboose; eight curved and one straight track; 6029 uncoupling section; and a 1014 40-watt transformer.

Comments: This was one of two sets that offered the second-rate NW-2 diesel switcher. The outfit box was the standard 1955 issue, but was only a single-tier box. The engine with two small cardboard inserts came in a Middle Classic box while the other components were unboxed. This outfit and 1001 or 501 were the two 1955 sets that had unusual combinations of boxed and unboxed contents. Earliest editions of this set have been known to contain the scarce gray frame with yellow end rails variation of the 600 switcher. This set, except for one with the gray-framed 600, stirs minimal interest for the advanced collector. The outfit box is more scarce than the items it contained. Please see page 70 for a picture of the contents and an example of this new packaging concept.   **210**   **350**

1526S or 515   O27 Gauge $29.95 Retail

Contents: 2037 steam locomotive with headlight, smoke, and Magnetraction; 2046T Lionel Lines non-whistle tender; 6465 Sunoco two-dome tank car; 6456 black Lehigh Valley hopper; 6257 SP-type caboose; eight curved and one straight track; 6029 uncoupling section; and a 1014 40-watt transformer.

Comments: This was another of the many 2037 sets to appear in the postwar era. The outfit box was standard 1955 issue. The engine came in the new corrugated carton without a liner while the balance of the nondescript rolling stock and the tender came in Middle Classic boxes.   **120**   **200**

1527 or 502   O27 Gauge $29.95 Retail

Contents: 1615 steam switcher with headlight; 1615T slope-back tender; 6462-125 red gondola with barrels; 6560 gray cab crane; 6119 red work caboose; eight curved and one straight track; 6029 uncoupling section; and a 1014 40-watt transformer.

Comments: The outfit box was the standard two-tier 1955 issue. The engine was boxed in the newly designed corrugated carton while the tender and rolling stock came in Middle Classic boxes. The gray crane is a very desirable piece and the all-red work caboose is not as common as one may think. This red work caboose came only in the reshaped 1955 box with a single-piece cardboard insert with "6119" printed on the end flaps. The -125 gondola box was still the elongated version with coupler protection flaps.   **350**   **600**

1529 or 503   O27 Gauge $29.95 Retail

Contents: 2028 Pennsylvania GP-7; 6311 brown pipe car; 6436 Lehigh Valley quad hopper; 6257 SP-type caboose; eight curved and one straight track; 6029 uncoupling section; and a 1014 40-watt transformer.

**1
9
5
5**

VG   LN

Comments: This was the introductory set for the newly designed GP-7. This was the bottom of the Geep line as it offered no horn, only minimal trim, and a light in the cab end only. The engine with either gold or yellow rubber-stamped lettering came in the new corrugated carton while the remainder of the rolling stock came in Middle Classic boxes. The 6311 with three pipes and seven stakes is a scarce car and was common only to this set, while either a black or a maroon hopper was an acceptable component. The maroon hopper always came in a box with a "-25" suffix. It is of interest that the only real difference between the 6257 caboose at $3.95 retail (for separate sale) and the 6017 caboose at $2.95 retail (for separate sale) is that the 6257 has SP logo and a brakewheel on one end.   **475   800**

1531W or 505   O27 Gauge $39.95 Retail

Contents: 2328 Burlington GP-7; 6462-125 red gondola with barrels; 6465 Sunoco two-dome tank car; 6456 black

VG   LN

Lehigh Valley hopper; 6257 SP-type caboose; eight curved and three straight track; 6019 uncoupling/operating section; and a 1033 90-watt transformer.

Comments: The outfit box was the standard two-tier 1955 issue. The -125 gondola box was usually the elongated version with coupler protection flaps. The engine could have been packed in either the new corrugated carton or a Middle Classic box with two small cardboard inserts, while the other components came in Middle Classic boxes. It was initially believed that the paper Geep engine box was designed for inclusion in sets, and that the corrugated carton was the method used to package separate-sale items. This assumption proves false because both the Burlington and the 2338 Milwaukee Road came in either type of box while the 2028 Pennsylvania came only in a corrugated carton. What a shame Lionel could not have put some of the new-issue rolling stock with the glistening silver Burlington Geep instead of run-of-the-mill carry-over equipment.   **400   750**

The contents of 600 MKT diesel switcher outfit 1525/500 in the "special" three-digit set box. This was one of two 1955 outfits that showed experimentation with unusual combinations of boxed and unboxed contents. Repacking outfits packaged in this manner was difficult, and it was for that reason that many of the liners and dividers were discarded. Lionel always included everything that was necessary to operate and maintain a train set right in the outfit box. M. Sokol Collection.

VG   LN

1533WS or 507   O27 Gauge $49.95 Retail

Contents: 2055 steam locomotive with headlight, smoke, and Magnetraction; 6026W Lionel Lines whistle tender; 3562-50 yellow operating barrel car; 6436 Lehigh Valley quad hopper; 6465 Sunoco two-dome tank car; 6357 illuminated SP-type caboose; eight curved and three straight track; 6019 uncoupling/operating section; and a 1033 90-watt transformer.

Comments: The outfit box was the standard 1955 issue. The engine came in the new corrugated carton, often with blue printing, while the tender and rolling stock came in Middle Classic boxes. The 6436 hopper could have been either black or maroon, and the earliest issues of the operating barrel car were the yellow-painted variation, often in a "-25" suffix box with the letter "Y" rubber stamped on the end flaps to designate yellow.   325   525

1534W or 508   O27 Gauge $49.95 Retail

Contents: 2328 Burlington GP-7; 2432 Clifton Vista Dome, 2434 Newark Pullman, and 2436 Summit observation in the silver-with-red-letter color scheme; eight curved and three straight track; 6019 uncoupling/operating section; and a 1033 90-watt transformer.

Comments: The outfit box was the standard two-tier 1955 issue. The engine was usually boxed in the new corrugated carton but may have come in a Middle Classic box. The passenger cars were individually boxed in either the 1954 dimension box or the slightly shorter and wider 1955 version of the Middle Classic box with the stock number printed on all four sides. The Burlington Geep in very difficult to obtain in collector condition as the silver paint has usually become dull from both age and exposure.   750   1500

1535W or 509   O27 Gauge $49.95 Retail

Contents: 2243P/2243C Santa Fe AB F-3 units; 6462-125 red gondola with barrels; 6436 Lehigh Valley quad hopper car; 6464-50 M St. L boxcar *or* 6468X tuscan B & O double-door automobile car; 6257 SP-type caboose; eight curved and five straight track; 6019 uncoupling/operating section; and a 1033 90-watt transformer.

Comments: This was the mystery set that contained the scarce tuscan double-door automobile car. This set was shown in the Advance Catalogues with a -50 M St. L boxcar that was most assuredly carry-over inventory, and the set was pictured in this manner to deplete that inventory. A problem arose when the inventory was prematurely depleted; i.e., Lionel was left with a void to fill. In order to solve the problem and remain consistent in the use of color, Lionel simply painted some 6468 shells in tuscan and rubber stamped a letter "X" on the box so as not to confuse them with the normal blue production items. Lionel became so conscious of cost that they did not even include an illuminated caboose with an F-3 outfit. The outfit box was the standard 1955 issue. The engine came in the new corrugated carton while the B unit was packed with a liner in the newly down-sized Middle Classic

VG   LN

box. The proper 2243C box for this set must have the stock number printed on all four sides. The balance of the rolling stock also came in Middle Classic boxes.   800   1600

1536W or 510   O27 Gauge $59.95 Retail

Contents: 2245P/2245C Texas Special AB F-3 units; two 2432 Clifton Vista Domes and 2436 Summit observation in the silver-with-red-letter color scheme; eight curved and three straight track; 6019 uncoupling/operating section; and a 1033 90-watt transformer.

Comments: This set was a near repeat of the 1954 outfit with an extra 2432 being substituted for the 2434. The outfit box was the standard 1955 issue, but from here on the analysis gets complicated. The 2245 was a repeat engine and the engine box was usually the larger 1954 corrugated type with a liner; the C box could have been either a larger 1954 carry-over or the new 1955 down-sized version. The passenger cars came in either the narrow, elongated 1954-style box or in the shorter, wider 1955 version, or in both styles. To further complicate matters, the B unit came two different ways; as the 1954 shells were depleted they were replaced with the less detailed, sans-porthole 1955 bodies. Some of the A units were even mounted on a black truck Santa Fe chassis. The simpler B unit shell without portholes is much more scarce and therefore more desirable to collectors than the 1954 counterpart, while the A units without portholes are perceived to be fraudulent items. The value of the set is predicated upon cab type, not chassis, as frames are easily switched. This is an exceptionally scarce outfit. The second edition of a repeat road name seldom sold as well as the first.   1200   2000

1537WS or 511   O27 Gauge $59.95 Retail

Contents: 2065 steam locomotive with headlight, smoke, and Magnetraction; 6026W Lionel Lines whistle tender; 3469 operating ore car; 6464-275 State of Maine boxcar; 3562-50 yellow operating barrel car; 6357 illuminated SP-type caboose; eight curved and five straight track; 6019 uncoupling/operating section; and a 1033 90-watt transformer.

Comments: The outfit box was the standard 1955 issue. The engine was packed in the new corrugated carton, while the tender and the rolling stock came in Middle Classic boxes. Earliest issues of the operating barrel car are the painted yellow variation often in a "-25" suffix box with the letter "Y" rubber stamped on the end flaps to designate yellow. This was also the introductory set for the -275 State of Maine boxcar whose earliest versions were the scarce solid-door type.   400   650

1538WS or 512   O27 Gauge $65 Retail

Contents: 2065 steam locomotive with headlight, smoke, and Magnetraction; 2046W Lionel Lines whistle tender; 2432 Clifton Vista Dome, 2434 Newark Pullman, 2435 Elizabeth Pullman, and 2436 Summit observation in the silver-with-red-letter color scheme; eight curved and five straight track; 6019 uncoupling/operating section; and a 1033 90-watt transformer.

	VG	LN

Comments: The outfit box was the standard 1955 issue. The engine was boxed in the new corrugated carton, while the tender and the passenger cars came in Middle Classic boxes with coupler protection flaps. The passenger cars could have come in either the narrow, elongated 1954-style box or the shorter, wider 1955 version. This was the only passenger set to contain all four differently numbered 2430 series cars. **650 1200**

1539W or 513   O27 Gauge $65 Retail

Contents: 2243P/2243C Santa Fe AB F-3 units; 3620 searchlight car; 6446 N & W covered hopper; 6561 depressed-center flatcar with cable reels; 6560 gray cab crane; 6419 work caboose; eight curved and five straight track; 6019 uncoupling/operating section; and a 1033 90-watt transformer.

Comments: This was the second Santa Fe set offered for the year. The outfit box was standard 1955 issue. The engine came in the new corrugated carton while the B unit was boxed with a liner in the newly down-sized paper box. The proper 2243C box must have the stock number printed on all four sides. The remainder of the rolling stock also came in Middle Classic boxes. The 6446 cement car could have come in either black or gray, while the work caboose with high stack came in the redesigned 6419 box. 1955 was a transition year for cranes and this set could have contained the basic red cab, the scarce gray cab, or even the more scarce red-orange cab on an unstamped 6460 chassis. This outfit has also been known to contain a variation of the searchlight car. The 3620 did not have a remote-controlled on/off mechanism, but it sometimes came on a discontinued 3520 body and had an "X" suffix added to the stock number on the end flaps of the box.

650 1300

1541WS or 514   O27 Gauge $69.95 Retail

Contents: 2065 steam locomotive with headlight, smoke, and Magnetraction; 2046W Lionel Lines whistle tender; 3482 operating milk car; 6415 Sunoco three-dome tank car; 3461-25 green operating log car; 3494-1 operating Pacemaker boxcar; 6427 Lionel Lines porthole caboose; 6019 uncoupling/operating section; and a 1033 90-watt transformer.

Comments: This was the third 2065 set offered in 1955 and was the top of the O27 line. The outfit box was standard issue. The engine was packed in the new corrugated carton, while the tender and the remainder of the rolling stock came in Middle Classic boxes. The 3494-1 was a new item in 1955 and was common only to this set. The "-25X" suffix attached to the log car box meant that it was green and that the unloading bin was not component boxed with the car itself, but placed loose inside the set box. **400 650**

2235W or A-20   O Gauge $39.95 Retail

Contents: 2338 Milwaukee Road GP-7; 6436-25 maroon Lehigh Valley quad hopper; 6362 flatcar with rail trucks; 6560-25 red cab crane; 6419 work caboose; eight curved and five straight track; and a UCS uncoupling/operating section.

	VG	LN

Comments: This was the first of three Milwaukee Road sets to be catalogued. It was introduced as O Gauge in 1955 but demoted to O27 Gauge in the two 1956 outfits. The outfit box was standard 1955 issue. The engine box could have been either the newly designed corrugated carton or the also newly designed paper Geep box, while the rolling stock all came in Middle Classic boxes. The crane car was usually red but bear in mind that both the gray and the scarce red-orange cranes were also 1955 items. Both the quad hopper and the rail truck car were new pieces of rolling stock, and the 6419 caboose with high stack came in the newly down-sized box. **425 700**

2237WS or A-21   O Gauge $49.95 Retail

Contents: 665 steam locomotive with headlight, smoke, and Magnetraction; 6026W Lionel Lines whistle tender; 3562-50 yellow operating barrel car; 6464-275 State of Maine boxcar; 6415 Sunoco three-dome tank car; 6417 Pennsylvania porthole caboose; eight curved and five straight track; and a UCS uncoupling/operating section.

Comments: The outfit box was the standard 1955 issue. The engine was packed in the newly designed corrugated carton while the tender and the balance of the rolling stock came in Middle Classic boxes. Earliest issues of the -50 barrel car are the painted yellow variation in a -25 box with the letter "Y" rubber stamped on the end flaps. Advance literature on this set was contradictory as some of it was shown not to include the -275 State of Maine — this boxcar is, however, a known set component. **275 450**

2239W or A-22   O Gauge $55 Retail

Contents: 2363P/2363C Illinois Central AB F-3 units; 6672 Santa Fe reefer; 6464-125 Pacemaker boxcar; 6414 auto loader; 6517 bay window caboose; eight curved and five straight track; and a UCS uncoupling/operating section.

Comments: The Illinois Central was a new road name added to the F-3 series. The outfit box was the standard 1955 circled-L issue and the powered unit came in the newly designed corrugated box, and the B unit came with a liner in the down-sized version of the Middle Classic box. The remainder of the rolling stock also came in Middle Classic boxes. This was the only set ever to contain the -125 Pacemaker, and was one of only two to contain the 6672 reefer. Scarce variations of the reefer exist, but none can be directly tied to this outfit. The auto loader and bay window caboose were new 1955 items, and the caboose usually had "Lionel" underscored. Remember, all component boxes must have the stock number printed on all four sides. The auto loader and caboose are much more common in later issue boxes. **1800 3000**

2241WS or A-23   O Gauge $55 Retail

Contents: 646 steam locomotive with headlight, smoke, and Magnetraction; 2046W Lionel Lines whistle tender; 3359 operating twin-bin ore car; 6446 N & W covered hopper; 3620 searchlight car; 6417 Pennsylvania porthole

VG   LN

caboose; eight curved and five straight track; and a UCS uncoupling/operating section.

Comments: The outfit box was the new 1955 issue but the 646 was a repeat. The engine and tender could have come in either the 1954-design boxes with liners or the newly designed corrugated carton and paper box without liners, while the balance of the components came in Middle Classic boxes. The 3359 dump car was new in 1955 and the cement car could have been either black or gray with "644625" stamped on the car sides or "546446", which was the initial stamp when the car made its debut in 1954.   **325   550**

2243W or A-24   O Gauge $59.95 Retail

Contents: 2321 gray roof Lackawanna F-M; 3662 operating milk car; 6511 brown pipe car; 6462-125 red gondola with

VG   LN

barrels; 6464-300 Rutland boxcar; 6417 Pennsylvania porthole caboose; eight curved and five straight track; and a UCS uncoupling/operating section.

Comments: The outfit box was the standard 1955 issue. The engine was boxed in a corrugated carton with a liner while the remaining components came in Middle Classic boxes. The 3662 milk car was new in 1955 as was the Rutland boxcar which was the rubber-stamped variation. Keep in mind that 1955 boxes must have the stock number printed on all four sides with specific attention given to the 3662 and the -300 Rutland, because they were catalogued in subsequent years and also came in Late Classic boxes. This was the third, last, and most scarce of the Lackawanna sets and was only one of two outfits to contain the Rutland boxcar. The more colorful Virginian no doubt had a negative sales influence on the Lackawanna set.   **1500   2500**

The contents of 682 steam turbine outfit 2245WS. This version of the steam turbine with lubricator linkage and a white running stripe was a handsome engine but a sales disappointment. This set most often contained the scarce red-orange variation of the 6560 crane on an unstamped plastic mold of a 6460 chassis that had the trucks attached with binding head screws instead of mounting clips. Greenberg's Guide to Lionel Trains, 1945-1969, Volume I, seventh edition contains detailed information on the crane. P. Sigrist Collection.

The contents of the 2340-25 green GG-1 freight set 2253W. The GG-1 was reissued in 1955 after a five-year absence from the catalogue. The 6414 auto loader and the 3361 operating log car were two new items contained in this set, and this outfit was one of only two to contain the -300 Rutland boxcar. The Rutland exists in several rare variations, and this example shows the extremely rare solid shield herald with a solid door. P. Sigrist Collection.

	VG	LN

2244W or A-25   O Gauge $65 Retail

Contents: 2367P/2367C Wabash AB F-3 units; 2530 Railway Express baggage car; 2531 Silver Dawn observation and 2533 Silver Cloud Pullman extruded-aluminum passenger cars; eight curved and seven straight track; and a UCS uncoupling/operating section.

Comments: The Wabash was a new road name added to the F-3 series, and this was one of two 2367 sets that were catalogued in 1955. The outfit box was the standard 1955 issue and the powered unit came in the new corrugated box. The B unit was packed with a liner in the down-sized version of the Middle Classic box, but consistency stops at this point. The aluminum cars usually came in Middle Classic boxes without liners, and the Pullman and observation cars should have been, by 1955 standards, the flat-channeled variety, but such was not always the case. Unsold pre-1955 inventory was still being depleted and this set surfaces with varying combinations of cars and boxes. Flat channels, ribbed-channel glued plates, and even hex heads are all possible, with flat channels being the most desirable to the collector. Whatever

the case, a matched set of passenger cars and boxes is always the best alternative.   **1800   3000**

2245WS or A-26   O Gauge $65 Retail

Contents: 682 steam turbine locomotive with smoke, headlight, Magnetraction, and lubricator linkage; 2046WX Pennsylvania whistle tender; 3562-25 gray operating barrel car; 6436-25 maroon Lehigh Valley quad hopper; 6561 depressed-center flatcar with cable reels; 6560-25 red cab crane; 6419 work caboose; eight curved and seven straight track; and a UCS uncoupling/operating section.

Comments: This was the second and last of the 682 sets that Lionel catalogued, and it was probably catalogued solely to move unsold 1954 inventory. Many 1955 outfits surface with a black unpainted tender. Although Lionel had an adequate supply of engines on hand, they ran short of tenders, and rather than sustaining the additional expense of painting a tender shell for an engine which was being depleted, they simply heat-stamped unpainted shells. The en-

VG   LN

gine and tender came with liners in Middle Classic boxes, with the tender box also stamped with "P.R.R." on the end flaps. The balance of the rolling stock also came in Middle Classic boxes. The crane car was often the scarce red-orange variation on an unstamped 6460 chassis with an "X" suffix rubber stamped on the end flaps of the box; bear in mind, though, that both the conventional red cab and gray cab cranes were also available in 1955. The 6419 caboose with a high stack came in the newly down-sized box with a single-piece cardboard insert. Please refer to page 73 for a picture of the contents.

600   1000

2247W or A-27   O Gauge $65 Retail

Contents: 2367P/2367C Wabash AB F-3 units; 6462-125 red gondola with barrels; 3662 operating milk car; 6464-150 Missouri Pacific boxcar; 3361 operating log car; 6517 bay window caboose; eight curved and seven straight track; and a UCS uncoupling/operating section.

Comments: The Wabash was a new road name added to the F-3 series and this was one of two sets that were catalogued in 1955. The outfit box was the standard 1955 issue and the powered unit came in the new corrugated box. The B unit was packed with a liner in the down-sized version of the Middle Classic box. This was only one of two sets to contain the -150 Missouri Pacific boxcar. The milk car, log dump car, and the bay window caboose were new 1955 items.

VG   LN

The 1955 version of the bay window caboose had "Lionel" underscored. Keep in mind that all 1955 boxes were still Middle Classic and had the stock number printed on all four sides. The rolling stock was all catalogued again in subsequent years, and most often surfaces in revised Late Classic boxes. See page 68 for an end view of the outfit box.

1650   2750

1 9 5 5

2249WS or A-28   O Gauge $69.50 Retail

Contents: 736 Berkshire steam locomotive with headlight, smoke, and Magnetraction; 2046W Lionel Lines whistle tender; 6464-275 State of Maine boxcar; 6414 auto loader; 3359 operating twin-bin ore car; 3562-50 yellow operating barrel car; 6517 bay window caboose; eight curved and seven straight track; and a UCS uncoupling/operating section.

Comments: The outfit box was standard 1955 issue. The engine came in the newly designed corrugated carton while the tender also and the balance of the rolling stock came in Middle Classic boxes. The set components, except for motive power, were exactly the same as the Virginian outfit 2251W. Please refer to that set for pertinent comments.

If one were to look at the cover of a 1955 catalogue, one would notice that both of these sets had the same freight cars in the same order and are pictured one above the other. Was the advertising department remiss, or was this poorly planned cover deliberately designed to over-expose certain items?

500   825

The contents of the 1955 edition of the Congressional set. Outfit 2254W was headed by the reissued and newly colored 2340 tuscan GG-1. The flat-channeled cars were developed for this set — some of the ribbing was removed from the sides of the extruded-aluminum bodies in order to accommodate the striping required for the 2540 series cars. P. Sigrist Collection.

**1
9
5
5**

VG   LN

2251W or A-29   O Gauge $69.50 Retail

Contents: 2331 Virginian F-M; 6464-275 State of Maine boxcar; 3562-50 yellow operating barrel car; 6414 auto loader; 3359 operating twin-bin ore car; 6517 bay window caboose; eight curved and seven straight track; and a UCS uncoupling/operating section.

Comments: The Virginian was the second road name offered in the F-M series and this was the first of four outfits to be catalogued through 1958. The outfit box was standard 1955 issue and the engine came in a corrugated carton with a liner. Early editions of this set contained the scarce black and yellow Virginian, while the later issues contained the extremely scarce blue- and yellow-painted variation on a gray body mold. The rolling stock, except for the barrel car, were all new 1955 items. Earliest issues of the -50 barrel car were the yellow-painted variation while the -275 State of Maine may have been the scarce solid-door variation, and the 1955 version of the bay window caboose usually had "Lionel" underscored. The rolling stock all came in Middle Classic boxes with the stock number printed on all four sides. Particular attention must be paid as each of these cars were also available in subsequent years and most often surface in later issue boxes. See page 68 for an end view of the outfit box.

2100   3500

2253W or A-30   O Gauge $75 Retail

Contents: 2340-25 green Pennsylvania five-stripe GG-1; 3361 operating log car; 6464-300 Rutland boxcar; 3620 searchlight car; 6414 auto loader; 6417 Pennsylvania porthole caboose; eight curved and seven straight track; and a UCS uncoupling/operating section.

Comments: The outfit box was the standard 1955 circled-L type. The engine was an updated version of the 2330 that was last catalogued in 1950. It came in a corrugated carton with a liner and "2340-25" stamped on one end flap. This was only one of two outfits to contain the -300 Rutland. The 6414 was a new item in 1955 as was the 3361 log dump

VG   LN

car. All component boxes must be Middle Classic and have the stock number printed on all four sides, and particular attention must be paid as each of these cars were also available in 1956 and later. This outfit, as with all other GG-1 sets, is a collector's dream. Please see page 74 for a picture of this outfit.

2100   3500

2254W or A-31   O Gauge $100 Retail

Contents: 2340 tuscan Pennsylvania five-stripe GG-1; 2541 Alexander Hamilton observation, 2542 Betsy Ross Vista Dome, 2543 William Penn Pullman, and 2544 Molly Pitcher Pullman extruded-aluminum passenger cars; eight curved and eleven straight track; and a UCS uncoupling/operating section.

Comments: The outfit box was standard 1955 issue and this was the set for which the flat-channeled cars were developed. This was the first time that a GG-1 was ever catalogued in tuscan. The engine was packed in a corrugated carton with a protective liner and "2340" stamped on one end flap, while the passenger cars came in Middle Classic boxes with coupler protection flaps and the stock number printed on all four sides. Note that the 1955 boxes differ from the 1956 in that the stock number was not retained on the sides of the 1956 boxes. Buyer beware as a substantial number of both engines and passenger cars have been re-striped, and even the 2340 box has been fraudulently reproduced. The proper engine box was made by St. Joe Paper Company and is usually dated "55" below the box manufacturer's seal. Many collectors feel that the acute shortage of regular flat-channeled passenger cars in today's market is due in large part to the inordinate amount of forgeries that exist in the Congressional and the Canadian Pacific series cars. The purchase of this set as a set saved the consumer only about 6-1/2 percent when compared to individually sold component pieces, less than any other 1955 outfit.

The Congressional set is one of the most prized postwar outfits and ranks near the top of any collector's list. Please see page 75 for a picture of this outfit.

3000   5000

1956

STILL A VINTAGE YEAR

As the title implies, Lionel production in 1956 gave us what has become some of the scarcest and most coveted of the postwar diesels, along with some striking motive power innovations and an impressive array of new operating cars and general rolling stock. Six new 6464 series boxcars were introduced. They were the -325 Sentinel, -350 Katy, -375 Central of Georgia, -400 B & O Timesaver, -425 New Haven, and the -450 Great Northern. Two 3494 series operating boxcars were introduced — the -150 Missouri Pacific and the -275 State of Maine. Other most notable new items were the 3530 generator car, 3424 Wabash brakeman, and the 3356 operating horse car. The previously mentioned innovations in motive power were the 44-ton center cab diesel, EP-5 electric, and the motorized 400 Budd RDC. The 2360 tuscan and green five-stripers, the 2240 Wabash, 2368 B & O, and 2378 Milwaukee Road F-3 units as well as the 2341 Jersey Central F-M all were 1956-only engines. They have become some of the most sought after and collectable of any postwar items.

The majority of the rolling stock was still of excellent quality. Bar-end metal trucks with extended tab couplers were the norm, but with a silver knuckle pin appearing on new rolling stock and passenger truck production. 1956 was the year in which the double circled-L appeared on the 6257 SP-type cabooses. The burro crane and the track cleaning car were new motorized units. The consumer catalogue (on page 36) shows an interesting assortment of replacement accessories, most of which came in individual component boxes!

The corrugated cardboard engine boxes remained the same as in 1955 and most were dated with the year "56" below the box manufacturer's seal. The paper boxes were essentially unchanged from the previous year, but since the stock number was removed from the four sides on all new issue and reordered boxes, these boxes will be termed *Late Classic*. Lionel continued the practice, begun in 1955, of running two separate but corresponding series of outfit numbers. The major change was in the graphics of the set boxes. The newly issued outfit box was basic tan, overprinted with a gray tone that gave the appearance of a loosely woven basket with medium blue lettering. Please refer to page 82 for some examples of outfit boxes. Of critical importance in 1956 is that Lionel, for the first time in the postwar era, released some outfits that did not have any of the individual contents component boxed. The first four O27 outfits were packaged in this manner.

curved and one straight track; 6029 uncoupling section; and a 1015 45-watt transformer.

Comments: This set was a late addition to the product line, one that was designed to meet buyer demands for a train outfit that retailed for under $20. Therefore, both the 1542 and 750 outfit numbers were out of numerical sequence; "1542" should have been reserved for a passenger set but the entire product line had already been numbered, with outfit 1543 or 700 at $25 retail being the planned introductory set. With no other option available, Lionel simply assigned the number "1542", which was one numeral lower than "1543", and then randomly chose the three-digit "750" number.

The outfit box was an undersized two-tier, basket weave type. Lionel totally broke with tradition and placed the contents *unboxed* inside the set box. The 520 was held in place by only a wraparound liner; a component box for this engine does not exist. The other components were separated by cardboard dividers. The rolling stock was low end yet still had bar-end metal trucks.   **150   250**

1543 or 700   O27 Gauge $25 Retail

Contents: 627 Lehigh Valley center cab; 6121 flatcar with pipes; 6112 black gondola with canisters; 6017 SP-type caboose; eight curved and one straight track; 6029 uncoupling section; and a 1015 45-watt transformer.

Comments: The center cab design was new for 1956. It was an attractive item but grossly out of proportion; as a 44-ton unit it should have been about half the size of the 80-ton 520 box cab electric, making it roughly equivalent to the size of a 41 or 51 motorized unit. The outfit box was the new basket weave type but had only one tier. Lionel again broke with tradition and placed the contents *unboxed* inside the set box. The engine was protected and held in place by a wraparound liner while the other components were separated by cardboard dividers. The rolling stock was low end yet still had bar-end metal trucks. The 627, when available for separate sale, came in a Late Classic box with two small cardboard inserts to hold the engine in place. Refer to page 78 for a picture of this outfit.   **150   250**

1545 or 701   O27 Gauge $29.95 Retail

Contents: 628 Northern Pacific center cab; 6424 flatcar with autos; 6014 red Baby Ruth boxcar; 6025 black Gulf single-dome tank car; 6257 SP-type caboose; eight curved and

---

1542 or 750   O27 Gauge $19.95 Retail

Contents: 520 GE box cab electric; 6014 red Baby Ruth boxcar; 6012 black gondola; 6017 SP-type caboose; eight

The contents of 627 Lehigh Valley center cab outfit 1543/700 in the "special" three-digit set box. Lionel totally broke with tradition and placed the contents unboxed inside the set box. The folded cardboard liner in front of the billboard sheet was used to protect and hold the engine in place. Repackaging outfits that did not come with component boxes was painstaking, and it was for that reason that most of the cardboard liners and dividers were discarded. It is extremely difficult to obtain sets packaged as such with a full complement of inserts. Also note that the outfit instruction sheet that came with this set had the misspelled "Mangetraction"! M. Sokol Collection.

VG   LN

three straight track; 6029 uncoupling section; and a 1015 45-watt transformer.

Comments: The center cab was a new design introduced in 1956. It was an attractive item but obviously out of proportion; as a 44-ton unit it should have been about half the size of the 80-ton 520 box cab electric, making it roughly equivalent to the size of a 41 or 51 motorized unit. The outfit box was the new basket weave type but had only one tier. Lionel again broke with tradition and placed the contents *unboxed* inside the set box. The components were separated and held in place by cardboard dividers. The rolling stock was run-of-the-mill yet still had bar-end metal trucks. The 628, when available for separate sale, came in a Late Classic box with two small cardboard inserts to hold the engine in place.   **175   300**

1547S or 702   O27 Gauge $33.50 Retail

Contents: 2018 steam locomotive with headlight and smoke; 6026T Lionel Lines non-whistle tender; 6121 flatcar with pipes; 6112 black gondola with canisters; 6014 red Baby

VG   LN

Ruth boxcar; 6257 SP-type caboose; eight curved and one straight track; 6029 uncoupling section; and a 1015 45-watt transformer.

Comments: The outfit box was the new two-tier basket weave type and the components were usually placed unboxed inside of the set box and were separated and held in place by cardboard dividers. The rolling stock was low-end, run-of-the-mill equipment yet still had bar-end metal trucks. The 6026 tender was most often an unpainted variation.   **150   250**

1549 or 703   O27 Gauge $35 Retail

Contents: 1615 steam switcher with headlight; 1615T slope-back tender; 6262 flatcar with wheels; 6560-25 red cab crane; 6119-25 orange work caboose; eight curved and three straight track; 6029 uncoupling section; and a 1015 45-watt transformer.

Comments: The outfit box was the new two-tier basket weave type. The engine was boxed in a corrugated carton with tucked-in end flaps, while the tender and the balance of the

VG   LN

VG   LN

components came in Late Classic boxes. The crane was sometimes the red cab variation with "656025" stamped on the frame. The work caboose was usually the all-orange 6119 but was occasionally the scarce all-brown variation. It came with an insert in a box with a "- 25" suffix that was often rubber-stamped onto the 1955 version of the 6119 box. The 6262 wheel car was most often the very scarce variation with the red body mold. This was the only known set to contain the 6262 in red, and was the second and last of the 1615 sets to be catalogued. **600**   **1000**

1551W or 704   O27 Gauge $39.95 Retail

Contents: 621 Jersey Central NW-2 switcher with horn; 6362 rail truck car; 6425 Gulf three-dome tank car; 6562-25 red gondola with canisters; 6257 SP-type caboose; eight curved and three straight track; 6029 uncoupling section; and a 1053 60-watt transformer.

Comments: The outfit box was the new two-tier basket weave type. This was one of two 621 sets to be catalogued in 1956. The engine, with two small cardboard inserts, and most of the components came in Late Classic boxes. Gulf was a new logo tank car that replaced the 6415 Sunoco. The 6362 was a repeat item and may have come in a 1955-style box. The 6562 was a new item; this example was red and came in a box with a "-25" suffix. **300**   **500**

1552 or 705   O27 Gauge $39.95 Retail

Contents: 629 Burlington center cab; 2432 Clifton Vista Dome, 2434 Newark Pullman, and 2436 Summit observation in the silver-with-red-letter color scheme; eight curved and three straight track; 6029 uncoupling section; and a 1015 45-watt transformer.

Comments: This was the third set from the 1956 product year to contain the new center cab design. It was an attractive item but greatly out of proportion; as a 44-ton unit it should have been about half the size of the 80-ton 520 box cab electric, making it roughly equivalent to the size of a 41 or 51 motorized unit. The outfit box was the new two-tier basket weave type and all of the items were component boxed. The 629 came in a Late Classic box with two small cardboard inserts to hold the engine in place; the passenger cars also came in Late Classic boxes with the stock number printed on the box flaps only. To collectors, the 629 is the most desirable of the center cab units and the easiest to obtain boxed; it always came boxed, whether as a set component or a separate-sale item. This is an extremely scarce set, and the engine is very difficult to obtain in collector condition as the silver paint has usually become dull with age and exposure.

   750   **1500**

1553W or 706   O27 Gauge $49.95 Retail

Contents: 2338 Milwaukee Road GP-7; 6430 flatcar with vans; 6462-125 red gondola with barrels; 6464-425 New Haven boxcar; 6346 Alcoa covered hopper; 6257 SP-type caboose; eight curved and three straight track; 6019 uncoupling/operating section; and a 1053 60-watt transformer.

Comments: This was the second of three Milwaukee Road Geep sets to be catalogued, and for 1956 it was demoted to O27 Gauge. The outfit box was the new two-tier basket weave type. The engine came in either a corrugated carton with tucked-in end flaps or in a Late Classic box with two small cardboard inserts, while the rolling stock and caboose all came in Late Classic boxes. The -425 New Haven was a new addition to the 6464 series, and both the 6430 and the Alcoa hopper were new pieces of rolling stock. The vans on the 6430 were usually gray and had Cooper-Jarrett nameplates. The -125 gondola box was again the short version that allowed the couplers to be turned inwards. **350**   **600**

1555WS or 707 O27 Gauge $49.95 Retail

Contents: 2018 steam locomotive with smoke and headlight; 6026W Lionel Lines whistle tender; 3361 operating log car; 6464-400 B & O boxcar; 6462-125 red gondola with barrels; 6257 SP-type caboose; eight curved and three straight track; 6019 uncoupling/operating section; and a 1053 60-watt transformer.

Comments: The outfit box was the new two-tier basket weave type. The engine came in a corrugated carton with tucked-in end flaps while the tender and the balance of the components came in Late Classic boxes. The -400 B & O was a new addition to the 6464 series and this was the only set of which it was a component. The -125 gondola box was again the short version that allowed the couplers to be turned inwards. **275**   **475**

1557W or 708   O27 Gauge $49.95 Retail

Contents: 621 Jersey Central NW-2 switcher with horn; 6436-25 maroon Lehigh Valley quad hopper; 6511 brown pipe car; 3620 searchlight car; 6560-25 red cab crane; 6119-25 orange work caboose; eight curved and three straight track; 6019 uncoupling/operating section; and a 1053 60-watt transformer.

Comments: This was the second 621 set to be catalogued. The outfit box was the new two-tier basket weave type. The engine, with two small cardboard inserts, and most of the components came in Late Classic boxes. The crane was usually the red cab variation with "656025" stamped on the frame and the all-orange work caboose came with an insert in a box with a "-25" suffix. The balance of the rolling stock were repeat items and as such may have come in Middle Classic boxes with the stock number printed on all four sides.

   350   **600**

1559W or 709   O27 Gauge $59.95 Retail

Contents: 2338 Milwaukee Road GP-7; 6414 auto loader; 3562-50 yellow operating barrel car; 6362 rail truck car; 3494-275 operating State of Maine boxcar; 6357 illuminated SP-type caboose; eight curved and three straight track; 6019 uncoupling/operating section; and a 1053 60-watt transformer.

Comments: This was the third and last of the Milwaukee Road Geep sets to be catalogued, and for 1956 it was

1956

	VG	LN

demoted to O27 Gauge. The outfit box was the new two-tier basket weave type. The engine came in either a corrugated carton with tucked-in end flaps or in a Late Classic box with two small cardboard inserts. The barrel car, rail truck car, and auto loader were repeat items and may surface in Middle Classic boxes, while the SP-type caboose came in a Late Classic box, usually with a "-25" suffix. The operating State of Maine was a new 1956 item and came in a Late Classic box with a "-275" suffix; furthermore, it was usually the scarce B.A.R.-only variation with "3494275" omitted. **475 800**

1561WS or 710 O27 Gauge $59.95 Retail

Contents: 2065 steam locomotive with headlight, smoke, and Magnetraction; 6026W Lionel Lines whistle tender; 3424 Wabash brakeman; 6262 flatcar with wheels; 6562-25 red gondola with canisters; 6430 flatcar with vans; 6257 SP-type caboose; eight curved and three straight track; 6019 uncoupling/operating section; and a 1053 60-watt transformer.

Comments: The outfit box was the new two-tier basket weave type. The engine came in a corrugated carton with tucked-in end flaps while the tender and the balance of the components came in Late Classic boxes. All of the rolling stock was new for 1956. The 6430 had gray vans with Cooper-Jarrett nameplates while the "-25" suffix applied to the canister car box meant that it was red, not black or gray, and came boxed as such. Although the 6262 was catalogued in red, this set came with the common black version. **425 725**

1562W or 711   O27 Gauge $59.95 Retail

Contents: 2328 Burlington GP-7; two 2242 Clifton Vista Domes, 2444 Newark Pullman, and 2446 Summit observation in the new silver with red-stripe/red-letter color scheme; eight curved and three straight track; 6019 uncoupling/operating section; and a 1053 60-watt transformer.

Comments: This was the third and last of the Burlington sets to be catalogued. The outfit box was the new two-tier basket weave type. The engine came in either a corrugated carton with tucked-in end flaps or in a paper box with two small cardboard inserts. The 2440 series passenger cars were new for 1956 and are common only to this set. They came in Late Classic boxes with coupler protection flaps. The 2445 Elizabeth Pullman was not included with the set but was available for separate sale, and as such is the scarcest and most sought after of the red-striped cars. These cars exist in two variations: a glossy red stripe and a flat red stripe, with the glossy version being the scarcer of the two. This outfit is underrated and extremely desirable to collectors. The Burlington Geep is very difficult to obtain in collector condition as the silver paint has usually become dull with age and exposure. **1250 2500**

1563W or 712   O27 Gauge $67.50 Retail

Contents: 2240P/2240C Wabash F-3 AB units; 6467 miscellaneous car; 3562-50 yellow operating barrel car; 6414 auto loader; 3620 searchlight car; 6357 illuminated SP-type caboose; eight curved and five straight track; 6019 uncoupling/operating section; and a 1033 90-watt transformer.

Comments: The Wabash was the third road name offered in the single-motored F-3 series, and this was the only set to be headed by the 2240. The outfit box was the new two-tier basket weave type. The engine came in a corrugated carton with tucked-in end flaps while the B unit, which was protected by a liner, and most of the other components came in Late Classic boxes. The 6467 was new for 1956, while the remainder of the rolling stock were repeat items and may surface in 1955-style boxes. The "-50" suffix applied to the barrel car meant that it was yellow and came in a box with "-50" on the end flaps. The proper B unit for the 2240 does not have the thin white stripe on the very ends of the unit itself as does the B unit for the twin-motored 2367. **1800 3000**

1565WS or 713 O27 Gauge $69.95 Retail

Contents: 2065 steam locomotive with headlight, smoke, and Magnetraction; 6026W Lionel Lines whistle tender; 3662 operating milk car; 3650 extension searchlight car; 6414 auto loader; 6346 Alcoa covered hopper; 6357 illuminated SP-type caboose; eight curved and five straight track; 6019 uncoupling/operating section; and a 1033 90-watt transformer.

Comments: The outfit box was the new two-tier basket weave type. The engine came in a corrugated carton with tucked-in end flaps, while the tender and most of the components came in Late Classic boxes. The searchlight car and the Alcoa hopper were new items, but the milk car and the auto loader were repeats and may surface in 1955-style boxes. **425 725**

1567W or 714   O27 Gauge $75 Retail

Contents: 2243P/2243C Santa Fe F-3 AB units; 3356 operating horse car; 3424 Wabash brakeman; 6430 flatcar with vans; 6672 Santa Fe reefer; 6357 illuminated SP-type caboose; eight curved and five straight track; 6019 uncoupling/operating section; and a 1033 90-watt transformer.

Comments: This was the third of four single-motored Santa Fe sets to be catalogued, and the outfit box was the new two-tier basket weave type. The engine came in a corrugated carton with tucked-in end flaps while the B unit, which was protected by a liner, and the remainder of the components usually came in Late Classic boxes. The 6672 was a repeat item while the balance of the rolling stock were new additions to the product line. The vans on the 6430 were gray and came with Cooper-Jarrett nameplates. This was the only O27 set ever to include the 3356 horse car. It came with the corral and a wraparound liner in an oversized Late Classic box. Both the horse corral and the horse car were available separately as replacement items, and each had an individual component box! **750 1500**

VG   LN

2255W or 800   O Gauge $39.95 Retail

Contents: 601 Seaboard NW-2 diesel switcher; 3424 Wabash brakeman; 6362 rail truck car; 6560-25 red cab crane; 6119-25 orange work caboose; eight curved and three straight track; and a UCS uncoupling/operating section.

Comments: The outfit box was the new basket weave type. The 601 was a new engine that was a grade above the 600 and 610 from 1955. It came in a Late Classic box with two small cardboard inserts and had a horn, Magnetraction, and operating couplers but no headlight. Caution is advised when examining a mid-1950s switcher as chassis changes are quite prevalent. The Wabash brakeman was a new 1956 item; so was the all-orange work caboose whose proper box must have "6119-25" on the end flaps. The red cab crane most often was the scarce variation with "656025" stamped on the chassis. These items came in Late Classic boxes while the 6362 was a repeat and may surface in a 1955-style box.   **350   600**

2257WS or 801 O Gauge $49.95 Retail

Contents: 665 steam locomotive with headlight, smoke, and Magnetraction; 2046W Lionel Lines whistle tender; 3361 operating log car; 6346 Alcoa covered hopper; 6467 miscellaneous car; 6462-125 red gondola with barrels; 6427 Lionel Lines porthole caboose; eight curved and three straight track; and a UCS uncoupling/operating section.

Comments: The outfit box was the new basket weave type and the engine was boxed without a liner in a 1955-design corrugated carton with tucked-in end flaps. The tender and the balance of the rolling stock came in Late Classic boxes. The 6346 and 6467 were newly issued items for 1956. The 6427 caboose now came in a box with "6427-1" stamped on the end flaps, and the -125 gondola box was downsized allowing for the couplers to be turned inwards.   **350   575**

2259W or 802   O Gauge $55 Retail

Contents: 2350 New Haven EP-5 electric; 6464-425 New Haven boxcar; 6430 flatcar with vans; 3650 extension searchlight car; 6511 brown pipe car; 6427 Lionel Lines porthole caboose; eight curved and five straight; and a UCS uncoupling/operating section.

Comments: The outfit box was the new basket weave type, and the EP-5 was a dramatic new design offered in two 1956 sets, both headed by the 2350 New Haven. The engine came without a liner in a 1955-design corrugated carton with tucked-in end flaps. The rolling stock all came in Late Classic boxes and all but the 6511 pipe car and the caboose were new items. The vans on the 6430 were gray and had Cooper-Jarrett nameplates, while the caboose now came in a box with "6427-1" stamped on the end flaps. The engine itself came in four known 1956 variations and the set value is predicated upon the variation, with the reversed-color units being the most desirable and commanding the highest price among collectors. The 2350 was pictured on the front of the 1956 catalogue with orange paint going through the door jamb. This variation usually surfaces on a yellow 2351 body mold

and was most probably the last run of the series, which would date the item to late 1957 or early 1958.   **600 1000**

2261WS or 803 O Gauge $59.95 Retail

Contents: 646 steam locomotive with headlight, smoke, and Magnetraction; 2046W Lionel Lines whistle tender; 3562-50 yellow barrel car; 6414 auto loader; 6436-25 maroon Lehigh Valley quad hopper; 6376 circus stock car; 6417 Pennsylvania porthole caboose; eight curved and five straight track; and a UCS uncoupling/operating section.

Comments: The outfit box was the new 1956-issue basket weave type. The engine came without a liner in the 1955-design corrugated carton with tucked-in end flaps, while the tender and most of the rolling stock came in Late Classic boxes. The -50 barrel car was now unpainted yellow plastic and the porthole caboose now came in a box with "6417-1" stamped on the end flaps. The 6414 and the 6436-25 were repeat items and as such may come in 1955-style boxes with the stock number printed on all four sides. The 6376 circus stock car was a new item; extreme caution is advised when cleaning this car because the red paint and heat stamping are quite apt to fade. Under no conditions should this car be washed in running water.   **450 775**

2263W or 804   O Gauge $65 Retail

Contents: 2350 New Haven EP-5 electric; 3359 operating twin-bin ore car; 6468-25 New Haven double-door automobile car; 6414 auto loader; 3662 operating milk car; 6517 bay window caboose; eight curved and seven straight track; and a UCS uncoupling/operating section.

Comments: The outfit box was the new basket weave type and this was one of two 1956 sets that introduced the dramatic new EP-5 design. The engine came without a liner in a 1955-design corrugated carton with tucked-in end flaps. The 6468-25 was a new road name for the automobile boxcar and may be the scarce reversed-color example, while the caboose and the remainder of the rolling stock were continuations of items first produced in 1955 and, as such, may surface in Middle Classic boxes with the stock number printed on all four sides. Kindly refer to outfit 2259W for additional comments on the 2350 engine.   **725 1200**

2265WS or 805 O Gauge $69.95 Retail

Contents: 736 Berkshire steam locomotive with headlight, smoke, and Magnetraction; 2046W Lionel Lines whistle tender; 3620 operating searchlight car; 3424 Wabash brakeman; 6430 flatcar with vans; 6467 miscellaneous car; 6517 bay window caboose; eight curved and seven straight track; and a UCS uncoupling/operating section.

Comments: The outfit box was the new basket weave type and the engine was boxed without a liner in the 1955-design corrugated carton with tucked-in end flaps. The tender and the balance of the rolling stock all came in Late Classic boxes. The Wabash brakeman, miscellaneous car, and the 6430 were new items for 1956, and the vans on the 6430 were

	VG	LN

1956 usually gray with Cooper-Jarrett nameplates. The search-light car and the bay window caboose were repeat items and, as such, may surface in Middle Classic boxes. **425** **725**

2267W or 806   O Gauge $69.95 Retail

Contents: 2331 Virginian F-M; 3562-50 yellow operating barrel car; 3359 operating twin-bin ore car; 3361 operating log ore car; 6560-25 red cab crane; 6419-50 work caboose; eight curved and seven straight track; and a UCS uncoupling/operating section.

Comments: This was the second of four Virginian sets that Lionel catalogued through 1958, and the outfit box was the new basket weave type. The engine was boxed in a corrugated carton with a protective liner and could have been the extremely scarce blue- and yellow-painted variation on a gray body mold that Lionel was in the process of depleting, but it was usually the new common version that was only yellow-painted on a blue body mold. All of the rolling stock were continuation items and may surface in Middle Classic boxes with the stock number printed on all four sides. The -50 barrel car was now unpainted yellow plastic, the red cab crane was most often the scarce variation with "656025" stamped on the chassis, and the work caboose was the reengineered short stack version that came in a Late Classic box with an insert and a "-50" suffix on the end flaps. **1500** **2500**

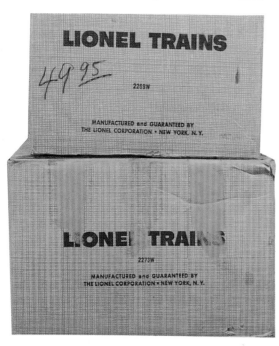

An end view of two rare 1956 sets in the new basket weave-type outfit box. (Top) 2269W B & O F-3 freight set box. Notice the marked down price of $49.95 written in black crayon. It will take more that 100 times that amount to purchase a collector condition example of this outfit in today's market. (Bottom) 2273W Milwaukee Road F-3 freight set. B. Myles Collection.

	VG	LN

2269W or 807   O Gauge $75 Retail

Contents: 2368P/2368C Baltimore & Ohio F-3 AB units; 3356 operating horse car; 6518 double-truck transformer car; 6315 Gulf chemical tank car; 3361 operating log car; 6517 bay window caboose; eight curved and seven straight track; and a UCS uncoupling/operating section.

Comments: The Baltimore & Ohio was a new road name in the F-3 series. It is a highly prized collector's item and one of the top three F-3 outfits, along with 2273W and 2296W. The outfit box was the new basket weave type, and the powered unit was boxed without a liner in the 1955-design corrugated carton while the B unit came with a protective liner in a Late Classic box. The 3356 was a new operating car and came with the corral and a wraparound liner in an oversized Late Classic box. Both the horse car and the corral were available separately as replacement items, and each had an individual component box! The chemical tank car and the transformer car were also new 1956 items, while the log dump car and the bay window caboose were carry-forward items and may surface in Middle Classic boxes with the stock number printed on all four sides. The underscoring of "Lionel" was eliminated from the caboose during 1956 production, and the transformer car came with two cardboard inserts that were common to this car only, and when properly inserted, helped to protect the fragile insulators. Please note that the powered A unit may have been the scarce blue-painted variation on a gray body mold. **3600** **6000**

2270W or 808   O Gauge $75 Retail

Contents: 2341 Jersey Central F-M; 2531 Silver Dawn observation, 2532 Silver Range Vista Dome, and 2533 Silver Cloud Pullman extruded-aluminum passenger cars; eight curved and seven straight track; and a UCS uncoupling/operating section.

Comments: The Jersey Central is another of the premier postwar sets. The outfit box was the new basket weave type and the engine, either high gloss or dull orange, came in a corrugated carton with a protective liner. Extreme caution is advised when pondering the purchase of a 2341 because both the box and the cab have been fraudulently reproduced. It is estimated that the number of forgeries exceeds the number of legitimate pieces in the marketplace, and many of the reproduction cabs were done over a decade ago! The passenger cars came without liners in boxes that were often a mixture of Middle Classic with the stock number printed on all four sides, and the new Late Classic with the stock number deleted. They should all be the flat-channeled type, but it is not inconceivable for a ribbed channel glued plate to surface with this set. Keep in mind that once a passenger car was boxed there was no sure way, other than reopening the box, of telling what type of car was in that box. Refer to page 83 for a picture of this outfit. **2700** **4500**

The contents of 2341 Jersey Central passenger set 2270W in the new basket weave outfit box. This is one of the premier sets of the postwar era. The Jersey Central was a one-year-only engine and is the most sought after of the F-M units. The outfit box alone commands a price of nearly $1000 in today's market. P. Sigrist Collection.

VG   LN

2271W or 809   O Gauge $79.50 Retail

Contents: 2360-25 green Pennsylvania five-stripe GG-1; 3424 Wabash brakeman; 3662 operating milk car; 6414 auto loader; 6418 double-truck girder car; 6417 Pennsylvania port-hole caboose; eight curved and seven straight track; and a UCS uncoupling/operating section.

Comments: The outfit box was the new basket weave design and the green 2360-25 was the replacement engine for the revised 2340-25. It came protected by a liner in a corrugated carton made by National and with "2360-25" stamped on one end flap. The milk car, girder car, and the auto loader were repeat items from 1955 and may be found in Middle Classic boxes with the stock number printed on all four sides. The brakeman car was a new item that came in a Late Classic box while the caboose, although a repeat, also came in a Late Classic box with "6417-1" printed on the end flaps. The 6418 girder car box is almost always torn because the double trucks are apt to twist when the car is removed from or replaced in the box. Earliest issues of the 6418 box had coupler protection flaps that were subsequently deleted in favor of two small

cardboard inserts used to hold the car in place. This outfit, as with all other GG-1 sets, is a collector's dream.

1950   3250

2273W or 810   O Gauge $85 Retail

Contents: 2378P/2378C Milwaukee Road F-3 AB units; 342 operating culvert loader with 6342 culvert gondola; 3562-50 yellow operating barrel car; 3662 operating milk car; 3359 operating twin-bin ore car; 6517 bay window caboose; eight curved and seven straight track; and a UCS uncoupling/operating section.

Comments: The Milwaukee Road was a new road name in the F-3 series. It was a 1956-only engine available in only one set, and is therefore an extremely coveted postwar item and one of the top three F-3 outfits, along with 2269W and 2296W. The outfit box was the new basket weave type and was oversized to accommodate the component-boxed culvert loader. The powered unit was boxed without a liner in the 1955-design corrugated carton, while the B unit came protected by a liner in a Late Classic box. The caboose and all

1956

	VG	LN

of the rolling stock, except for the 6342 culvert gondola, were repeat items from 1955 and may surface in Middle Classic boxes with the stock number printed on all four sides. The culvert gondola was unboxed when packed inside the 342 corrugated carton but was component boxed when available for separate sale; it was "stuffed" into an overstamped, undersized 6462 gondola box. The AB units exist in three variations: yellow roof line stripes, no roof line stripes, and A without and B with roof line stripe. These are all legitimate pairs, with the yellow-striped variation being the most desirable. The large nose decal on the A unit often shows deterioration, and a decal in poor condition measurably lessens the value of the AB pair. Please see page 82 for an end view of the outfit box.

	VG	LN
With yellow roof line stripes	3900	6500
Other variations	3600	6000

2274W or 811   O Gauge $100 Retail

Contents: 2360 tuscan Pennsylvania five-stripe GG-1; 2541 Alexander Hamilton observation, 2542 Betsy Ross Vista Dome, 2543 William Penn Pullman, and 2544 Molly Pitcher Pullman extruded-aluminum passenger cars; eight curved and eleven straight track; and a UCS uncoupling/operating section.

Comments: The outfit box was the new basket weave type and this was the follow-up outfit to the 2254W Congressional set from 1955. The passenger cars remained the same except that they now came in Late Classic boxes without the stock number printed on the four sides. The 2340 from the 1955 set was replaced with a 2360 that came in a corrugated carton with a protective liner, made by National with a "56" date below the box manufacturer's seal, and with "2360" stamped on one end flap. Many collectors feel that the desirability of the Canadian Pacific and the Congressional sets has caused an acute shortage of regular flat-channeled passenger cars in the marketplace because of their use in the creation of forgeries. Reproduction striping and window inserts are readily available. Extreme caution is recommended when considering purchasing a Congressional set since even the engine boxes have been fraudulently reproduced.

VG	LN
3000	5000

1957

A Giant Step — Sideways

This was the year in which Super O track was introduced by Lionel, and the catalogue pictured an adequate assortment of all three gauges. Lionel offered innovations that ranged from good to bad to indifferent; hence, the end result was a side step. 1957 is one of the more difficult years to analyze: suffixes were used with abandon on box flaps, outfits were assembled and packaged in unusual combinations of both boxed and unboxed components, and plastic AAR trucks were introduced for the O27 rolling stock.

The O27 and O Gauge outfit boxes remained unchanged from 1956 and Lionel continued the practice of running two separate but corresponding series of outfit numbers. The initial Super O set box was a recolored tan/brown version of the basket weave design with motive power scenes added to the four sides. The corrugated cardboard engine boxes with tucked-in end flaps were the same as those introduced in 1955, and the Late Classic boxes were essentially unchanged, although some new production had a slightly reddish tint.

A new inexpensive version of the Alco made its debut in three road names. On the positive side, however, 1957 was the introductory year for the mighty 746 Norfolk & Western; the Canadian Pacific and Rio Grande were new road names on F-3 units as were the Wabash and the Milwaukee Road in the Geep and EP-5 series respectively.

Some interesting F-3 variations occurred in 1957. The 2243, 2373, and the 2379 are all known to exist on *orange* body molds. Why orange? The 2363 Illinois Central was issued in 1955; the A unit initially came on a gray body mold while the B unit utilized an orange body mold. The production department proceeded to then mold orange A unit cabs, but the Illinois Central was discontinued! Faced with a problem, Lionel did what any business would, and that was to deplete inventory by any means possible; hence, orange cab Santa Fes, Canadian Pacifics, and Rio Grandes. These are scarce variations, but they have not piqued much collector interest. Most collectors would be happy to own a Canadian Pacific or Rio Grande in Like New condition no matter what color the body molds.

Available data suggests that all production on the 746 and the heat-stamped 746W took place in 1957 — both the engine and tender boxes show characteristics that were common to 1957 only; no other variations of the boxes exist, and the original instruction sheet that accompanied the engine was dated "10-57". There were at least two production runs on the tender. The first run was probably the heat-stamped short-striped version with stamped numberboards, followed, possibly in 1958, by the rubber-stamped long-striped variation. The more desirable long-striped tender is the one that is often forged. The production sequence of the tender was in direct opposition to the one Lionel normally followed. Rubber

stamping was usually the first or early process that was then followed by heat stamping. Lionel must have expected a sales bonanza with the 746, but it turned out to be a disappointment. In subsequent years, Lionel tried desperately to deplete inventory on the 746 by heading the 2545WS military-related outfit with it in 1959, by cataloguing it as a separate-sale item in 1960, and finally by offering it to Sears in an outfit with a complement of military cars in 1961. The 746 engine but not the tender was available at Madison Hardware to "preferred" customers nearly to the very end of their long and storied history. (Madison Hardware, located on 23rd Street in New York City, was the Mecca for train collectors for over sixty years until it was sold in 1989 to Richard Kughn.)

The now famous and highly sought Girls' Set also graced the consumer catalogue. The freight roster included four (or six, if the -510 and -515 Girls' cars are counted) new 6464 series boxcars. They were the -475 Boston and Maine, -500 Timken, -525 M St. L, and the -650 Rio Grande. Two new 3494 series operating boxcars were introduced as the -550 Monon and the -625 Soo. Other notable new items were the 3444 cop and hobo animated gondola, the 6800 airplane car, and the 6801 boat car. The vast majority of rolling stock, except for the stamped sheet metal flatcar, was still quality merchandise, and even the 6476 hopper, 6646 stock car, and 6482 reefer, which were strictly O27 items, included steps. This was also the year in which heat-stamped numberboards began to appear on some of the 2046W and 6026W tender production.

6111 and 6121 flatcars were ubiquitous throughout the O27 line in varying colors. It is nearly impossible to accurately determine which color of car came with an individual set, but this flatcar was always referred to in Advance literature as the 6111 "with logs" and the 6121 "with pipes." These cars were stamped with only "Lionel" on the frame, which allowed for the log and pipe loads to be completely interchangeable. Most colors other than red or gray were stamped with black lettering, but an occasional scarce white-lettered variation surfaces. To further complicate matters, these cars were often unboxed when included in sets. This is clearly evidenced by the fact that although the cars themselves are as common as dust, the boxes are seldom seen.

Another new and cost-saving item, the 1008 camtrol uncoupling unit, made a quiet debut in three O27 outfits. This unit allowed Lionel to discontinue the inclusion of the more costly 6029 uncoupling track with their low-end sets. The 6029 now became standard issue for all other O27 outfits, replacing the more expensive 6019.

It appears that the major shortcoming of Super O track was the absence of a combined uncoupling/operating section of track that would function similarly to a UCS. Although Lionel was already half-way home with the development of the

1957

No. 37 uncoupling section, it took the time and expense to develop both insulated track sections and the No. 43 power track when a No. 61 ground lockon and No. 62 power lockon would have sufficed. The No. 36 power blades, essential for operating cars, were unsightly and required painstaking effort to install. In addition, the lack of an appropriate integrated Super O uncoupling/operating section required major revisions of the instruction sheets for operating cars. Lionel was subsequently forced to include a No. 36 power blade in the instruction envelope of the operating horse car, circus car, and then the 44 and 45 missile-launching units. How much simpler life could have been with a *super* UCS!

A Note on the 1957-1958 Suffixes and Boxes

The usage of the suffixes and two styles of printing on boxes that was prevalent in 1957 and 1958 is baffling. Concise analysis of their use is difficult because data is contradictory, as explained below, and many items were not boxed as set components in 1957. The most commonly used suffixes are "-60" and "-85". These are widely used in the O27 product line and usually indicate items that have AAR trucks. A notable exception is the O Gauge Virginian porthole caboose with metal trucks; it came in a Late Classic box with an over-stamped "-60" suffix. It can also be stated most assuredly that bold print box type was introduced as early as late 1957, but was most common to 1958. Not all 1958 boxes, however, were printed with bold type. Some exceptions are the 6556 Katy stock car, the 6818 transformer car, and the 6800 series military load flatcars.

Two O27 items with suffixes from 1958 that can be positively identified are the 6017-50 U.S.M.C. caboose (the only car known to have come in box "6017-60"), and the gray 6017 Lionel Lines caboose with black letters that always came in box "6017-85". Each caboose came in only one set, and each was the only component in the set to come in a box with a suffix.

The production of 6024s, 6014s, and 6112s exemplifies the confusion underlying Lionel's apparently capricious combinations of products and boxes during these years. Catalogued in 1957 only, the 6024 Nabisco boxcar has no major variations. It often surfaces with metal trucks in a Late Classic box with only "6024" on the end flaps, and usually with early AAR trucks in a Bold Classic box that is numbered "6024-60". Could the "-60" suffix be the means by which one can identify truck type? It is difficult to say because the Nabisco boxcar was a component of three catalogued sets and several Sears outfits during this two-year span.

Two other O27 boxcars were offered during this period — the 6014 Frisco, made in red or white, and the 6014 Bosco, produced in red, orange, or white. Adding up the color variations, one would expect as many as five different boxes, yet only three exist. They are the regular 6014 boxes (some of which had been overstamped), and boxes numbered "6014-60" and "6014-85".

Complications continue. The 6112 canister car from this two-year period was available in three variations (black, blue, and white) yet four boxes exist. They are boxes regularly stamped with the numerals "6112", "6112-1", "6112-85", and "6112-135", but note that colors and boxes were neither specifically nor consistently correlated. Could the canister box suffix have something to do with either the color or the number of canisters? It is again difficult to say because both red and white canisters were used with this component, and the number of canisters included with the car was reduced from four in 1957 to three in 1958. Lionel also used three colors of boats for their 6801 flatcar. Yellows appear to be the most scarce while blues are the most common; blue boats have been observed in both -50 and -75 boxes.

The following chart lists some additional items that were O27 set components in 1957 and 1958, along with their possible boxes.

Components:	Boxes:
6025:	6025 and 6025-60
6111:	6111-75 and 6111-110
6121:	6121-60 and 6121-85
6424:	6424, 6424-60, and 6424-85
6465:	6465 and 6465-60
6476:	6476, 6476-60, and 6476-85
6801:	6801, 6801-50, and 6801-75

It would seem that the use of a particular suffix was not limited to an individual set. This is most evident by an analysis of the rolling stock boxes that came with the 1958 Texas Special Alco outfit number 1599.

1599 Components:	Possible Suffixes:
6801 flatcar with boat	-50, -75
6014 orange Bosco boxcar	-60, -85
6424 flatcar with autos	-60, -85
6112 black canister car	-1, -85, -135
6465 gray two-dome tank car	-60
6017 SP-type caboose	None

As you can see from the above example using outfit 1599, there is no one suffix that was used consistently throughout the set. Which car came in which box? The question may be unanswerable. Could suffixes be used solely for cars that were designated to be set components? Highly unlikely. The matter is still a mystery, and may never be satisfactorily explained.

1569 or 725   O27 Gauge $25 Retail

Contents: 202 Union Pacific Alco A unit; 6014 white Frisco boxcar; 6111 flatcar with logs; 6112 blue gondola with canisters; 6017 SP-type caboose; eight curved and two straight track; 1008 camtrol; and a 1015 45-watt transformer.

Comments: This was the introductory set for the new Alco series. The quality Alco pairs that were last catalogued

VG   LN   VG   LN

in 1954 were replaced by units of lesser quality. The outfit box was standard issue but had only a single tier. The engine, and all of the components with newly designed plastic AAR trucks, were placed unboxed inside the set box. The engine was held in place by a wraparound liner while the other components were separated by cardboard dividers. The 202 was component boxed when available for separate sale. It came in a corrugated carton with tucked-in end flaps.   **150**   **250**

Comments: The blue Missouri Pacific units were another road name offered in the new Alco series. The outfit box was standard two-tier issue but the 205 units were placed unboxed on the bottom level. They were separated and held in place by cardboard dividers while the balance of the components was a mixture of both boxed and unboxed items. The rolling stock usually came with the newly designed plastic AAR trucks. Beware of cracked and/or repaired struts on the Alco units as they are exceptionally fragile.   **250**   **400**

1571 or 726   O27 Gauge $29.95 Retail

Contents: 625 Lehigh Valley center cab; 6424 flatcar with autos; 6476 red Lehigh Valley hopper; 6121 flatcar with pipes; 6112 white gondola with canisters; 6017 SP-type caboose; eight curved and two straight track; 1008 camtrol; and a 1015 45-watt transformer.

Comments: The black and red 625 was a new color combination in the center cab series and was equipped with fixed couplers at both ends. The run-of-the-mill rolling stock all came with the new plastic AAR trucks, but the 6112 was usually the scarce white variation. Early examples of the O27 line version of the 6424 had the AAR trucks riveted to a mounting bracket in the same manner as those with metal trucks. Subsequent issues had the trucks riveted directly to the car. This outfit came packaged in two ways, either in a single-tier basket weave box with all of the contents unboxed and separated by cardboard dividers, or in a conventional two-tier basket weave box with component boxes. When boxed the engine, with two small cardboard inserts, and the other items came in Late Classic types.

Boxed	300	500
Unboxed	250	400

1573 or 727   O27 Gauge $29.95 Retail

Contents: 250 red-striped steam locomotive with headlight; 250T Pennsylvania red-striped non-whistle tender; 6112 black gondola with canisters; 6025 orange Gulf single-dome tank car; 6476 red Lehigh Valley hopper; 6464-425 New Haven boxcar; 6017 SP-type caboose; eight curved and four straight track; 1008 camtrol; and a 1015 45-watt transformer.

Comments: The outfit box was standard two-tier issue. The engine came in a corrugated carton with tucked-in end flaps while the tender, canister car, and boxcar came in Late Classic boxes. The tank car, hopper car, and caboose were usually unboxed and were placed strategically inside the set box so as not to be damaged by the track and the unboxed transformer. The tender and all other rolling stock came with the newly designed plastic AAR trucks.   **195**   **325**

1575 or 728   O27 Gauge $37.50 Retail

Contents: 205P/205T Missouri Pacific Alco AA units; 6121 flatcar with pipes; 6112 blue gondola with canisters; 6111 flatcar with logs; 6560 red cab crane; 6119-100 red cab work caboose; eight curved and three straight track; 6029 uncoupling section; and a 1015 45-watt transformer.

1577S or 729   O27 Gauge $37.50 Retail

Contents: 2018 steam locomotive with headlight and smoke; 1130T Lionel Lines non-whistle tender; 6014 red Frisco boxcar; 6121 flatcar with pipes; 6464-475 Boston and Maine boxcar; 6111 flatcar with logs; 6112 black gondola with canisters; 6017 SP-type caboose; eight curved and three straight track; 6029 uncoupling section; and a 1015 45-watt transformer.

Comments: The outfit box was standard two-tier issue with the contents a mixture of both boxed and unboxed items. The 2018 came in a corrugated carton with tucked-in end flaps and a "57" date below the box manufacturer's seal. All of the other components, including the tender, came fitted with the newly designed plastic AAR trucks. The -475 boxcar, the canister car, and the caboose came in Late Classic boxes while the other components, usually unboxed, were strategically placed to avoid damage along with cardboard dividers inside the set box. Six of the O27 Gauge outfits catalogued in 1957 included an O Gauge boxcar.   **195**   **325**

1578S or 730   O27 Gauge $43.75 Retail

Contents: 2018 steam locomotive with headlight and smoke; 1130T Lionel Lines non-whistle tender; 2432 Clifton Vista Dome, 2434 Newark Pullman, and 2346 Summit or Mooseheart observation in the silver-with-red-letter color scheme; eight curved and three straight track; 6029 uncoupling section; and a 1015 45-watt transformer.

Comments: The outfit box was standard two-tier issue. The engine and tender were usually unboxed and held in place by cardboard dividers along with the track and transformer on the bottom level of the set box. The passenger cars came in Late Classic boxes without the stock number printed on the four sides. The 2436 was shown as a Summit in the Advance Catalogue and as a Mooseheart in the consumer catalogue. Either name is acceptable, but Mooseheart is preferred by collectors.   **300**   **550**

1579S or 731   O27 Gauge $43.75 Retail

Contents: 2037 steam locomotive with headlight, smoke, and Magnetraction; 1130T Lionel Lines non-whistle tender; 6476 red Lehigh Valley hopper; 6121 flatcar with pipes; 6468-25 New Haven double-door automobile car; 6111 flatcar with logs; 6112 blue gondola with canisters; 6025 black Gulf single-dome tank car; 6017 SP-type caboose; eight curved

VG   LN

1957

and three straight track; 6029 uncoupling section; and a 1043 60-watt transformer.

Comments: The outfit box was standard two-tier issue with the contents a mixture of both boxed and unboxed items. By Lionel's standards this was a long train. It included seven cars along with an engine and tender. The 2037 came in a corrugated carton with tucked-in end flaps and a "57" date below the box manufacturer's seal. The rolling stock with the exception of the 6468-25, which always came with metal trucks, had the newly designed plastic AAR trucks. Six of the O27 Gauge outfits catalogued in 1957 included an O Gauge boxcar. The tender, -25 automobile car, canister car, and caboose came in Late Classic boxes while the other components, usually unboxed, were strategically placed to avoid damage along with cardboard dividers inside the set box.

210   350

1581 or 732   O27 Gauge $43.75 Retail

Contents: 611 Jersey Central NW-2 switcher; 6464-650 Rio Grande boxcar; 6424 flatcar with autos; 6024 Nabisco boxcar; 6025 black Gulf single-dome tank car; 6476 red Lehigh Valley hopper; 6560-25 red cab crane; 6119-100 red cab work caboose; eight curved and three straight; 6029 uncoupling section; and a 1043 60-watt transformer.

Comments: The outfit box was standard two-tier issue with the contents a mixture of both boxed and unboxed items. This too was a long train by Lionel's standards. It included seven pieces of varied rolling stock that accompanied the engine. It is of interest to note that six of the O27 Gauge outfits catalogued in 1957 included an O Gauge boxcar. The 611, with fixed couplers at both ends, came in a Late Classic box, often overstamped, with two small cardboard inserts to hold the engine in place. The -650 Rio Grande and the 6024 also came component boxed and were the only two items in the set to have metal trucks. The Rio Grande boxcar was a new addition to the 6464 series and this was the only outfit in which it was a component. The other components were equipped with the newly designed plastic AAR trucks. The crane usually came boxed while the other components, usually unboxed, were strategically placed to avoid damage along with cardboard dividers inside the set box. Early examples of the O27 line version of the 6424 had the AAR trucks riveted to a mounting bracket in the same manner as the metal truck version. Subsequent issues had the trucks riveted directly to the car.

425   700

1583WS or 733 O27 Gauge $49.95 Retail

Contents: 2037 steam locomotive with headlight, smoke, and Magnetraction; 6026W Lionel Lines whistle tender; 6482 refrigerator car; 6112 blue gondola with canisters; 6646 orange stock car; 6121 flatcar with pipes; 6476 black Lehigh Valley hopper; 6017 SP-type caboose; eight curved and three straight track; 6029 uncoupling section; and a 1053 60-watt transformer.

Comments: The outfit box was standard two-tier issue. The engine came in a corrugated carton with tucked-in end flaps while the tender came in a Late Classic box. The tender

VG   LN

still retained metal trucks but all of the other components came with the newly designed plastic AAR trucks. Usually this set had no additional items, other than the caboose, that were component-boxed. This is one of the better 2037 sets as it contained two scarce items, namely the 6482 and 6646, that were catalogued only in 1957 and were included as components in this set only.

275   475

1585W or 734   O27 Gauge $49.95 Retail

Contents: 602 Seaboard NW-2 switcher with horn; 6014 white Frisco boxcar; 6111 flatcar with logs; 6464-525 M St. L boxcar; 6025 black Gulf single-dome tank car; 6121 flatcar with pipes; 6112 blue gondola with canisters; 6476 gray Lehigh Valley hopper; 6024 Nabisco boxcar; 6017 SP-type caboose; eight curved and five straight track; 6029 uncoupling section; and a 1053 60-watt transformer.

Comments: The outfit box was standard two-tier issue with the contents a mixture of both boxed and unboxed items. This was the longest train Lionel catalogued during the postwar era. It included nine pieces of rolling stock to accompany the engine. As noted earlier, six of the O27 Gauge outfits catalogued in 1957 included an O Gauge boxcar. The 602 with headlight, horn, and dummy couplers at both ends came in a Late Classic box with two small cardboard inserts to hold the engine in place. The -525 M St. L was a new addition to the 6464 series and, along with the 6024, usually came boxed. These were the only two items in the set to have metal trucks. The other components were equipped with the newly designed plastic AAR trucks. The canister car and the caboose most often came boxed while the other components, usually unboxed, were strategically placed to avoid damage with cardboard dividers inside the set box.

450   750

1586 or 735   O27 Gauge $49.95 Retail

Contents: 204P/204T Santa Fe Alco AA units; two 2432 Clifton Vista Domes and 2436 Summit or Mooseheart observation in the silver-with-red-letter color scheme; eight curved and five straight track; 6029 uncoupling section; and a 1043 60-watt transformer.

Comments: The blue and yellow Santa Fe units were another road name offered in the new Alco series. The P and T units each came in its own corrugated carton with tucked-in end flaps. The 204T was the only non-powered unit in the entire Alco series ever to come with a headlight. Beware of cracked and/or repaired struts as they are exceptionally fragile. The outfit box was standard two-tier issue. The passenger cars came in Late Classic boxes without the stock number printed on the four sides. The 2436 was shown as a Summit in the Advance Catalogue and as a Mooseheart in the general catalogue. Either name is acceptable, but Mooseheart is preferred by collectors.

425   750

1587S or 736   O27 Gauge $49.95 Retail

Contents: 2037-500 pink steam locomotive with headlight, smoke, and Magnetraction; 1130T-500 pink Lionel Lines non-whistle tender; 6462-500 pink gondola with canisters; 6464-515 yellow Katy boxcar; 6436-500 lilac Lehigh Valley quad hopper; 6464-510 blue-green Pacemaker boxcar; 6427-500 blue Pennsylvania porthole caboose; eight curved and five straight track; 6029 uncoupling section; and a 1043-500 60-watt white transformer with white cord.

Comments: This outfit is the both famous and infamous Girls' Set — a prize today, but a disaster in 1957. The outfit box was a two-tier basket weave type but it was on a special pink/mauve background used exclusively for this set. The engine came in a standard 2037 corrugated carton with tucked-in end flaps and has the "-500" suffix rubber-stamped on the box ends. This box is easily and often forged, so at least be aware that the proper box was usually made by National and has a "57" date below the box manufacturer's seal. The

other components all came with metal trucks in Late Classic boxes with the appropriate suffixes printed during the manufacturing process on the end flaps. The transformer even has a special tan corrugated box and is numbered "1043-500". Forgeries permeate the marketplace. It is advisable to consult a knowledgeable collector when considering the purchase of any Girls' item. Also be advised that until recently original replacement tops for the transformers were available, and they have often been switched with a regular 1043 black shell in order to bring a premium price. The correct transformer must have an off-white cord and plug that has usually yellowed with age. Refer to page 90 to see a color comparison of outfit boxes.

	VG	LN
	2400	4000

1957

The both famous and infamous Girls' Set 1587S. Yesterday's nightmare is today's dream as this outfit has become a prized collector item. Note that Lionel even colored a complementary transformer for this outfit. The set was catalogued as O27 Gauge, yet contained two 6464 series boxcars and a quad hopper along with an illuminated porthole caboose that were usually O Gauge items.

The outfit box was also unique. It was printed in a shade of mauve as opposed to the gray that was used for all other basket weave outfit boxes. Sales on the Girls' Set were so poor that it was catalogued again in 1958 solely to assist dealers in moving unsold inventory. A horror story about this set emanated from Madison Hardware — store personnel distinctly recall repainting untold numbers of engines from pink to black simply to make them salable at any price. All Girls' Set items, except the engine, were available through Madison Hardware to "preferred" customers throughout the decade of the 1970s and into the early 1980s. P. Sigrist Collection.

VG   LN   VG   LN

1589WS or 737   O27 Gauge $59.95 Retail

Comments: 2037 steam locomotive with headlight, smoke, and Magnetraction; 6026W Lionel Lines whistle tender; 6424 flatcar with autos; 6464-450 Great Northern boxcar; 6025 orange Gulf single-dome tank car; 6024 Nabisco boxcar; 6111 flatcar with logs; 6112 black gondola with canisters; 6017 SP-type caboose; eight curved and five straight track; 6029 uncoupling section; and a 1044 90-watt transformer.

Comments: This was the top-of-the-line O27 set for 1957. The outfit box was standard two-tier issue, and all of the components were usually boxed. The engine came in a corrugated carton with tucked-in end flaps while the other components came in Late Classic boxes. The -450 boxcar came with metal trucks and was included with this set merely to deplete existing inventory. Six of the O27 Gauge outfits catalogued in 1957 included an O Gauge boxcar. The 6024 was a new O27 boxcar and, oddly enough, it was often issued with metal trucks. It was catalogued in red but does not exist as such as part of regular production. The 6424 flatcar with autos sometimes came with metal trucks while the other cars were fitted with the newly designed plastic AAR trucks.

                                            325   550

2275W or 815   O Gauge $49.95 Retail

Contents: 2339 Wabash GP-7; 3444 animated gondola; 6464-475 Boston and Maine boxcar; 6425 Gulf three-dome tank car; 6427 Lionel Lines porthole caboose; eight curved and five straight track; and a UCS uncoupling/operating section.

Comments: The outfit box was the standard basket weave type. The 2339 was a new road name in the GP series and it came in a Late Classic box with two cardboard inserts; a corrugated carton does not exist for this item. The balance of the rolling stock also came in Late Classic boxes. The Gulf logo replaced the Sunoco name in 1956 on the three-dome tank car, necessitating a number change from 6415 to 6425. The -475 Boston and Maine was a new addition to the 6464 series and the cop chasing hobo around the animated gondola was an interesting new operating car.   **475   800**

2276W or 816   O Gauge $49.95 Retail

Contents: 404 Budd motorized RDC mail-baggage car; two 2559 Budd passenger cars; eight curved and seven straight track; and a UCS uncoupling/operating section.

Comments: The outfit box was the standard basket weave type. The Budd motorized unit made an inauspicious debut as the 400 passenger car in the rear of the 1956 catalogue, and a mail-baggage car was developed for the 1957 line and appeared as both the 404 powered unit and the 2550 (non-powered) trailer. This set was headed by the new 404 which came in a conventional carton with a protective liner and "404" stamped on one end flap. The 2559 was the non-powered (trailer) version of the motorized 400, and came without liners in Late Classic boxes with coupler protection flaps. Ironically, the non-powered 2550 and 2559 command

An end view of two 1957 basket weave type set boxes. Outfit 2276W is the O Gauge 404 Budd set, while 1587S is the extremely scarce Girls' Set. Outfit box 1587S is unique; it was printed in a mauve tone as opposed to the usual gray tone that was used for all other basket weave outfit boxes. B. Myles Collection.

higher prices than the powered units, with the 2550 being the more desirable.   **1200   2000**

2277WS or 817   O Gauge $49.95 Retail

Contents: 665 steam locomotive with headlight, smoke, and Magnetraction; 2046W Lionel Lines whistle tender; 6446-25 N & W gray covered hopper; 3650 extension searchlight car; 6560-25 red cab crane; 6119-75 gray work caboose; eight curved and five straight track; and a UCS uncoupling/operating section.

Comments: The outfit box was the standard basket weave type. The engine was boxed without a liner in a corrugated carton with tucked-in end flaps while the remaining components came in Late Classic boxes. All of the rolling stock, except the caboose, were repeat items. The crane was the normal red cab type while the work caboose was all gray on a gray frame, with a "-75" suffix as part of the stock number on the end flaps. Both of these items still included a cardboard insert as part of component packaging.   **375   625**

2279W or 818   O Gauge $55 Retail

Contents: 2350 New Haven EP-5 electric; 3424 Wabash brakeman; 6464-425 New Haven boxcar; 6424 flatcar with autos; 6477 miscellaneous car with pipes; 6427 Lionel Lines porthole caboose; eight curved and seven straight track; and a UCS uncoupling/operating section.

Comments: This was the third and last of the 2350 catalogued sets, and the outfit box was the standard basket weave type. The engine was boxed without a liner in a corrugated carton with tucked-in end flaps while the rolling stock came in Late Classic boxes. The rolling stock was run-of-the-mill with only the 6477 being a nearly new item. It was an

VG   LN

upgrade of the 6467 which had previously been issued without pipes. The 2350 came in five known variations but this set usually contained the most common decaled white N version.

600   1000

2281W or 819   O Gauge $59.95 Retail

Contents: 2243P/2243C Santa Fe F-3 AB units; 6464-150 Missouri Pacific boxcar; 3361 operating log car; 3562-75 orange operating barrel car; 6560-25 red cab crane; 6119-75 gray work caboose; eight curved and seven straight track; and a UCS uncoupling/operating section.

Comments: This was the fourth and last of the 2243 sets to be catalogued, and for this encore it was upgraded to O Gauge. The outfit box was the standard basket weave type while the powered unit was boxed without a liner in a corrugated carton with tucked-in end flaps. Most powered unit boxes are datable as they usually include a "55", "56", or "57" below the box manufacturer's seal. The B unit, protected by a liner, and the remainder of the rolling stock came in Late Classic boxes. This was one of only two outfits to contain the -150 Missouri Pacific boxcar. The "-75" suffix attached to the barrel car designated the color orange while the "X" suffix applied to the log dump car box meant that the unloading bin was placed loose inside of the outfit box as opposed to being packed with the car itself. The crane was the normal red cab type while the work caboose was all gray on a gray frame, and came in a box with a "-75" suffix. Both of these items still included a cardboard insert as part of component packaging.

750   1500

2283WS or 820   O Gauge $59.95 Retail

Contents: 646 steam locomotive with headlight, smoke, and Magnetraction; 2046W Lionel Lines whistle tender; 3424 Wabash brakeman; 3361 operating log car; 6464-525 M St. L boxcar; 6562-50 black gondola with canisters; 6357 illuminated SP-type caboose; eight curved and seven straight track; and a UCS uncoupling/operating section.

Comments: The outfit box was the standard basket weave type. The engine was boxed without a liner in a corrugated carton with tucked-in end flaps while the remaining components came in Late Classic boxes. The -525 M St. L boxcar was a new 1957 addition to the 6464 series while the Wabash brakeman, the canister car, and the log dump car were repeat items. The "-50" suffix on the canister car box meant that it was black, not red or gray. Each canister car box is identifiable because of its suffix.

425   725

2285W or 821   O Gauge $69.95 Retail

Contents: 2331 Virginian F-M; 6418 double-truck girder car; 6414 auto loader; 6425 Gulf three-dome tank car; 3662 operating milk car; 6517 bay window caboose; eight curved and seven straight track; and a UCS uncoupling/operating section.

Comments: This was the third of four Virginian sets to be catalogued by Lionel. The outfit box was the standard basket weave type and the engine was boxed in a corrugated

carton with a protective liner. All of the rolling stock were repeat items and came in Late Classic boxes. The Gulf logo replaced the Sunoco name on the three-dome tank car in 1956, necessitating a number change from 6415. This was one of only two outfits to contain the 6418 girder car; the box for the girder car is almost always torn as the double trucks are apt to twist when removing or replacing the car in the box, and two small cardboard inserts, which are most often lost, are required to hold the car in place.

1500   2500

2287W or 822   O Gauge $69.95 Retail

Contents: 2351 Milwaukee Road EP-5 electric; 342 culvert loader with 6342 culvert gondola; 6464-500 Timken boxcar; 3650 extension searchlight car; 6315 Gulf chemical tank car; 6427 Lionel Lines porthole caboose; eight curved and nine straight track; and UCS uncoupling/operating section.

Comments: The Milwaukee Road was the second road name to appear on the EP-5 series electrics. The outfit box was the standard basket weave type but was oversized to include the component-boxed culvert loader. The engine was boxed without a liner in a corrugated carton with tucked-in end flaps while the balance of the rolling stock came in Late Classic boxes. The -500 Timken was a new road name in the 6464 series and this was one of only two sets in which it was a component. The 6342 culvert gondola was unboxed inside the 342 corrugated carton, but boxed when available for separate sale; it was "stuffed" into an overstamped, undersized 6462 gondola box. The early 6315 is a collectable item, and was included as a component in only two sets. This is a scarce and undervalued outfit.

1500   2500

An end view of the outfit box for the scarce 2287W Milwaukee Road EP-5 electric freight set. B. Myles Collection.

2289WS or 823   Super O $75 Retail

Contents: 736 Berkshire steam locomotive with headlight, smoke, and Magnetraction; 2046W Lionel Lines whistle tender; 3359 operating twin-bin ore car; 3494-275 State of Maine operating boxcar; 3361 operating log car; 6430 flatcar with vans; 6427 Lionel Lines porthole caboose; twelve curved, three straight, and one insulated straight track; and a 39-20 operating packet.

Comments: The old reliable Berkshire was given the honor of being the "first to make the run on Super O track."

The contents of Berkshire outfit 2289WS. This set was "the first to make the run on Super O track." Every component of the set was a repeat item, but the outfit box was a new design introduced exclusively for Super O sets. It had a tan basket weave look with motive power scenes on all four sides. P. Sigrist Collection.

	VG	LN

The outfit box was the new tan/brown basket weave look that was introduced exclusively for Super O. The engine was boxed without a liner in a corrugated carton with tucked-in end flaps, while the tender and the balance of the components came in Late Classic boxes. The rolling stock were all repeat items and the only major variable with this set was that the 6430 most often came with white rather than gray vans with Cooper-Jarrett nameplates. **450   750**

	VG	LN

tion could have sold if this practice were the norm rather than the exception? The -525 M St. L was a new addition to the 6464 series while the 3444 was a new operating car. The generator car, usually with a long white stripe and a blue fuel tank, and the operating barrel car were repeat items. The "-75" suffix applied to the barrel car meant that it was the color orange, and that it came in a box stamped as such. Please refer to page 93 for a picture of this outfit.

1800   3000

2291W or 824   Super O $79.95 Retail

Contents: 2379P/2379C Rio Grande F-3 AB units; 3562-75 orange operating barrel car; 3530 generator car; 3444 animated gondola; 6464-525 M St. L boxcar; 6657 illuminated Rio Grande SP-type caboose; twelve curved, three straight, and one insulated straight track; and a 39-20 operating packet.

Comments: The colorful Rio Grande was a new road name for the F-3 series, and this was one of two sets to include the 2379 units. The set box was the new tan/brown basket weave look that was introduced exclusively for Super O. The engine came without a liner in a corrugated carton with tucked-in end flaps. The B unit, which was protected with a liner, and the balance of the components came in Late Classic boxes. At long last Lionel finally released a caboose other than a Pennsylvania porthole that truly matched the engine. Can you imagine how many more cabooses the old Lionel Corpora-

2292WS or 825   Super O $85 Retail

Contents: 646 steam locomotive with headlight, smoke, and Magnetraction; 2046W Lionel Lines whistle tender; 2530 Railway Express baggage car, 2531 Silver Dawn observation, 2532 Silver Range Vista Dome, and 2533 Silver Cloud Pullman extruded-aluminum passenger cars; twelve curved, three straight, and one insulated straight track; and a 39-5 operating packet.

Comments: The outfit box was the new tan/brown basket weave look that was introduced exclusively for Super O. The engine came without a liner in a corrugated carton with tucked-in end flaps while the tender and the passenger cars came in Late Classic boxes. This was the first of the aluminum passenger outfits in which the cars were all guaranteed to make a matched set; they were the flat-channeled variation. The proper boxes are even scarcer than the passenger cars, with the 2530 box being extremely difficult to find. This outfit

The contents of 2379 Rio Grande outfit 2291W. This was one of seven Super O sets that Lionel catalogued in 1957. This was an extremely colorful and visually appealing outfit that included the complementary 6657 Rio Grande SP-type caboose, and the long white-striped variation of the 3530 generator car. Note the No. 36 power blades in the lower left corner that were essential to the operation of the barrel car. P. Sigrist Collection.

	VG	LN

and 2526W from 1958 were the only two sets to include a baggage car boxed as such. This was the second time that a 646 headed a 2530 series passenger set, the other being with outfit 2222WS from 1954, but this is the more difficult of the two sets to acquire.   **1050   1750**

2293W or 826   Super O $87.50 Retail

Contents: 2360 tuscan Pennsylvania solid-stripe GG-1; 3662 operating milk car; 3650 extension searchlight car; 6414 auto loader; 6518 double-truck transformer car; 6417 Pennsylvania porthole caboose; twelve curved, three straight, and one insulated straight track; and a 39-20 operating packet.

Comments: The outfit box was the new tan/brown basket weave type that was introduced exclusively for Super O. The proper engine for this set was the solid rubber-stamped striped version with uneven ventilators, and the corrugated carton with a liner was made by National with a "57" date below the box manufacturer's seal. All of the rolling stock were repeat items that came in Late Classic boxes, but two variations are known components of this set: the 6417 caboose was the scarce, without "New York Zone", example and always came in a box with "6417-1" on the end flaps, while the 3650 was most often the dark gray frame version. Also note that the transformer car came with two cardboard inserts that

	VG	LN

were common only to this car and, when properly inserted, helped to protect the fragile insulators. This 1957 rubber-stamped GG-1 is extremely scarce and more difficult to acquire in collector condition than any other of the 2360 series electrics, even the more highly sought five-stripers. This outfit, as with all other GG-1 sets, is a collector's dream.

2400   4000

2295WS or 827   Super O $87.50 Retail

Contents: 746 N & W steam locomotive with headlight, smoke, and Magnetraction; 746W N & W whistle tender; 342 operating culvert loader with 6342 culvert gondola; 3530 generator car; 3361 operating log car; 6560-25 red cab crane; 6419-100 N & W work caboose; twelve curved, three straight, and one insulated straight track; and a 39-20 operating packet.

Comments: The streamlined, bullet nose Norfolk & Western was a new engine for 1957 and was the only 4-8-4 Northern that Lionel made during the postwar era. This was one of five N & W sets that were catalogued through 1959. The outfit box was the new tan/brown basket weave type that was introduced exclusively for Super O.

The engine came without a liner in a corrugated carton with tucked-in end flaps while the tender and rolling stock, except for the 342, came in Late Classic boxes. The culvert gondola was unboxed inside the 342 corrugated carton, but

1
9
5
7

The contents of the 2373 Canadian Pacific passenger set 2296W. In terms of collector desirability and market value, this is one of the top five postwar sets. As sent from the factory, this set contained three Skyline 500 Vista Domes. However, many customers wanted more variety in the passenger cars, so dealers frequently substituted Blair Manor and Craig Manor Pullmans for two of the Vista Domes. Regrettably, forgeries of the Canadian Pacific items permeate the marketplace today, and even the engine boxes have been fraudulently reproduced. P. Sigrist Collection.

	VG	LN

boxed when available for separate sale: it was "stuffed" into an overstamped, undersized 6462 gondola box. The entire set was comprised of repeat items, but the N & W road name was a new logo for the work caboose; it came in a box with cardboard insert and had a "-100" suffix stamped on the end flaps end as part of the stock number, while the generator car was the long-striped variation with a blue fuel tank. Lastly, the 1957 outfits are purported to include the scarce long-striped tender with a rubber-stamped "X" suffix on the end flaps of the box, but this was not the case as the more common short-striped tender was the usual component of this set.

1800   3000

2296W or 828   Super O $100 Retail

Contents: 2373P/2373T Canadian Pacific F-3 AA units; 2551 Banff Park observation, 2552 Skyline 500 Vista Dome, 2553 Blair Manor Pullman, and 2554 Craig Manor Pullman extruded-aluminum passenger cars; twelve curved, seven straight, and one insulated straight track; and a 39-5 operating packet.

Comments: This outfit was catalogued with three Vista Domes, but the 2553 and 2554 Pullmans are listed above

solely for the reason that this outfit caused the most noted instance of component switching. Many collectors balked at the lack of variety offered in the passenger cars and opted for an alternative, which was to switch two Vista Domes for the separate-sale Pullmans. This is another of the "upper echelon" of postwar sets. The outfit box was the new tan/brown basket weave type that was introduced exclusively for Super O. The extraordinary price that this set commands today has led to a deluge of forgeries. Reproductions that are virtually undistinguishable to the untrained eye exist in the metallic striping, window inserts, and the cabs and boxes for the engines. Many knowledgeable people feel that the extreme desirability of this and the previously issued Congressional sets has caused an acute shortage of regular flat-channeled passenger cars in the marketplace because of their use in the creation of forgeries.

The P and T units came individually boxed without liners in corrugated cartons with tucked-in ends flaps while the passenger cars came without protective liners in Late Classic boxes with coupler protection flaps. A minor quirk occurred in 1957 in that the authentic 2373P carton was made by Express while the 2373T was made by National. These are legitimate boxes! Furthermore, this outfit is sometimes offered on the market as a six-car set that includes the separate-sale 2553 and 2554, and is most sought after as such. Mint condition, boxed examples of the scarce 2553 and 2554 Pullmans were available at Madison Hardware to "preferred" customers up until the time the doors closed.

	VG	LN
As six-car set	4200	7000
As four-car set with four different cars	3900	6500
As catalogued	3600	6000

2297WS or 829   Super O $110 Retail

Contents: 746 N & W steam locomotive with headlight, smoke, and Magnetraction; 746W N & W whistle tender; 264 operating forklift with 6264 lumber car; 3356 operating horse car; 3662 operating milk car; 345 operating culvert unloader with 6342 culvert gondola; 6517 bay window caboose; twelve curved, five straight, and one insulated straight track; and a 39-20 operating packet.

Comments: The streamlined bullet nose Norfolk & Western was a new engine for 1957 and was the only 4-8-4 Northern that Lionel made during the postwar era. This was the most expensive set that Lionel catalogued during the 1950s and it was one of five N & W sets that were catalogued through 1959. The outfit box was the new tan/brown basket weave type exclusive to Super O, and was oversized to accommodate the boxed accessory items.

The engine came without a liner in a corrugated carton with tucked-in end flaps. The horse and the milk cars, protected by liners, and the tender all came in Late Classic boxes while the forklift and the culvert unloader came in their own corrugated cartons. The culvert gondola was unboxed inside the 345 carton but was boxed when available for separate sale; it was "stuffed" into an overstamped, under-sized 6462 gondola box. The forklift was a new accessory for 1957. The 6264 was placed unboxed inside the 264 carton but it too was boxed when available for separate sale; it came in a Late Classic box with "6264" printed on the end flaps. The component boxes for both the culvert gondola and the 6264 lumber car are very scarce.

The 1957 outfits are purported to include the scarce long-striped tender with a rubber-stamped "X" suffix on the end flaps of the box. Such was not the case as the more common short-striped tender was the usual component of this set.

Note that the 3356 came with an amended instruction envelope that included information about the enclosed No. 36 power blade that was essential to the operation of the car on Super O track. Both the horse car and the corral were available separately as replacement items, and each had an individual component box.   2250   3750

1958

A SLIGHT STEP BACKWARDS

One could sense trouble on the horizon when military-related items were introduced in the 1958 catalogue. The new 175 rocket launcher was featured on the cover and on page two of the consumer catalogue. New noteworthy rolling stock was introduced in the form of 6800 series military unit flatcars, 6519 Allis Chalmers car, 6572 REA reefer, 6434 illuminated poultry car, and the scarce 6556 Katy stock car. In addition, two collectable cabooses were introduced this year: the 6557 smoking SP-type caboose and the 6427-60 Virginian porthole caboose.

The only truly new piece of motive power was the 2329 Virginian rectifier electric, and it was a sales disaster. The scarce 613 U P switcher was a new road name as were the 2348 M St. L Geep and the 2352 Pennsylvania EP-5 electric. The 2242 single-motored New Haven was new to the F-3 series and the Santa Fe returned to a twin-motored AA combination as 2383. The inferior Alcos were catalogued in four new road names. They were the 209 New Haven, 210 Texas Special, 212 U.S.M.C., and 216 Burlington. Buyer beware as chassis changes are quite prevalent in the Alco series. The units mentioned above, except for the 212, came with two-axle Magnetraction and three-position E-units, and must have the proper chassis with the appropriate trucks.

O Gauge outfits disappeared from the product line, not to be seen again until 1964. The outfit roster included twelve new O27 sets (or thirteen, if the repeat of 1587S is counted) and sixteen Super O sets. Plastic early version AAR trucks were the norm for O27 rolling stock, while metal trucks were retained on some Super O items. Because Lionel was still developing their AAR truck replacement, metal trucks were most common on cars that required a contact roller or pickup shoe. A cost-saving frame was also introduced for the SP-type cabooses. The new tab frame eliminated the use of screws as a means of attaching the cab to the chassis.

The O27 outfit box was the same basket weave type that was used in 1956 and 1957, and the Super O box was a repeat of the tan/brown type from 1957 with motive power scenes on all four sides. The corresponding three-digit outfit numbering system that began in 1955 was abandoned. The component boxes were still done in the Late Classic style, but some new and/or reorder issues were now printed with distinctive bolder-face type on the end flaps. The corrugated cardboard steam engine boxes remained the same, but a new slightly oversized corrugated box was developed for the 2329 Virginian rectifier. This oversized box with two cardboard inserts was necessary to properly protect the pantograph, and this same size box was also used for the 2348 M St. L Geep. The Alco box was also reengineered for 1958 production only. This new corrugated carton was usually manufactured by the Star Company, was shorter than the 1957 issue, had conventional

end flaps rather than those that tucked in, and included two cardboard rings, often lost, that were used as coupler protectors.

For additional information on suffixes, please refer to the earlier discussion in **1957**.

1587S **O27 Gauge** **$49.95 Retail**

Comments: The "Lady Lionel" train set (Girls' Set) was catalogued again solely to help dealers move unsold 1957 outfits. The Girls' Set was a sales disaster at the time but is highly coveted by collectors today. Please refer to **1957** for more detailed information. **2400** **4000**

1590 **O27 Gauge** **$25 Retail**

Contents: 249 red-striped steam locomotive; 250T Pennsylvania red-striped non-whistle tender; 6014 red Bosco boxcar; 6151 flatcar with Range Patrol vehicle; 6112 blue gondola with three canisters; 6017 SP-type caboose; eight curved and two straight track; 1008 camtrol; and a 1015 45-watt transformer.

Comments: The 249 was a close copy of the 250 from 1957, except that it had no headlight and only a two-position reversing unit. This outfit was a late addition to the product line as evidenced by the outfit number which is incorrect for a freight set. Please refer to the **Prologue** for additional details.

The outfit box was the standard O27 basket weave type. The engine was packed in a corrugated carton with tucked-in end flaps while the repeat tender with AAR trucks came in a Late Classic box. The balance of rolling stock, also with AAR trucks, came in Bold Classic boxes. The only new item was the 6151, and it was common only to this set; it was the same flatcar body that was introduced in 1955 for the 6111 and also used for the 6121 in 1956; it has only "Lionel" stamped, usually in black, on the frame and came in yellow, cream, or orange with a Pyro Range Patrol vehicle.

The 6014 and 6112 usually came in boxes with suffixes; please refer to the earlier discussion on suffixes in **1957**. **175** **300**

1591 **O27 Gauge** **$29.95 Retail**

Contents: 212 U.S.M.C. Alco A unit; 6803 flatcar with military units; 6807 flatcar with military DKW; 6809 flatcar with military units; 6017-50 U.S.M.C. SP-type caboose; eight

VG   LN

curved and two straight track; 1008 camtrol; and a 1015 45-watt transformer.

Comments: The outfit box was the standard O27 basket weave type. The engine came in a new corrugated carton made by the Star Company with standard end flaps that was used only in 1958. Interior packaging included two cardboard rings that were inserted as coupler protectors, even though the 212 did not have a front coupler. The military flatcars, all with AAR trucks, came in Late Classic boxes. The U.S.M.C. caboose was on a tab frame and came in a Bold Classic box with a "-60" suffix. The military flatcar loads, except for the 6807, were extremely fragile and are highly desirable in the collector market. This is an extremely scarce set as each component was common only to this outfit.   **900   1500**

1593   O27 Gauge $35 Retail

Contents: 613 Union Pacific NW-2 switcher; 6476 Lehigh Valley hopper; 6818 flatcar with transformer; 6660 flatcar with boom crane; 6112 black gondola with three canisters; 6119-100 red cab work caboose; eight curved and two straight track; 1008 camtrol; and a 1015 45-watt transformer.

Comments: The outfit box was the standard O27 basket weave type. The 613 was a new 1958 item and is now a scarce switcher. The engine, with two small cardboard inserts, and most of the rolling stock with AAR trucks came in Bold Classic boxes. The 6476 was catalogued in orange but came in either red or black. The 6660 and 6818 were new additions to the rolling stock roster. This was one of only two sets to include the 6660 boom crane; the car came with a special cardboard insert, most often lost, to hold it in place. The 6476 and 6112 usually came in boxes with suffixes; please refer to the earlier discussion on suffixes in **1957**.

    500   850

1595   O27 Gauge $37.50 Retail

Contents: 1625 steam switcher with headlight; 1625T slope-back tender; 6804, 6806, and 6808 flatcars with military units; 6017 gray SP-type caboose with black letters; eight curved and one straight track; 6029 uncoupling section; and a 1015 45-watt transformer.

Comments: The 1625 was simply another version of the 1615 with a dummy front coupler, and the 1625T was nothing more than a 1615T with AAR trucks. The outfit box was the standard O27 basket weave type. The engine came without a liner in a corrugated carton with tucked-in end flaps while the tender came in a Bold Classic box. The military flatcars, all with AAR trucks, came in Late Classic boxes. The loads on these flatcars were all extremely fragile and are highly desirable in the collector market. The caboose was also common only to this set; it was gray with black "Lionel Lines" lettering on a tab frame and came in a Bold Classic box with an "-85" suffix. This is an extremely scarce set as each component was common only to this outfit.   **1050   1750**

1597S   O27 Gauge $39.95 Retail

Contents: 2018 steam locomotive with headlight and smoke; 1130T Lionel Lines non-whistle tender; 6014 orange Bosco boxcar; 6818 flatcar with transformer; 6476 red Lehigh

VG   LN

Valley hopper; 6025 black Gulf single-dome tank car; 6112 blue gondola with three canisters; 6017 SP-type caboose; eight curved and three straight track; 6029 uncoupling section; and a 1015 45-watt transformer.

Comments: The outfit box was the standard O27 basket weave type. The engine came without a liner in a corrugated carton with tucked-in end flaps. The tender and the rolling stock all came with AAR trucks in a mixture of Late and Bold Classic boxes. The components were rather bland, and the only new item was the 6818 transformer car. Please refer to the earlier discussion on suffixes in **1957**. Most low and moderate steam outfits arouse minimal collector interest today.   **210   350**

1599   O27 Gauge $39.95 Retail

Contents: 210P/210T Texas Special Alco AA units; 6801 flatcar with boat; 6014 orange Bosco boxcar; 6424 flatcar with autos; 6112 black gondola with three canisters; 6465 gray Gulf two-dome tank car; 6017 SP-type caboose; eight curved and three straight track; 6029 uncoupling section; and a 1015 45-watt transformer.

Comments: The outfit box was the standard O27 basket weave type. The P and T units each came in the new Alco corrugated carton made by Express in this instance, rather than the Star Company, with standard end flaps that were exclusive to 1958. Interior packaging included two cardboard rings that were inserted as coupler protectors. Beware of cracked and/or repaired struts as they are extremely fragile. The rolling stock all came with AAR trucks in a mixture of Late and Bold Classic boxes. The only new item other than the engines was the 6465 tank car that was reintroduced, after missing the 1957 product year, with Gulf logo. Please refer to the earlier discussion in **1957** on suffixes that are known to come with this set. Diesel outfits, even with common equipment, are far more collectable that their steam counterparts.   **250   400**

1600   O27 Gauge $39.95 Retail

Contents: 216 Burlington Alco A unit; 6572 Railway Express Agency reefer; 2432 Clifton Vista Dome and 2436 Mooseheart observation in the silver-with-red-letter color scheme; eight curved and three straight track; 6029 uncoupling section; and a 1015 45-watt transformer.

Comments: This was a unique set as it included the new 6572 REA reefer. This reefer, not to be confused with the reissue from 1963, was painted dark green and had metal trucks. It has been known to surface as a set component with 2400 series passenger trucks, but that variation is easily retrofitted by taking 2430 series rear observation trucks and adding magnetic couplers. The engine came in the new corrugated carton made by the Star Company with standard end flaps that was exclusive to 1958. Interior packaging included two cardboard rings that were inserted as coupler protectors. Beware of a cracked and/or repaired strut as it is extremely fragile. The outfit box was the standard O27 basket weave type and the passenger cars, along with the REA reefer, came in Late Classic boxes. This outfit and the 1608W New Haven are the two most highly sought conventional Alco sets.   **500   1000**

	VG	LN

1958

1601W   O27 Gauge $49.95 Retail

Contents: 2337 Wabash GP-7; 6800 flatcar with airplane; 6464-425 New Haven boxcar; 6801 flatcar with boat; 6810 flatcar with van; 6017 SP-type caboose; eight curved and three straight track; 6029 uncoupling section; and a 1053 60-watt transformer.

Comments: The 2337 was a carbon copy of the 2339 from 1957 except that it was now catalogued as O27 Gauge and was fitted with dummy couplers. The outfit box was the standard O27 basket weave type. The engine, with two small cardboard inserts, came in a Bold Classic box, while the rolling stock with AAR trucks came in a mixture of both Late and Bold Classic boxes. The only new item in the set was the 6810, which was nothing more than a lower-quality version of a 6430 without a mounting rack and with only one van, either gray or white, with a Cooper-Jarrett nameplate. Nevertheless, the 6810 is a scarce car because it was included as a component in this set only. This outfit is much scarcer that the 2275W Wabash O Gauge set from 1957.   **600   1000**

1603WS   O27 Gauge $49.95 Retail

Contents: 2037 steam locomotive with headlight, smoke, and Magnetraction; 6026W Lionel Lines whistle tender; 6424 flatcar with autos; 6014 white Bosco boxcar; 6818 flatcar with transformer; 6112 black gondola with three canisters; 6017 SP-type caboose; eight curved and three straight track; 6029 uncoupling section; and a 1053 60-watt transformer.

Comments: The outfit box was the standard O27 basket weave type. The engine came without a liner in a corrugated carton with tucked-in end flaps while the tender, usually with metal trucks but often unpainted, came in a Late Classic box. The balance of the components came with AAR trucks in both Late and Bold Classic boxes. The 6818 was a new 1958 item and the Bosco car in white is a scarce color. Please refer to the earlier discussion on suffixes in **1957**.   **275   475**

1605W   O27 Gauge $55 Retail

Contents: 208P/208T Santa Fe Alco AA units; 6800 flatcar with airplane; 6464-425 New Haven boxcar; 6801 flatcar with boat; 6477 miscellaneous car with pipes; 6802 flatcar with girders; 6017 SP-type caboose; eight curved and three straight track; 6029 uncoupling section; and a 1053 60-watt transformer.

Comments: The outfit box was the standard O27 basket weave type. The P and T units each came in the new style corrugated carton made by the Star Company with standard end flaps that was exclusive to 1958. Interior packaging included two cardboard rings that were inserted as coupler protectors. Beware of cracked and/or repaired struts as they are quite susceptible to breakage. The "208" number on the engines was changed from "204" in 1957, because of the addition of a horn to the P unit and the removal of the headlight from the T unit. The rolling stock all came with AAR trucks in both Late and Bold Classic boxes. The only new item was the 6802 that came with two black U.S. Steel girders, while the repeat 6801 surfaces with boats of various colors, any of which would be acceptable to collectors.   **250   400**

1607WS   O27 Gauge $59.95 Retail

Contents: 2037 steam locomotive with headlight, smoke, and Magnetraction; 6026W Lionel Lines whistle tender; 6465 Gulf two-dome tank car; 6818 flatcar with transformer; 6464-425 New Haven boxcar; 6112 blue gondola with three canisters; 6119-100 red cab work caboose; eight curved and five straight track; 6029 uncoupling section; and a 1044 90-watt transformer.

Comments: The outfit box for this set was the standard O27 basket weave type. The engine came without a liner in a corrugated carton with tucked-in end flaps while the tender, with metal trucks but often unpainted, came in a Late Classic box. The rolling stock all came with AAR trucks in a mixture of both Late and Bold Classic boxes. The 6818 and 6660 were new additions to the rolling stock roster. The 6465 was almost new in that it was reintroduced, after missing the 1957 catalogue, with Gulf logo; it was catalogued in orange but came in either black or gray. This was one of only two sets to include the 6660 boom crane; the car came with a special cardboard insert, usually lost, to hold it in place. The 6465 and 6112 usually came in boxes with suffixes; please refer to the discussion of suffixes in **1957**.   **325   550**

1608W   O27 Gauge $65 Retail

Contents: 209P/209T New Haven Alco AA units; two 2432 Clifton Vista Domes, 2434 Newark Pullman, and 2436 Mooseheart observation in the silver-with-red-letter color scheme; eight curved and five straight track; 6029 uncoupling section; and a 1053 60-watt transformer.

Comments: This was the top-of-the-line O27 set for 1958. It was more expensive than four of the Super O outfits, and equal in price to two others! The outfit box was the standard O27 basket weave type. The P and T units each came in the new corrugated carton made by the Star Company with standard end flaps that was exclusive to 1958. Interior packaging included two cardboard rings that were inserted as coupler protectors. Beware of cracked and/or repaired struts as they are easily broken. The passenger cars came in Late Classic boxes, and this was the last set to include the red-lettered 2430 series cars. The New Havens are the most coveted Alcos today, and are common only to this set.   **900   1800**

2501W   Super O Gauge $49.95 Retail

Contents: 2348 M St. L GP-9; 6464-525 M St. L boxcar; 6802 flatcar with girders; 6560 red cab crane; 6119-100 red cab work caboose; twelve curved, three straight, and one insulated straight track; and a 39-5 operating packet.

Comments: The 2348 was the first GP-9 to be offered by Lionel. It came without a liner in a slightly oversized corrugated carton, made by the Star Company, with two small cardboard inserts that fit over the front and rear railing to hold the engine in place; these inserts are now almost always missing because they were difficult for the consumer to reuse in repackaging. The rolling stock came in a mixture of Late and Bold Classic boxes. The 6802 was a new item and was fitted with AAR trucks, while the other components consisted of repeat items that most often came with AAR trucks. The

VG   LN

outfit box was the standard Super O design developed in 1957 and carried forward for the entire 1958 line. Keep in mind that both the work caboose and crane still came with cardboard inserts.   **550   900**

2502W   Super O Gauge $59.95 Retail

Contents: 400 Budd RDC passenger car; 2550 Budd mail-baggage car; 2559 Budd passenger car; twelve curved, three straight, and one insulated straight track; and a 39-5 operating packet.

Comments: This was the second and last of the Budd sets to be catalogued. It was introduced as O Gauge in 1957 but was upgraded to Super O in 1958 when all O Gauge was temporarily shelved. The outfit box was standard Super O design. The powered unit came in a corrugated carton with a liner while the 2550 and 2559 came in Late Classic boxes with coupler protection flaps. The 2550 was the non-powered (trailer) version of the powered 404 unit. Ironically, the non-powered 2550 and 2559 command higher prices than the powered units, with the 2550 being the most desirable of all the Budd units.   **1500   2500**

2503WS   Super O Gauge $59.95 Retail

Contents: 665 steam locomotive with headlight, smoke, and Magnetraction; 2046W Lionel Lines whistle tender; 3361 operating log car; 6434 poultry car; 6801 flatcar with boat; 6536 M St. L quad hopper; 6357 illuminated SP-type caboose; twelve curved, three straight, and one insulated straight track; and a 39-20 operating packet.

Comments: The outfit box was standard Super O issue. The engine came boxed without a liner in a corrugated carton with tucked-in end flaps, while the tender and the balance of the components came in a combination of Late and Bold Classic boxes. The poultry car and the 3361 unquestionably came with metal trucks while only the earliest examples of the M St. L hopper and the 6357 caboose had the same. The 6801 was fitted with AAR trucks. The "X" suffix applied to the box of the log dump car meant that the unloading bin was placed loose inside the set box rather than being packed with the car itself. A component box for the 6536 is the most difficult item to obtain from the entire set.   **400   675**

2505W   Super O Gauge $59.95 Retail

Contents: 2329 Virginian rectifier electric; 6805 atomic energy disposal car; 6519 Allis Chalmers car; 6800 flatcar with airplane; 6464-500 Timken boxcar; 6357 illuminated SP-type caboose; twelve curved, three straight, and one insulated straight track; and a 39-5 operating packet.

Comments: The rectifier was a new, and not well-received, design for the 1958 product year. It came without a liner in a slightly oversized corrugated carton made by the Star Company, with one large and one small cardboard insert that fit over the front and rear railing to protect the pantograph and to hold the engine in place; these inserts are almost always missing since they were difficult for the train enthusiast to use in repackaging.

The outfit box was standard Super O issue. The rolling stock all came in a blend of Late and Bold Classic boxes. The

---

VG   LN

6805 and 6519 were new items, and because of the need for a contact roller, the atomic energy car received metal trucks while the Allis Chalmers car had AAR trucks. The brakewheels on the 6519 were extremely fragile and are now usually broken; so are the handles on top of the radioactive waste canisters on the 6805. The 1958 edition of the 6800 came only with AAR trucks while the -500 Timken could have come either way. The Timken boxcar has been purported to be the scarce Type II-B on a gray body mold, but it could possibly be the earliest version of the Type III body mold.   **1200   2000**

2507W   Super O Gauge $65 Retail

Contents: 2242P/2242C New Haven AB F-3 units; 3444 animated gondola; 6464-425 New Haven boxcar; 6424 flatcar with autos; 6468-25 New Haven double-door automobile car; 6357 illuminated SP-type caboose; twelve curved, three straight, and one insulated straight track; and a 39-5 operating packet.

Comments: The single-motored New Haven was a new road name in the F-3 series and, because the Alcos dominated the O27 line, it was designated as Super O. The outfit box was standard Super O issue. The engine came without a liner in a corrugated carton with tucked-in end flaps while the B unit, protected by a liner, came in a Late Classic box. The remaining components came in a mixture of both Late and Bold Classic boxes. All of the rolling stock were repeat or carry-forward items; the 6468 and the 3444 retained metal trucks but the -425 and the 6424 now came with AAR trucks. The 1958 edition of the 6357 caboose also came with metal trucks. This was one of two New Haven F-3 outfits to be catalogued, the other being 2537W from 1959.   **1800   3000**

2509WS   Super O Gauge $65 Retail

Contents: 665 steam locomotive with headlight, smoke, and Magnetraction; 2046W Lionel Lines whistle tender; 6414 auto loader; 3650 extension searchlight car; 6464-475 Boston and Maine boxcar; 6805 atomic energy disposal car; 6357 illuminated SP-type caboose; twelve curved, three straight, and one insulated straight track; and a 39-5 operating packet.

Comments: The outfit box was standard Super O issue. The engine came boxed without a liner in a corrugated carton with tucked-in end flaps while the tender and the remaining components came in a mixture of both Late and Bold Classic boxes. The 6805 was a new item for 1958, and was given metal trucks because of the need for a contact roller. Please note that the handles on top of the radioactive waste canisters on the 6805 were extremely fragile and are often found broken. The 3650 searchlight car was a carry-forward item and still retained metal trucks, while the 1958 editions of the 6414 and -475 were usually fitted with AAR trucks.   **425   725**

2511W   Super O Gauge $69.95 Retail

Contents: 2352 Pennsylvania EP-5 electric; 3562-75 orange operating barrel car; 3424 Wabash brakeman; 3361 operating log car; 6560 red cab crane; 6119-100 red cab work

---

99

VG   LN

caboose; twelve curved, three straight, and one insulated straight track; and a 39-10 operating packet.

Comments: The Pennsylvania was a new road name in the EP-5 series and was offered in only two sets. The outfit box was standard Super O issue. The engine came boxed without a liner in a corrugated carton with tucked-in end flaps while the balance of the components came in a mixture of both Late and Bold Classic boxes. The rolling stock were all repeat items, and the barrel car, Wabash brakeman, and the log dump car still retained metal trucks while the crane and the caboose usually came with AAR trucks. This was the only Super O set to ever include the 3424, and it required a unique operating packet that included the No. 38-95 adapter sections necessary to operate the Wabash brakeman car. To see a picture of the envelope, please see the photograph on page 20 that accompanies Chart IX.   **1200   2000**

2513W   Super O Gauge $69.95 Retail

Contents: 2329 Virginian rectifier electric; 6556 Katy stock car; 6425 Gulf three-dome tank car; 6414 auto loader; 6434 poultry car; 3359 operating twin-bin ore car; 6427-60 Virginian porthole caboose; twelve curved, three straight, and one insulated straight track; and a 39-20 operating packet.

Comments: The rectifier was a new, and not well-received, design for the 1958 product year. It came without a liner in a slightly oversized corrugated carton made by the Star Company, with one large and one small cardboard insert that fitted over the front and rear railing to protect the pantograph and to hold the engine in position; these inserts are almost always missing since they required a little time and patience, on the part of the consumer, for proper repackaging.

The outfit box was standard Super O issue. The rolling stock came in a mixture of both Late and Bold Classic boxes. All of the components had metal trucks except for the 6414 auto loader. For those who are sticklers for detail, the earliest editions of the auto loader with AAR trucks had the trucks riveted to a mounting bracket in the same manner as the metal truck version. Subsequent issues had the trucks riveted directly to the car. The poultry car, Katy stock car, and the Virginian caboose were new items for 1958, and this was the only set ever to include the 6556 and the 6427-60. The Virginian caboose came in a 6427-1 box that had the "-1" overstamped with a "-60" suffix. This is an extremely scarce and highly desirable set today.   **2100   3500**

2515WS   Super O Gauge $75 Retail

Contents: 646 steam locomotive with headlight, smoke, and Magnetraction; 2046W Lionel Lines whistle tender; 3662 operating milk car; 6424 flatcar with autos; 3444 animated gondola; 6800 flatcar with airplane; 6427 Lionel Lines porthole caboose; twelve curved, three straight, and one insulated straight track; and a 39-20 operating packet.

Comments: The outfit box was standard Super O issue and this was the last of the 646 catalogued sets. The engine came without a liner in a corrugated carton with tucked-in end flaps while the tender and the balance of the components came in a combination of Late and Bold Classic boxes. The rolling stock were all repeat items. The milk car, animated gondola,

VG   LN

and the caboose still retained metal trucks while the airplane and automobile flatcars came with AAR trucks.

          500   825

2517W   Super O Gauge $75 Retail

Contents: 2379P/2379C Rio Grande AB F-3 units; 6519 Allis Chalmers car; 6805 atomic energy disposal car; 6434 poultry car; 6800 flatcar with airplane; 6657 Rio Grande SP-type caboose; twelve curved, three straight, and one insulated straight track; and a 39-5 operating packet.

Comments: This was the follow-up set to outfit 2291W from 1957. It is much harder to find than its predecessor. The second edition of a repeat road name seldom sold as well as the first. The outfit box was standard Super O issue, and the engine came without a liner in a corrugated carton with tucked-in end flaps. The B unit came in a Late Classic box with a liner while the balance of the components came in a blend of Late and Bold Classic boxes. The Rio Grande caboose was a repeat, or more likely, a carry-forward item with metal trucks from 1957. The 6800 was also a repeat but now came with AAR trucks. The 6434, 6805, and 6519 were new additions to the rolling stock roster; the poultry car and the atomic energy car were given metal trucks because of their need for a contact roller, while the Allis Chalmers car was fitted with AAR trucks. The brakewheels on the 6519 were extremely fragile as were the handles on top of the radioactive waste containers on the 6805; both items are usually found broken.   **2100   3500**

2518W   Super O Gauge $75 Retail

Contents: 2352 Pennsylvania EP-5 electric; 2531 Silver Dawn observation; 2533 Silver Cloud Pullman; 2534 Silver Bluff Pullman; twelve curved, three straight, and one insulated straight track; and a 39-5 operating packet.

Comments: The Pennsylvania was a new road name in the EP-5 series and was offered in only two sets. The outfit box was standard Super O issue. The engine came without a liner in a corrugated carton with tucked-in end flaps while the passenger cars came without liners in Late Classic boxes with coupler protection flaps. The passenger cars were the flat-channeled variation and this was the only set to include the flat-channeled 2534. This outfit is scarce and somewhat undervalued in today's market.   **1800   3000**

2519W   Super O Gauge $79.95 Retail

Contents: 2331 Virginian F-M; 6434 poultry car; 3530 generator car; 6801 flatcar with boat; 6414 auto loader; 6464-275 State of Maine boxcar; 6557 smoking caboose; twelve curved, three straight, and one insulated straight track; and a 39-5 operating packet.

Comments: This was the fourth and last of the 2331 catalogued sets. The outfit box was standard Super O issue. The engine came in a corrugated carton with a liner while the remainder of the components came in a mixture of Late and Bold Classic boxes. The 6434 and the 6557 were new items for 1958 and came with metal trucks because of their need for contact rollers, as did the 3530 generator car; the 6801, 6414, and -275 were fitted with AAR trucks. The -275 State of Maine

VG LN

was usually on a Type III body mold. This was one of only three sets to include the scarce smoking caboose.

1800 3000

2521WS   Super O Gauge $89.95 Retail

Contents: 746 N & W steam locomotive with headlight, smoke, and Magnetraction; 746W N & W whistle tender; 6805 atomic energy disposal car; 3361 operating log car; 6430 flatcar with vans; 3356 operating horse car; 6424 flatcar with autos; 6557 smoking caboose; twelve curved, three straight, and one insulated straight track; and a 39-15 operating packet.

Comments: This was the third of five catalogued N & W sets. The outfit box was standard Super O issue. The engine came without a liner in a corrugated carton with tucked-in end flaps, while the tender and rolling stock came in a combination of both Late and Bold Classic boxes. The 6430 with metal trucks came with either white or gray Cooper-Jarrett vans. The 6805 and smoking caboose were new items for 1958 and were given metal trucks because of their need for contact rollers, while the 6424 most often had AAR trucks. The 3356 horse car still retained metal trucks and usually came in the bolder-faced 1958-lettered box. An interesting point about the 3356 is that it contained an amended instruction envelope because of the inclusion of a No. 36 power blade that was necessary to operate the car on Super O track.

The 746W tender was catalogued again with a long stripe, but most often surfaces with the common short stripe. Please note that the handles on top of the radioactive waste canisters were extremely fragile and often found broken. Kindly refer to **1957** for additional comments pertaining to the 746.   **1800 3000**

2523W   Super O Gauge $95 Retail

Contents: 2383P/2383T Santa Fe AA F-3 units; 264 operating forklift with 6264 lumber car; 6434 poultry car; 6800 flatcar with airplane; 3662 operating milk car; 6517 bay window caboose; twelve curved, three straight, and one insulated straight track; and a 39-20 operating packet.

Comments: The twin-motored Santa Fe reappeared in the 1958 catalogue in an AA combination to replace the discontinued single-motored 2243. The outfit box was standard Super O issue. The powered and tender units came without liners in corrugated cartons with tucked-in end flaps made by the Star Company. These Star boxes without perforated fronts are dated to 1958 only; do not accept sets with the Santa Fe units in Mead or perforated-front boxes, which were later issue. The 6264 came unboxed inside the 264 corrugated carton while the balance of the rolling stock came in both Late and Bold Classic boxes. The 6434 with metal trucks was new for 1958 while the remaining components were repeat items. The milk car and the bay window caboose, because of their need for pickup shoes and a contact roller, still retained metal trucks while the 6800 always, and the 6264 usually, came with AAR trucks.   **1050 1750**

VG LN

2525WS   Super O Gauge $100 Retail

Contents: 746 N & W steam locomotive with headlight, smoke, and Magnetraction; 746W N & W whistle tender; 342 operating culvert loader with 6342 culvert gondola; 345 operating culvert unloader with 6342 culvert gondola; 6519 Allis Chalmers car; 6518 double-truck transformer car; 6560 red cab crane; 6419-100 N & W work caboose; twelve curved, five straight, and one insulated straight track; and a 39-5 operating packet.

Comments: This was the fourth and most coveted of the five catalogued N & W sets. The outfit box was standard Super O issue but approximated the size of a footlocker. The engine came without a liner in a corrugated carton with tucked-in end flaps while the 342 and 345 came in corrugated cartons that each contained an unboxed 6342 culvert gondola with metal trucks. The 6342 culvert gondola was boxed when available for separate sale; it was "stuffed" into an overstamped, undersized 6462 gondola box. The rolling stock all came in Late Classic boxes. The N & W work caboose with metal trucks was a repeat item and came only in a box with a "-100" suffix. The crane and transformer cars were also repeat items; the 6518 came with two cardboard inserts that were common only to this car and that helped to protect the fragile insulators. The Allis Chalmers car was a new item with AAR trucks; also note that the brakewheels were extremely fragile and are often found broken. The 746W tender was catalogued again with a long stripe but most often surfaces with the common short stripe. Please refer to **1957** for additional comments pertaining to the 746.   **2400 4000**

2526W   Super O Gauge $100 Retail

Contents: 2383P/2383T Santa Fe AA F-3 units; 2530 Railway Express baggage car; 2531 Silver Dawn observation; two 2532 Silver Range Vista Domes; twelve curved, seven straight, and one insulated straight track; and a 39-5 operating packet.

Comments: The twin-motored Santa Fe reappeared in the 1958 catalogue in an AA combination to replace the discontinued single-motored 2243. The outfit box was standard Super O issue. The powered and tender units came without liners in corrugated cartons with tucked-in end flaps made by the Star Company. These Star boxes without perforated fronts are dated only to 1958; do not accept sets with the Santa Fe units in Mead or perforated-front boxes, which were later issue. The passenger cars were the flat-channeled variation that, along with the 2530, came without liners in Late Classic boxes with coupler protection flaps. The proper boxes are scarcer than the cars, with the 2530 box being extremely difficult to find. This outfit and 2292WS from 1957 were the only two sets to include a baggage car boxed as such. This was the last of the 2530 series passenger sets.   **1500 2500**

1959

A TIME WARP—PAST MEETS FUTURE

This was definitely a year of major changes. The glossy solid orange perforated-front box made its debut for rolling stock and passenger cars. This new box will be termed *Orange Perforated* in the text. Even the corrugated cardboard engine boxes, both diesel and steam, now had a tear-out panel. Cardboard inserts disappeared from the work caboose boxes, and the insert for the crane was further simplified and now consisted of a single cardboard strip. *All* of the outfit boxes were changed to a *yellow* background, and some sets began to appear in display boxes. These display boxes were designed for flat packaging and had a perforation cut into the attached lid. This allowed the box to be folded and creased in a manner that permitted the illustration to be shown vertically while revealing the interior contents at the same time.

Three versions of this display box were used in 1959. *Type A* had inner liners folded into channels that separated and protected the *unboxed* contents. *Type B* had a one-piece die-cut filler that held the *unboxed* contents in place. *Type C* had no inner liner, and the contents, except track and transformer, were individually boxed. A colored cardboard filler with a railroad logo was often used to fill the space not taken up by component contents. Lionel also developed an orange coated stock sleeve to slide over the engine box for Type C packaging that gave the contents a uniform look. Type C packaging also allowed the dealer to remove the perforated fronts of the component boxes from a floor sample in order to expose the contents to a potential customer.

This was also the year in which specific numbered outfit instruction sheets began to appear in the O27 sets.

The Super O set boxes retained the same design as the original 1957 issue, but as mentioned earlier, were printed with a yellow background. A new development in 1959 Super O outfits was the inclusion of the No. 43 power track with outfits which replaced the No. 61 ground and No. 62 power lockons. An interesting but incorrect picture of the new No. 43 is shown on page 39 of the consumer catalogue. The introduction of the No. 43 required Lionel to revise their Super O instruction sheet, with the new number being "39-7". The basic Super O operating packet was revised and was now referred to as "No. 39-25" in its simplest form.

Sometime during the production year changes occurred in both Super O and O27 track. From its inception in 1957 Super O used blackened metal for the basic support structure, but in 1959 it changed to grayish-silver. (This can be easily seen by simply turning a piece of track upside down.) In addition, black rail ties began to disappear from O27 track, replaced by ties of the same grayish-silver color.

The arch bar truck was another new 1959 item. It was developed for the General cars, but also became the most commonly used truck type for Advance and uncatalogued sets. AAR trucks were the norm with only a few operating cars that retained metal trucks. Those that did were equipped as such only to deplete existing inventory or to fulfill a need, since the AAR version of the pickup shoe required by the horse, circus, milk, and Bosco cars was not yet released. The contact roller assembly for AAR trucks was fully developed and began to appear on cars such as the 3435 traveling aquarium and the 6357 caboose.

Military and space-related items were a dominant part of the 1959 product line, and many interesting and highly collectable items were presented. The General was introduced and available in three sets. The 614 Alaska was a new switcher, the 2349 Northern Pacific a new road name in the Geep series, as was the 2358 Great Northern in the EP-5 series. The 217 Boston and Maine was a new Alco unit, and it was paired with the first issue of an Alco B unit. The 44 U.S. Army missile launcher was also new, and two highly coveted motorized units were introduced as the 57 AEC and the 58 Great Northern rotary snow blower. The Bosco and circus cars, the chicken sweeper, and the traveling aquarium were new operating cars. Other noteworthy new rolling stock were the 6816 flatcar with bulldozer, 6817 flatcar with earthscraper, 3512 fireman and ladder car, and the 3540 TV monitor car along with the various Alaska series items.

The blue-striped 2412/14/16 Santa Fe passenger cars were introduced for the O27 line to replace the discontinued 2430 series cars. It is interesting to note that the 2432 Clifton and the 2436 Mooseheart occasionally surface in Orange Perforated boxes; they were catalogued and boxed in this manner simply to deplete existing inventory. Mint examples of the Mooseheart were available through Madison Hardware up until the time the doors finally closed. Across the nation, most collectors place a higher value on the Mooseheart than on the Summit observation. This is not the case on the East Coast because the Mooseheart is just as easily obtained as the Summit, while the Summit is more difficult to acquire in collector condition.

The 2530 series O Gauge extruded-aluminum passenger cars were no longer available in an outfit. They were catalogued solely to deplete inventory, but were never available in Orange Perforated boxes. They were replaced by the 2560 series Santa Fe red-striped cars. These cars were catalogued for three years but are every bit as scarce and prized as the 1957 Canadian Pacific cars.

	VG	LN
1105 Advance Catalogue	**O27 Gauge**	**No Retail**

Contents: 1055 Texas Special Alco A unit; 6045 gray Lionel Lines two-dome tank car; 6044 blue Airex boxcar; 6042 or 6112 black gondola with two canisters; 6047 red SP-type caboose; eight curved and two straight track; and a 1026 25-watt transformer.

Comments: The origin of this set stemmed from Lionel's desire, as the 1959 Advance Catalogue states, "To meet the needs of the low price mass toy market." It came in a unique Type A, white background, display-style outfit box titled "The Texas Special" with blue and orange print. The contents were separated by loose cardboard dividers instead of channels. The rolling stock was equipped with the new arch bar trucks with fixed couplers. This was Lionel at its lowest ebb but, paradoxically, at its marketing best. Advance Catalogue sets are far more collectable than most of the consumer catalogue starter outfits. **120   200**

	VG	LN
1609	**O27 Gauge**	**$19.95 Retail**

Contents: 246 steam locomotive with headlight and Magnetraction; 1130T Lionel Lines non-whistle tender; 6162-25 blue gondola with canisters; 6476 red Lehigh Valley hopper; 6057 SP-type caboose; eight curved and one straight track; 1008-50 camtrol uncoupling section; and a 1016 35-watt transformer.

Comments: This set is known to have come in either the Type A with unboxed contents or in the Type C display-style outfit box with component boxes. The blue gondola does *not* have "6162-25" stamped on the side. The tender and rolling stock were equipped with AAR trucks. This is the only set in which a 6057 caboose *ever* came boxed, and is only one of two sets that included a 1016 transformer.

	VG	LN
Type A Box	60	100
Type C box	120	200

614 Alaska diesel switcher freight set 1611 in a Type B display-style box. This packaging was Lionel's first use of a one-piece die-cut filler. The Alaska boxcar and hopper were not included with the catalogued set. M. Sokol Collection.

	VG	LN

1 9 5 9

1611   O27 Gauge $25 Retail

Contents: 614 Alaska NW-2 switcher; 6825 flatcar with trestle; 6162-60 Alaska gondola with canisters; 6465 black Lionel Lines two-dome tank car; 6027 Alaska SP-type caboose; eight curved and one straight track; 1008-50 camtrol uncoupling section; and a 1016 35-watt transformer.

Comments: This set usually came in a die-cut Type B display-style outfit box, but also came in a small single-tier tan corrugated box with all of the components boxed. The rolling stock all came with AAR trucks as original issue. Boxes for the 6162-60 gondola and the 6027 caboose *do exist*. This set, along with 1609, are the only ones that included a 1016 transformer. Each component of this outfit was new issue for 1959 and when boxed, came in the new Orange Perforated style. Please note that the Alaska switcher also has a scarce variation. It is one on which the phrase "Built by Lionel" is outlined in yellow. Refer to page 103 for a picture of the Alaska set.

	VG	LN
Tan box	600	1000
Type B box	475	800

An end view of some of the General set boxes: (top) the General Frontier (gift) pack from 1959; (2nd from top) outfit 1612 in a rare conventional tan corrugated box that came with individually boxed components; (3rd from top) outfit 1644 from 1961 in a half-orange, half-white display-style box; (4th from top) Super O outfit 2528WS from 1959 in a Type C display-style box that included individually boxed components. Note that the dimensions are smaller that the other 2528WS box; (bottom) Super O outfit 2528WS in a Type B display-style box. This set included unboxed components that were held in place by a die-cut filler. Because of the absence of component boxes, it does not command the same price as the other 2528WS outfit. M. Sokol Collection.

1612   O27 Gauge $29.95 Retail

Contents: 1862 General with headlight; 1862T tender; 1866 mail-baggage car; 1865 passenger car; eight curved and two straight track; and a 1015 45-watt transformer.

Comments: This set usually came in a die-cut Type B display-style outfit box, but also came in a small single-tier tan corrugated box with all of the contents boxed. When component boxed the 1862 came in an oversized, perforated-front corrugated box with a special cardboard insert while the tender and the passenger cars came in Orange Perforated boxes. It was the General sets for which the arch bar trucks were developed. The passenger cars were non-illuminated and came with non-self-centering, fixed die-cast couplers.

	VG	LN
Tan box	475	800
Type B box	425	700

1613S   O27 Gauge $29.95 Retail

Contents: 247 blue-striped steam locomotive with smoke and headlight; 247T B & O blue-striped non-whistle tender; 6826 flatcar with Christmas trees; 6819 flatcar with helicopter; 6821 flatcar with crates; 6017 SP-type caboose; eight curved and one straight track; 1008-50 camtrol uncoupling section; and a 1015 45-watt transformer.

Comments: The engine came in a corrugated carton with tucked-in end flaps and an orange sleeve, while the tender and the balance of the components came with AAR trucks in Orange Perforated boxes. This set came in a Type C display-style outfit box. All of the components, other than the caboose, were new for 1959. The 6826 is a scarce car, and both the 6819 and 6821 are collectable. Refer to page 105 for a picture of Type C packaging and a boxed example of this set.

	250	400

1615   O27 Gauge $39.95 Retail

Contents: 217P/217C Boston and Maine Alco AB units; 6800 flatcar with airplane; 6464-475 Boston and Maine boxcar; 6812 track maintenance car; 6825 flatcar with trestle; 6017-100 Boston and Maine SP-type caboose; eight curved and five straight track; 6029 uncoupling section; and a 1015 45-watt transformer.

Comments: This set came in a Type C display-style box with component boxes. The Boston and Maine was a new road name in the Alco series and it was paired with a new-issue B unit. The engine came in a perforated-front corrugated carton with tucked-in end flaps and an orange sleeve while the B unit came in an Orange Perforated box.

All of the rolling stock came with AAR trucks. The 6812, 6825, and -100 caboose were new-issue items and came in Orange Perforated boxes while the 6800 came in a carry-over Late Classic box. Early versions of this set have been known to contain the rare purple -100 caboose. This caboose was created from leftover unstamped shells of the 6017-50 U.S.M.C. caboose from 1958.

	360	600

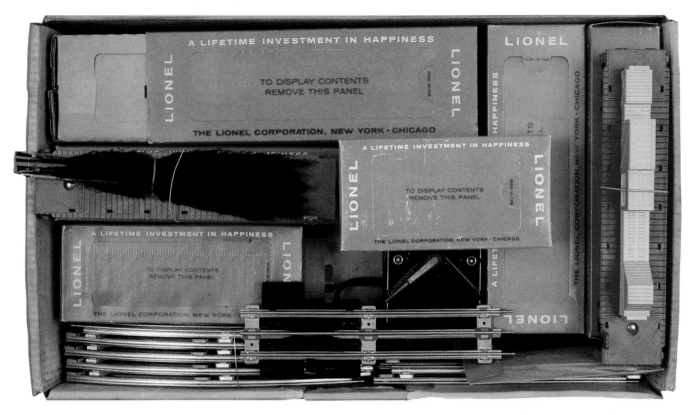

247 steam freight set 1613S in a Type C display-style box that included component boxes. The orange perforated boxes were new for 1959; notice that the corrugated engine box in the upper left corner also had a perforated front and was covered with a perforated-front orange sleeve. This orange sleeve enabled Lionel to give the contents a uniform look which hopefully would enhance sales. B. Myles Collection.

	VG	LN

1617S   O27 Gauge $39.95 Retail

Contents: 2018 steam locomotive with headlight and smoke; 1130T Lionel Lines non-whistle tender; 6816 flatcar with dozer; 6536 M St. L quad hopper; 6812 track maintenance car; 6119-100 red cab work caboose; eight curved and three straight track; 6029 uncoupling section; and a 1015 45-watt transformer.

Comments: This set came in the Type C display-style outfit box with component boxes. The engine came in a corrugated carton with tucked-in end flaps and an orange sleeve while the tender and the other components, except for the 6536, came in Orange Perforated boxes. All of the components came with AAR trucks. The somewhat scarce M St. L hopper came in a Late Classic box, and this was the only set that ever included the new 6670 derrick car. The 6670 is known to have come in an overstamped Bold Classic box, and the fragile 6816 is an exceptionally desirable item for collectors.

	350	600

1619W   O27 Gauge $49.95 Retail

Contents: 218P/218T Santa Fe Alco AA units; 6819 flatcar with helicopter; 6802 flatcar with girder; 6801 flatcar with boat; 6519 Allis Chalmers car; 6017-185 gray Santa Fe SP-type caboose; eight curved and three straight track; 6029 uncoupling section; and a 1053 60-watt transformer.

	VG	LN

Comments: This set came in the Type C display-style outfit box with all of the contents component boxed. The rolling stock came with AAR trucks and each piece is collectable. The 6819 and the -185 caboose were new while the 6519, 6801, and 6802 were repeat items that now came in Orange Perforated boxes. Caution is advised as the brakewheels on the 6519 were exceptionally fragile and are often found broken.

The Santa Fe was a repeat road name in the Alco series, but the silver and red war bonnet paint scheme was new. Beware of broken and/or repaired struts on the Alco units as they are also exceptionally fragile. The 218P came in a perforated-front corrugated carton with tucked-in end flaps and an orange sleeve, while the 218T came in Orange Perforated box. This was a change in packaging since Lionel had previously boxed their T units in corrugated cartons.

	360	600

1621WS   O27 Gauge $49.95 Retail

Contents: 2037 steam locomotive with headlight, smoke, and Magnetraction; 6026W Lionel Lines whistle tender; 6825 flatcar with trestle; 6519 Allis Chalmers car; 6062 black gondola with cable reels; 6464-475 Boston and Maine boxcar; 6017 SP-type caboose; eight curved and three straight track; 6029 uncoupling section; and a 1053 60-watt transformer.

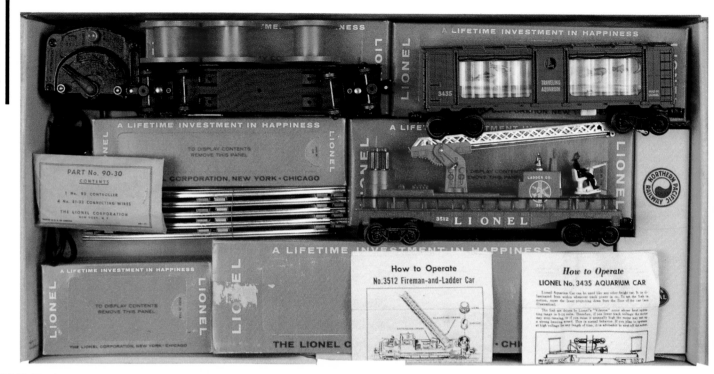

2349 Northern Pacific Geep set 1623W in a Type C display-style box with perforated-front component boxes. The Northern Pacifi[c] was catalogued as O27 in 1959 and then upgraded to Super O in 1960. This is a scarce and desirable set. The 3512 was sometime[s] the scarce silver ladder variation; be advised that three silver hose nozzles are required for a complete car, and pay particula[r] attention to the 6062 gondola. It utilized a discontinued metal underframe as a means to attach the trucks. Later examples ha[ve] the trucks riveted directly to the body. Also note the odd-shaped yellow filler on the right side of the set box. B. Myles Collection.

VG LN

Comments: This set came in the Type C display-style outfit box with component boxes. The tender and rolling stock came with AAR trucks, and early versions of this set have been known to include the 6062 with the metal underframe. The 6519 was a repeat item but now came in an Orange Perforated box. Caution is advised as the brakewheels on the 6519 are exceptionally fragile and are often found broken.

275 475

1623W   O27 Gauge $59.95 Retail

Contents: 2349 Northern Pacific GP-9; 3512 fireman and ladder car; 3435 traveling aquarium car; 6424 flatcar with autos; 6062 black gondola with cable reels; 6017 SP-type caboose; eight curved and three straight track; 6029 uncoupling section; and a 1053 60-watt transformer.

Comments: This set came in the Type C display-style outfit box with component boxes. The engine came in a perforated-front corrugated carton with an orange sleeve and tucked-in end flaps, while the other components came with AAR trucks in Orange Perforated boxes.

Experienced collectors find this to be a very desirable set. The catalogue illustration shows the 6424 in red, but its legitimacy is questionable, and the 6062 in red is not known to exist. The new aquarium car is known to have come with the rare gold letters and tank 1/tank 2 designation, while the new 3512 occasionally surfaces in the very desirable silver ladder variation.

775 1300

VG LN

1625WS   O27 Gauge $59.95 Retail

Contents: 2037 steam locomotive with headlight, smoke, and Magnetraction; 6026W Lionel Lines whistle tender; 6636 Alaska hopper; 3512 fireman and ladder car; 6470 exploding boxcar; 6650 flatcar with IRBM launcher; 6017 SP-type caboose; eight curved and five straight track; 6029 uncoupling section; and a 1053 60-watt transformer.

Comments: Because this was a premium O27 set, it came in a conventional two-tier yellow outfit box with all of the contents individually boxed. The engine came in a perforated-front corrugated carton with tucked-in end flaps and an orange sleeve, while the other components came in Orange Perforated boxes. The rolling stock was all new, and all components, even the tender, came with AAR trucks. The 6636 and the 3512 are collectable pieces.

325 550

1626W   O27 Gauge $65 Retail

Contents: 208P/208T Santa Fe Alco AA units; 3428 operating U.S. Mail boxcar; two 2412 Vista Domes and 2416 observation with blue-striped Santa Fe markings; eight curved and five straight track; 6029 uncoupling section; and a 1053 60-watt transformer.

Comments: This was the top-of-the-line O27 set, and at $65 was more expensive than four Super O sets offered in 1959. It came in a conventional two-tier yellow outfit box with

An end view of outfit box 1626W from 1959. It contained a pair of 208 Santa Fe Alco units and the blue-striped passenger cars along with a 3428 operating U.S. mail boxcar. This conventional type box on a solid yellow background was used for only two better O27 sets in 1959. All other O27 sets came in display-style outfit boxes. M. Sokol Collection.

	VG	LN

all of the contents individually boxed. The blue-striped Santa Fe passenger cars were new issue, and came in Orange Perforated boxes. Although the 1626W was one of five sets that included these cars, it was the only outfit to be headed by the matching blue Alco units. The operating 3428 with AAR trucks was also new, and it was included as a component in only two outfits. The 208 was a carry-forward item so both the P and T units came in 1958-style corrugated boxes, made by the Star Company, that included two cardboard rings as coupler protectors. Beware of broken and/or repaired struts on the Alco units as they are exceptionally fragile.

450   800

1800   **O27 Gauge**   **$25 Retail**

Contents: 1862 General with headlight; 1862T tender; 1866 mail-baggage car; 1865 passenger car; 1877 flatcar with horses; and the General story book.

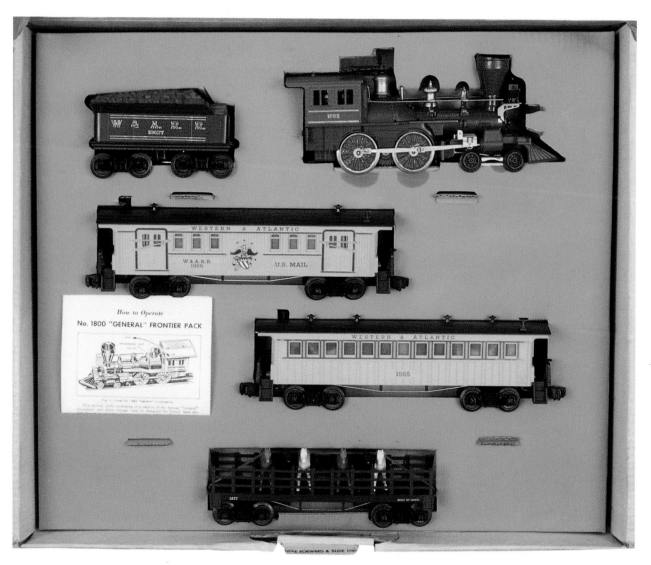

The O27 Gauge 1862 General "Frontier" gift pack 1800 in a Type B display-style box with die-cut filler. This was a new packaging venture for Lionel as gift packs included neither track nor transformer. B. Myles Collection.

107

**1
9
5
9**

VG   LN

Comments: This was Lionel's first gift box, and it was geared for the railroader who already had track and transformer. It came in a Type B die-cut display-style outfit box, and as the catalogue says, "was ready to put right under the Christmas tree." The new arch bar trucks were developed for the General sets, and even the 1877 flatcar often came with arch bar trucks with fixed couplers. The passenger cars were non-illuminated and came with non-self-centering fixed diecast couplers. Refer to pages 104 and 107 for pictures of this outfit.   **450   750**

2527   Super O Gauge $39.95 Retail

Contents: 44 U.S. Army missile launcher; 3419 flatcar with operating helicopter; 6844 missile-carrying flatcar; 6823

VG   LN

flatcar with IRBM missiles; 6814 medical caboose; 943 exploding ammo dump; twelve curved, one straight, and one insulated straight track; and a 39-25 operating packet.

Comments: This set came in a Type C display-style outfit box with the contents component boxed in Orange Perforated types. All of the space-related rolling stock was new and came with AAR trucks. The 3419 usually came with a twin-blade helicopter, and the 6844 is known to have come in the rare red body mold instead of the usual black. The 6814 is scarce and the accent pieces, namely the stretchers and oxygen tanks, are often missing. A mint example of this outfit also contained a cardboard game sheet titled, "The Great Locomotive Race." How prevalent inclusion of this game sheet was in 1959 is open to conjecture. Refer to page 120 for pictures that pertain to this outfit.   **325   550**

1872 Super O General passenger set 2528WS in a Type B display-style box. Most Super O and O Gauge outfits included only track and not a transformer. Note the inclusion of The Great Locomotive Race booklet, and a bottle of smoke fluid along with oil capsules, shown on center left. Type B display boxes require extreme caution when removing or replacing contents; brakewheels on the passenger cars and the whistle on top of the engine are easily damaged. This outfit came in three distinctly different set boxes, which was very unusual for Lionel. Refer to page 109 for another variation, and to page 104 for a side view of various General set boxes. M. Sokol Collection.

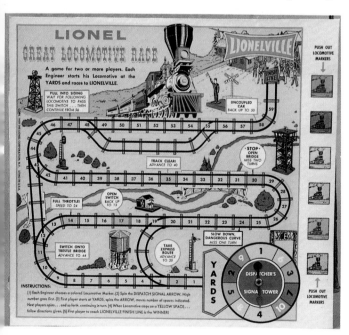

1872 Super O General passenger set 2528WS in a Type C display-style box with perforated-front component boxes. The 1875W had a punched-out window stripe that allowed the whistle sound to be more easily heard. Super O required twelve sections of curved track to make a circle, while O27 and O Gauge needed only eight. Note the inclusion of a cardboard filler at the center of the box. This outfit came in three distinctly different set boxes. Refer to page 108 for another variation, and to page 104 for a side view of various General set boxes. M. Sokol Collection.

2528WS   Super O Gauge $49.95 Retail

Contents: 1872 General with headlight, smoke, and Magnetraction; 1872T tender; 1877 flatcar with horses; 1876 illuminated mail-baggage car; 1875W illuminated passenger

The "Great Locomotive Race". This cardboard game sheet was a sometimes component in 1959 outfits. M. Sokol Collection.

VG   LN

1959

car with whistle; twelve curved, one straight, and one insulated straight track; and a 39-25 operating packet.

Comments: The 1872 was an upgrade of the 1862 and came with the addition of smoke and Magnetraction. Strangely enough, the most desirable of the General cars is the 1875 passenger car because it was never included in a set. This outfit is known to have come in both the Type B and the Type C display-style outfit boxes, and in a conventional design, two-tier tan corrugated box. The conventional box and the Type C display style included component boxes. The engine came in an oversized perforated-front corrugated box with a special cardboard insert while the tender, passenger cars, and the 1877 came in Orange Perforated boxes. (This is the only outfit that has been observed that came in three distinctly different set boxes.) The 1877 came with arch bar trucks as did the passenger cars. The O Gauge General cars were always illuminated and came with self-centering operating couplers. It was the General sets for which the new arch bar trucks were developed. Please see pages 104 and 108 for pictures that pertain to this outfit.

	VG	LN
Type B box	500	850
Type C or tan box	600	1000

2529W   Super O Gauge $59.95 Retail

Contents: 2329 Virginian rectifier electric; 3512 fireman and ladder car; 6819 flatcar with helicopter; 6812 track maintenance car; 6560 red cab crane; 6119-25 orange work caboose; twelve curved, three straight, and one insulated straight track; and a 39-25 operating packet.

Comments: This was the third and last of the rectifier sets, and was catalogued only to deplete surplus inventory as the 2329 was a sales disappointment. All of the rolling stock, except the caboose, came with AAR trucks in Orange Perforated boxes. The caboose was an all-orange 6119-25 that was originally catalogued in 1956 — another prime example of depleting dated inventory! The outfit box itself was an over-stickered tan/brown 1958 issue, and by its dimensions, appears to be a 2501W. Please refer to Outfit 2505 from **1958** for additional comments on the rectifier.   **1200   2000**

2531WS   Super O Gauge $59.95 Retail

Contents: 637 steam locomotive with headlight, smoke, and Magnetraction; 2046W Lionel Lines whistle tender; 3435 traveling aquarium car; 6817 flatcar with scraper; 6636 Alaska quad hopper; 6825 flatcar with trestle; 6119-100 red cab work caboose; twelve curved, three straight, and one insulated straight track; and a 39-25 operating packet.

Comments: The outfit box was the two-tier yellow 1959 issue. The 637 was a new steam engine and all of the rolling stock were new in 1959. The engine came in a corrugated carton while the tender and all other components came with AAR trucks in Orange Perforated boxes. This set has been known to contain the rare 6817 scraper with windshield. The aquarium car and the Alaska hopper are two other desirable items.   **500   850**

1959

	VG	LN

2533W   Super O Gauge $65 Retail

Contents: 2358 Great Northern EP-5 electric; 6650 flatcar with IRBM launcher; 6414 auto transport; 3444 animated gondola; 6470 exploding boxcar; 6357 illuminated SP-type caboose; twelve curved, three straight, and one insulated straight track; and a 39-25 operating packet.

Comments: The outfit box was a two-tier yellow 1959 issue. The engine came in a perforated-front corrugated carton with tucked-in end flaps, and all of the contents, except the 3444 which was a carry-over from 1958, came with AAR trucks in Orange Perforated boxes. The Great Northern is a scarce and undervalued piece. The original nose decals are almost always in an advanced stage of deterioration. The collector should be aware of reproduction decals; an original is water soluble while the reproductions are usually the adhesive type. It is unfortunate that the space age items do not seem to relate to the other components in this set.

1800   3000

2535WS   Super O Gauge $69.95 Retail

Contents: 665 steam locomotive with headlight, smoke, and Magnetraction; 2046W Lionel Lines whistle tender; 3434 chicken sweeper car; 6823 flatcar with IRBM missiles; 3672 operating Bosco car; 6812 track maintenance car; 6357 illuminated SP-type caboose; twelve curved, three straight, and one insulated straight track; and a 39-35 operating packet.

Comments: The outfit box was standard yellow 1959 issue with perforated fronts for the engine and the rest of the other contents, except for the 3672 Bosco car. The Bosco box was the same size as the existing 3662 milk car but with new graphics; because of the size and weight of the contents, the box was never perforated. This set has the honor of having two new-in-1959 cars, namely the 3434 and the 3672, whose earliest versions still retained metal trucks. The 6812 and the 6823 were also new issue but they and the caboose came with AAR trucks. The 39-35 operating packet differed from the 39-25 in that it contained an extra controller and No. 36 power blades necessary to operate the Bosco car. This was another set in which the rolling stock mix was not complementary.

500   850

2537W   Super O Gauge $75 Retail

Contents: 2242P/2242C New Haven AB F-3 units; 3435 traveling aquarium car; 3650 extension searchlight; 6464-275 State of Maine boxcar; 6819 flatcar with helicopter; 6427 Lionel Lines porthole caboose; twelve curved, three straight, and one insulated straight track; and a 39-25 operating packet.

Comments: This was the second and last of the New Haven F-3 sets to be catalogued. It is more scarce than its predecessor. The second edition of a repeat road name seldom sold as well as the first. The outfit box was standard yellow 1959 issue, but the contents were a nearly equal mixture of old and new. The 2242P, 2242C, and the 3650 and 6427 with metal trucks were carry-over items from 1958, while the -275 State of Maine was a repeat road name but now came with

AAR trucks on a Type III body mold. The remainder of the contents came with AAR trucks in Orange Perforated boxes. The aquarium car has become a highly desirable collector item. Buyer beware as some very high quality "fakes" of the 3650 have appeared in red on the market; avoid them like The Plague.

2100   3500

2539WS   Super O Gauge $79.95 Retail

Contents: 665 steam locomotive with headlight, smoke, and Magnetraction; 2046W Lionel Lines whistle tender; 3361 operating log car; 6464-825 Alaska boxcar; 3512 fireman and ladder car; 6812 track maintenance car; 6357 illuminated SP-type caboose; twelve curved, three straight, and one insulated straight track; 39-35 operating packet; and a 464 saw mill.

Comments: The outfit box was an oversized yellow 1959 issue. The engine and tender were repeat items and usually came in 1958-style boxes while the rolling stock, except for the carry-over 3361 with metal trucks, came with AAR trucks in Orange Perforated boxes. The 3512 is a very desirable item and this was the only set ever to include the new Alaska boxcar. The 3361 and most probably the 464 saw mill were excess inventory from 1958. This is one of the few times that Lionel offered a "major" accessory as part of an outfit. A 39-35 operating packet was included with this outfit because of the power blades required to operate the 3361 log dump car.

650   1100

2541W   Super O Gauge $89.95 Retail

Contents: 2383P/2383T Santa Fe AA F-3 units; 3356 operating horse car; 3512 fireman and ladder car; 6519 Allis Chalmers car; 6816 flatcar with dozer; 6427 Lionel Lines porthole caboose; twelve curved, three straight, and one insulated straight track; and a 39-25 operating packet.

Comments: The outfit box was standard yellow 1959 issue, and the rolling stock, except for the carry-over 6427 and 3356, came with AAR trucks in Orange Perforated boxes. Even the 2383 P and T corrugated boxes had perforations and as such are datable to 1959 or 1960 only. One other interesting note about the 3356, besides the fact that it still retained metal trucks, is that it contained a revised instruction envelope with a power blade that was necessary to operate the car on Super O track.

1200   2000

2543WS   Super O Gauge $95 Retail

Contents: 736 Berkshire steam locomotive with headlight, smoke, and Magnetraction; 2046W Lionel Lines whistle tender; 264 forklift with 6264 lumber car; 3435 traveling aquarium car; 6823 flatcar with IRBM missiles; 6434 poultry car; 6812 track maintenance car; 6557 smoking caboose; twelve curved, three straight, and one insulated straight track; and a 39-25 operating packet.

Comments: The outfit box was standard yellow 1959 issue, but this set too was a combination of both old 1958 and new 1959 items. The 3435, 6823, and the 6812 came with AAR

VG   LN

trucks in Orange Perforated boxes while the 6434 and the 6557 were carry-over items with metal trucks in a Bold and Late Classic box respectively. Lionel must have been experiencing a seriously over-stocked position on the 264 forklift as this was the third time in as many years that it was offered as part of an outfit. The 6264, now with AAR trucks, came unboxed inside the 264 corrugated carton. The 6264 lumber car with metal trucks was available component boxed as a separate-sale item in 1957 and 1958. The military style of the 6823 did not complement the more traditional cars in this set.

725   1200

2544W   Super O Gauge $100 Retail

Contents: 2383P/2383T Santa Fe AA F-3 units; 2530 Railway Express baggage car; 2561 Vista Valley observation, 2562 Regal Pass Vista Dome, and 2563 Indian Falls Pullman with red-striped Santa Fe markings; twelve curved, five straight, and one insulated straight track; and a 39-25 operating packet.

Comments This outfit box was standard yellow 1959 issue. The Santa Fe units came in perforated-front corrugated cartons and are therefore datable to 1959 or 1960 only. This is one of the premier postwar sets rivaling the more notable 2296W Canadian Pacific. A unique component of this set was the 2530 baggage car. It had a much shinier finish than its predecessors and is extremely difficult to find in the proper box. The red-striped Santa Fe passenger cars were new in 1959, replacing the discontinued 2530 series cars, and came in Orange Perforated boxes. These cars were catalogued for

VG   LN

three consecutive years but are extremely scarce. They came with both large- and small-letter Santa Fe logos. Either size is acceptable, but a matched set of cars is always preferred.

2700   4500

2545WS   Super O Gauge $100 Retail

Contents: 746 N & W steam locomotive with headlight, smoke, and Magnetraction; 746W N & W whistle tender; 6175 flatcar with rocket; 6470 exploding boxcar; 3419 flatcar with operating helicopter; 6650 flatcar with IRBM launcher; 3540 radar scanning car; 6517 bay window caboose; twelve curved, three straight, and one insulated straight track; 39-25 operating packet; and a 175 rocket launcher.

Comments: This was the fifth and last of the 746 sets. The outfit box was an oversized yellow 1959 issue, and all of the rolling stock, except for the caboose, came with AAR trucks in Orange Perforated boxes. The engine, tender, flatcar with rocket, and caboose were carry-over items, and this was the outfit that always contained the scarce long-striped tender. Evidently Lionel was significantly overstocked with the 746, and the creation of this set was a step to alleviate the problem. It did not succeed, as the 746, 1957 vintage, was still being offered for separate sale in the 1960 catalogue. Yesterday's nightmare is today's dream as this set has become a prized collector item. It has not gained the same recognition as the more famous outfit 2525WS, but it is every bit as scarce. The 3540 is one of the most desirable space age cars, and the 175 rocket launcher was a fragile accessory that is extremely difficult to obtain complete and unbroken.

2550   4250

1959

1960

THE HEIGHT OF MEDIOCRITY

The corrugated engine boxes, and the Orange Perforated boxes for rolling stock and passenger cars remained the same as in 1959, but another major color change occurred on the outfit boxes. The Super O outfit box retained the same design as the original 1957 issue, but was now printed on a field of solid orange coated stock. The yellow Types A, B, and C display-style boxes that were introduced in 1959 were all utilized again along with a new half-orange, half-white display box that included a sketch of a 4-6-2 steam engine on the upper portion of the lid.

Lionel continued to issue numbered instruction sheets for most of the low and moderate O27 sets. Super O was offered in eight outfits, and of the eight, four had "unique" track plans. 1960 was the last year in which the No. 48 insulated straight would be included as part of the outfit package.

The newness that was so evident in the 1959 line was not apparent in 1960. Military and space-related items were still a major part of the product line. Early AAR trucks were the norm with only a few carry-forward operating cars and tenders retaining metal trucks. The square 243W tender was introduced with AAR trucks and an operating coupler to pair with the new 243 steam engine. The 224 U.S. Navy and the 225 C & O were new road names in the Alco series, and the 45 was a recolored mobile missile launcher with Marine Corps markings. The 69 maintenance car was an interesting new motorized unit.

New noteworthy rolling stock included the 3376 giraffe car, 6475 pickle vat car, the 6827 and 6828 Harnischfeger cars, the 3830 and 6830 flatcars with submarines, the 6544 missile firing car, the 3535 security car, and the 6219 C & O work caboose. The -900 NYC Central was a new addition to the

1055 Texas Special Advance Catalogue freight set 1107 in a Type A display-style box. Take special note of the folded accessory catalogue on the bottom right. It was placed there as such to occupy the space formerly allotted to the extra car that was included with outfit 1105 from 1959. Refer to page 114 for a picture of the lid of the Texas Special outfit box. B. Myles Collection.

VG LN

6464 series and the 6428 was the new non-operating U.S. mail car. The 736W with Pennsylvania markings occasionally surfaced as a set component late in the product year as inventory on the 2046W was depleted. The highlight of the year was the coveted 2555W outfit, which was a combined Santa Fe Super O and HO set that has come to be known as the "Father and Son" set, and contained the rare illuminated 6357-50 Santa Fe caboose.

1107 Advance Catalogue — O27 Gauge / No Retail

Contents: 1055 Texas Special Alco A unit; 6112 blue gondola with two canisters; 6044 blue Airex boxcar; 6047 SP-type caboose with end rails; eight curved and two straight track; and a 1026 25-watt transformer.

Comments: The outfit box was a Type A white background display style that was titled "The Texas Special" with blue and orange print. The contents were separated by loose cardboard dividers instead of channels. The outfit box was identical to 1105 from 1959 and often was an over-stickered 1105 example. The rolling stock was equipped with arch bar trucks with fixed couplers. These inexpensive Advance Catalogue sets are difficult to obtain in collector condition. Refer to pages 112 and 114 for pictures pertaining to this outfit.

90 150

VG LN

1109 Advance Catalogue — O27 Gauge / No Retail

Contents: 1060 steam locomotive; 1060T streamlined tender; 6404 black flatcar with brown gray-bumpered auto; 3386 giraffe car; 6047 SP-type caboose with end rails; eight curved and two straight track; and a 1026 25-watt transformer.

Comments: The outfit box was either a Type A white background display style that was titled "the 2-4-2 Steam Freighter" with blue and orange print and with the contents separated by loose cardboard dividers, or the box was a single-tier tan corrugated type with the contents packed upright and separated by cardboard dividers. The rolling stock was equipped with arch bar trucks with fixed couplers, and this was the first set to have included a highly collectable gray-bumpered auto. The 1050T was a basic slope-back tender with Lionel Lines markings and arch bar trucks with a fixed coupler that was introduced with the uncatalogued 1050 engine in 1959. Refer to page 114 for pictures pertaining to this outfit.

175 300

1609 — O27 Gauge / $19.95 Retail

Comment: This was a carry-forward outfit from 1959. Please refer to **1959** for more information.

	VG	LN
Type A box	60	100
Type C box	120	200

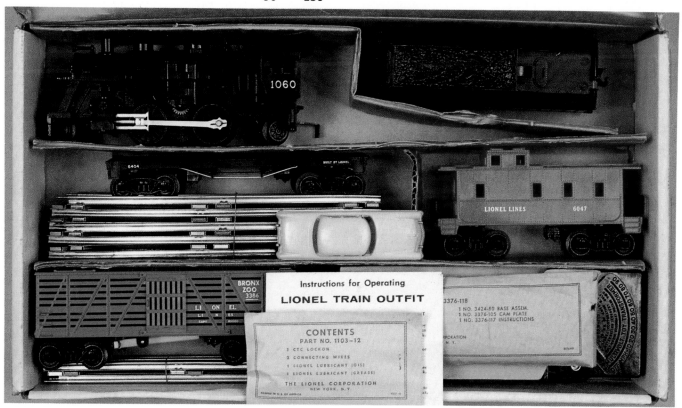

1960 Advance Catalogue steam freight set 1109 in a Type A display-style box with cardboard dividers. This was the first outfit to include a very collectable gray-bumpered auto, and the black 6404 flatcar which was the only General-type flatcar, other than 1877 and 6405, that had a heat-stamped stock number. Refer to page 114 for more particulars on the outfit boxes. M. Sokol Collection.

These are the unique outfit boxes for two Advance Catalogue sets. The graphics on 1109 (bottom) were used in 1960 only while the Texas Special artwork (top) was introduced in 1959 for outfit 1105. Refer to pages 112 and 113 for pictures of the contents of outfits 1107, which was the 1960 edition of the Texas Special set, and 1109, respectively. B. Myles Collection.

	VG	LN

1612   O27 Gauge $29.95 Retail

Comment: This was another carry-forward outfit from 1959. Please see **1959** for details.

	VG	LN
Tan box	475	800
Type B box	425	700

1627S   O27 Gauge $25 Retail

Contents: 244 steam locomotive with headlight and smoke; 244T slope-back tender; 6062 black gondola with cable reels; 6825 flatcar with trestle; 6017 SP-type caboose; eight curved and one straight track; 1008-50 camtrol uncoupling section; and a 1015 45-watt transformer.

Comments: This set came in a yellow Type A display-style outfit box with unboxed contents. The run-of-the-mill rolling stock all came with AAR trucks and operating couplers at both ends. The 244T was for all intents a 1625T that was last catalogued in 1958, but was now referred to as 244T because it was paired with the new 244 engine. It came with Lionel Lines lettering and AAR trucks with an operating

An end view of a regular 1109 Advance Catalogue outfit box (top) and a variation. The tan corrugated box (bottom) was probably made in response to a special packaging request by a customer, such as one that did mail-order business. The dimensions and strength of the corrugated carton were suitable for shipment via the U.S. Postal Service. B. Myles Collection.

	VG	LN

coupler. The tender was a Type A display-style set component only; therefore an original box for this item does not exist.

	90	150

1629   O27 Gauge $29.95 Retail

Contents: 225 C & O Alco A unit; 6650 flatcar with IRBM launcher; 6470 exploding boxcar; 6819 flatcar with helicopter; 6219 C & O work caboose; eight curved and one straight track; 1008-50 camtrol uncoupling section; and a 1015 45-watt transformer.

Comments: This set came in a yellow Type A display-style outfit box with unboxed contents. The rolling stock came with AAR trucks and operating couplers at both ends. The 225 with front coupler was a new Alco unit and this was the only set to contain the 6219 work caboose. This was one of the few instances in the postwar era in which Lionel issued a matching road name caboose. A box does not exist for the 6219, but because the 225 was available for separate sale, it came in a perforated-front corrugated carton with tucked-in end flaps. Beware of a broken and/or repaired strut on the Alco unit as it is exceptionally fragile. A starter diesel outfit is usually in much greater demand by collectors than most steam counterparts. Please refer to page 115 for a picture of this outfit.

	275	400

1631WS   O27 Gauge $39.95 Retail

Contents: 243 steam locomotive with headlight and smoke; 243W Lionel Lines whistle tender; 6519 Allis Chalmers car; 6812 track maintenance car; 6465 Cities Service two-dome tank car; 6017 SP-type caboose; eight curved and three straight track; 1008-50 camtrol uncoupling section; and a 1053 60-watt transformer.

Comments: This set came in a yellow Type A display-style outfit box with the components unboxed. The outfit box was usually over-stickered and had some interior modifica-

25 C & O Alco set 1629 in a Type A display-style box. This was one of the few postwar outfits to include a complementing color *nd* road name caboose. Notice the yellow filler in the transformer compartment that held the transformer in place and provided *orage* for the cord along with the miscellaneous packets and paperwork. M. Sokol Collection.

	VG	LN		VG	LN

tions. Please refer to page 116 for further comments. The tender was an AAR truck version of the 6026W and usually had "243W" stamped on the side. Cities Service was a new logo for the two-dome tank car. The brakewheels on the 6519 are extremely fragile and usually broken.

225   375

1633   O27 Gauge $39.95 Retail

Contents: 224P/224C U.S. Navy Alco AB units; 6544 missile firing car; 6830 flatcar with submarine; 6820 flatcar with helicopter and missiles; 6017-200 U.S. Navy SP-type caboose; eight curved and three straight track; 6029 uncoupling section; and a 1015 45-watt transformer.

Comments: This set came in a half-orange, half-white Type A display-style outfit box with unboxed components. Every item in the set was new for 1960. This is an extremely desirable set, but buyer beware, as the cars are extremely fragile and susceptible to breakage, and reproduction helicopters with missiles are prevalent in the marketplace.

Each item in this set was available for separate sale and consequently had a component box. The 224P came in a corrugated carton with perforated front and tucked-in end flaps while the 224C came in an Orange Perforated box, and even these Alco units came in a master carton when available for separate sale. Component boxes for the 6820 and the -200 caboose are rare. Beware of a broken and/or repaired strut on the Alco unit as it is exceptionally fragile. Refer to page 117 for a picture of this outfit.   **725   1200**

1635WS   O27 Gauge $49.95 Retail

Contents: 2037 steam locomotive with headlight, smoke, and Magnetraction; 6026W or 243W Lionel Lines whistle tender; 6361 timber transport; 6826 flatcar with Christmas trees; 6636 Alaska quad hopper; 6821 flatcar with crates; 6017 SP-type caboose; eight curved and three straight track; 6029 uncoupling section; and a 1053 60-watt transformer.

Comments: This set came in a yellow Type C display-style outfit box with individually boxed components. The engine came in a perforated-front carton while the tender and rolling stock with AAR trucks came in Orange Perforated boxes. The 6826 is a scarce repeat item as is the Alaska hopper. The 6361 was new issue for 1960, and was available throughout most of the remaining decade.   **325   525**

1637W   O27 Gauge $49.95 Retail

Contents: 218P/218T Santa Fe Alco AA units; 6475 pickle vat car; 6175 flatcar with rocket; 6464-475 Boston and Maine boxcar; 6801 flatcar with boat; 6017-185 gray Santa Fe SP-type caboose; eight curved and three straight track; 6029 uncoupling section; and a 1053 60-watt transformer.

Comments: This set came in a half-orange, half-white Type C display-style outfit box with individually boxed components. The powered unit came in a perforated-front corrugated carton while the 218T and the balance of the components came in Orange Perforated boxes. The Santa Fe was a repeat

243 steam freight set 1631WS in a Type A display-style box. Some interior modifications were necessary to accommodate the components; the left and center vertical dividers were eliminated, and upon close examination you will notice that the center channel is also reversed, no doubt by accident at the factory. M. Sokol Collection.

	VG	LN		VG	LN

road name in the Alco series, and all of the rolling stock were repeat items, except for the 6475. An Orange Perforated box for the 6801 is a scarce item. Beware of broken and/or repaired struts on the Alco units as they are exceptionally fragile.

360   600

1639WS   O27 Gauge $59.95 Retail

Contents: 2037 steam locomotive with headlight, smoke, and Magnetraction; 6026W or 243W Lionel Lines whistle tender; 6816 flatcar with dozer; 6817 flatcar with scraper; 6812 track maintenance car; 6530 fire prevention car; 6560 red cab crane; 6119-100 red cab work caboose; eight curved and three straight track; 6029 uncoupling section; and a 1053 60-watt transformer.

Comments: This set came in a half-orange, half-white Type C display-style outfit box with individually boxed components. The engine came in a perforated-front corrugated carton while the tender and rolling stock with AAR trucks came in Orange Perforated boxes. This is one of the most desirable of the sixteen catalogued postwar 2037 sets. It contained two scarce repeat items, namely the 6816 and 6817. The 6530 was a new item based on the body mold of the 3530 generator car.

450   750

1640W   O27 Gauge $65 Retail

Contents: 218P/218T Santa Fe Alco AA units; 3428 operating U.S. Mail boxcar; two 2412 Vista Domes and 2416 observation with blue-striped Santa Fe markings; eight curved and three straight track; 6029 uncoupling section; 1053 60-watt transformer; and a 1640-100 Presidential whistle stop kit.

Comments: This set came in the new half-orange, half-white Type C display-style outfit box with all of the components individually boxed. It is the most desirable of the seven postwar 218 sets to the collector, and to be complete it must contain the 1640-100 Presidential kit which had its own thin orange cardboard box.

This was the second of five sets to be catalogued with the blue-striped Santa Fe cars. It was nearly identical to outfit 1626W from 1959, except that the red and silver Santa Fe units replaced the blue 208P and 208T. Beware of broken and/or repaired struts on the Alco units as they are exceptionally fragile. The 218P came in a perforated-front corrugated carton with tucked-in end flaps while the 218T, 3428, and the passenger cars came in Orange Perforated boxes. This was a change in packaging that was instituted in 1959 for Alco T units. Please see page 118 for a picture of this component-boxed outfit.

600   1000

224 U.S. Navy color-coordinated military set 1633 in a Type A display-style box. This is an extremely desirable and fragile set. The 6820 flatcar with helicopter and "Little John" missiles is one of the rarer military items. Notice the orange filler that was included in the transformer compartment that held the transformer in place and provided storage for the cord along with the miscellaneous packets and paperwork. B. Myles Collection.

	VG	LN

1800   O27 Gauge $25 Retail

Comments: This was a repeat of the 1959 General gift pack. It was identical to 1959 production and came in a die-cut Type B display-style outfit box that was either a carry-over yellow or the new half-orange, half-white coloration. Please refer to **1959** for more detailed information.   **450**   **750**

1805   O27 Gauge $35 Retail

Contents: 45 olive U.S.M.C. missile launcher; 3429 olive U.S.M.C. flatcar with operating helicopter; 3820 olive U.S.M.C. flatcar with operating submarine; 6640 olive U.S.M.C. flatcar with IRBM launcher; and 6824 olive medical caboose.

Comments: This set was referred to as the "Land-Sea-and-Air" gift pack in the 1960 catalogue and on the box lid. It is an extremely desirable and scarce set. It came in the new half-orange, half-white die-cut Type B display-style outfit box,

	VG	LN

and to be correct, it must have a helicopter with U.S.M.C. markings. Component boxes do not exist for any items in this outfit other than the motorized 45 unit. This is one of the top three military/space-related outfits for the serious collector; the other two are the "Enforcer" gift pack 12512 from 1962 and the Santa Fe 11385 from 1963. Please refer to photos on page 119 for additional comments.   **1200**   **2000**

2527   Super O Gauge $39.95 Retail

Comments: This was a repeat of the 1959 outfit, and came in either a yellow carry-over or the newly colored Type C display-style outfit box with component boxes. This set is more difficult to obtain in the half-orange, half-white outfit box. Please refer to **1959** for more detailed information, and to page 120 for a picture of the set and an end view of the outfit boxes.

	VG	LN
Half-orange, half-white box	350	600
Yellow box	325	550

	VG	LN

1
9
6
0

2528WS   Super O Gauge $49.95 Retail

Comments: This was yet another repeat from 1959. Even though this set came in three distinctly different outfit boxes, it is not known to exist with 1960 half-orange, half-white graphics. Please refer to pages 104, 108, and 109 for pictures and to **1959** for further information.

Type B box	500	850
Type C or tan box	600	1000

2544W   Super O Gauge $100 Retail

Comments: This was a repeat of the 1959 outfit, but was packaged in a 1960 set box with an orange field. Please refer to **1959** for more information. Refer to page 120 for an end view of the outfit box.   **2700   4500**

2547WS   Super O Gauge $49.95 Retail

Contents: 637 steam locomotive with headlight, smoke, and Magnetraction; 2046W Lionel Lines whistle tender; 3330 flatcar with submarine kit; 6475 pickle vat car; 6361 timber transport; 6357 illuminated SP-type caboose; twelve curved, one straight, and one insulated straight track; and a 39-25 operating packet.

Comments: This outfit came in a newly colored half-orange, half-white Type C display-style Super O set box with individually boxed components. The engine came in a perforated-front corrugated carton with tucked-in end flaps while the tender, which was usually unpainted, came with metal trucks. The other components came in Orange Perforated boxes. All of the rolling stock was new for 1960. The 3330 submarine in kit form is a scarce car as it was included in only three sets, and is difficult to obtain complete and unassembled. Interestingly, the submarine kit was sold separately. It came in a unique box numbered "3330-100" and was highlighted on page 22 of the 1960 catalogue.   **425   700**

2549W   Super O Gauge $59.95 Retail

Contents: 2349 Northern Pacific GP-9; 3540 radar scanner; 6470 exploding boxcar; 6819 flatcar with helicopter; 6650 flatcar with IRBM launcher; 3535 security car; eighteen curved, two straight, five half-straight, and one insulated straight track; 90° crossing; and a 39-25 operating packet.

Comments: This outfit was packaged in a new orange two-tier Super O outfit box with all of the contents individually boxed. The 2349 came in a corrugated carton with tucked-in end flaps, and was a repeat engine that had been upgraded from O27 in 1959 to Super O. The 3535 security car was new issue and it, along with the other repeat rolling stock, came with AAR trucks in an Orange Perforated box. The security

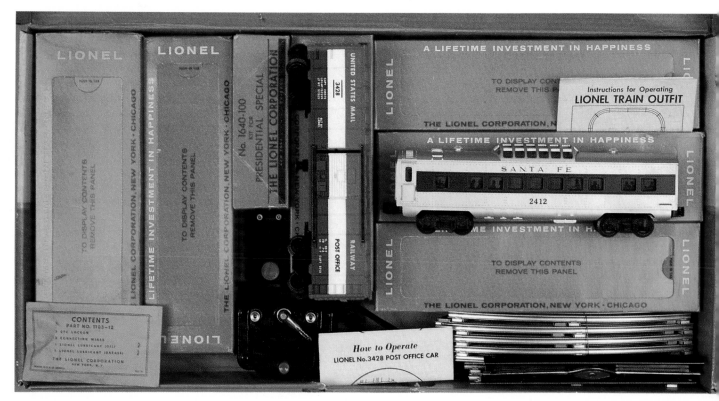

218 Santa Fe passenger set 1640W in a Type C display-style box that included component boxes. The powered unit came in a perforated-front corrugated carton with an orange sleeve, and was packaged to the extreme left of the set box. This was the top-of-the-line O27 outfit for 1960 and at $65 was more expensive than four Super O sets. Pay particular attention to the component-boxed 1640-100 Presidential whistle stop kit. It alone is valued at nearly $100. B. Myles Collection.

The U.S.M.C. "Land-Sea-and-Air" gift pack 1805 in one of the premier military/space related sets. The outfit box was a Type B display style that included neither track nor transformer. This set and outfit 1633 shown on page 117 were the only two completely color-coordinated outfits of the postwar era. Special attention must be paid to the 3429 helicopter car. It must come with a helicopter lettered "USMC" as opposed to the more common Navy markings. B. Myles Collection.

The attached perforated lid of the U.S.M.C. gift pack 1805. The contents are scarce and collectable but the outfit box itself is rare. Refer to photograph at top of page for an interior picture and an example of a Type B display-style box. M. Sokol Collection.

VG   LN

car had an unusual appearance; the chassis was a black flatcar that utilized a 3620 searchlight hood and mechanism, the cab was one that had been previously used on the 520 electric from 1956, and the guns on top were the same as those used with the Pyro military vehicles that came with flatcars 6804 and 6809. The Figure 8 layout was one of four unique track plans offered in 1960.   **850   1400**

2551W   Super O Gauge $75 Retail

Contents: 2358 Great Northern EP-5 electric; 6828 flatcar with Harnischfeger crane; 3512 fireman and ladder car; 6827 flatcar with Harnischfeger power shovel; 6736 Detroit & Mackinac quad hopper; 6812 track maintenance car; 6427 Lionel Lines porthole caboose; twenty-four curved, thirteen straight, and one insulated straight track; No. 110 graduated trestle set; and a 39-25 operating packet.

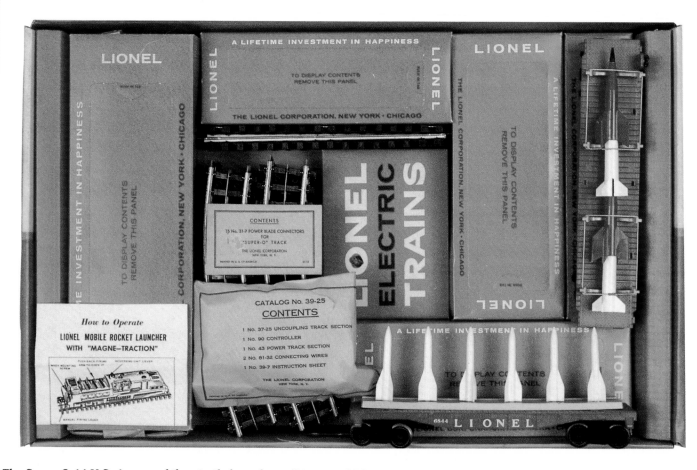

The Super O 44 U.S. Army mobile missile launcher military set 2527 in a Type C display-style box. This set was also available in 1959 and came in a yellow background Type C display box with slightly different dimensions. Refer to photograph at lower left for a side view of both the 1959 and 1960 variations. Note that the rare red 6844 was a sometime component of this set, and a component-boxed 943 exploding ammo dump was packed in the center of the box. B. Myles Collection.

Comments: This outfit came in the standard 1960 issue Super O set box with all of the contents component boxed. The Great Northern engine came in a perforated-front corrugated carton with tucked-in end flaps, and is a scarce and undervalued piece. The original nose decals are almost always in an advanced stage of deterioration. Be aware of

reproduction decals; an original is water soluble while the reproductions are usually the adhesive type. The 6427 was a

An end view of the set box for the 1960 edition of the Super O 2544W Santa Fe red-striped passenger set. The background on the Super O set boxes was changed form a yellow field to an orange field in 1960. Also note that 1960 was the last year in which the motive power scenes, adopted in 1957, were retained on all four sides of the box. M. Sokol Collection.

An end view of two different 2527 outfit boxes. The top example was a yellow background 1959 issue while the bottom box was the half-orange, half-white 1960 issue. M. Sokol Collection.

VG   LN

carry-forward item from 1958 in a Late Classic box that retained metal trucks. The fireman and ladder car was a repeat while the 6736 hopper, and the 6827 and 6828 Harnischfeger cars were new issue. The Harnischfeger items each came unassembled in their own white, black, and yellow thin cardboard boxes; the box was placed on top of the black flatcar and then repackaged in an oversized Orange Perforated box.

This outfit contained one of four unique track plans offered in 1960. It was a plan that utilized a complete trestle set and included a hairpin turn. This set is extremely scarce and somewhat undervalued in today's market, and it is much more visually appealing than 2533W from 1959.

2400   4000

2553W   Super O Gauge $100 Retail

Contents: 736 Berkshire steam locomotive with headlight, smoke, and Magnetraction; 2046W Lionel Lines whistle tender; 3830 flatcar with operating submarine; 3435 traveling aquarium car; 3419 flatcar with operating helicopter; 3672 operating Bosco car; 6357 illuminated SP-type caboose; eighteen curved, seven straight, two half-curved, six half-straight, and one insulated straight track; 90° crossing; left-hand manual switch; 260 bumper; and a 39-35 operating packet.

Comments: The outfit box was standard 1960 Super O issue, with all of the contents component boxed. The engine came in a perforated-front corrugated carton while the tender and the balance of the components, except for the Bosco car, came with AAR trucks in Orange Perforated boxes. The 3830 was new issue while everything else was a repeat.

The Bosco box is unique. It was the same size as the 3662 but was recolored in 1959 to include a picture of the car and the stand. The 3672 box, because of the size and weight of the contents, was never perforated. The Bosco car still retained metal trucks as a set component, but very late issues, probably separate-sale items, were unpainted yellow plastic and sometimes came with the newly released plastic AAR truck version of the pickup shoe assembly.

This outfit contained one of four unique track plans offered in 1960 — a

Figure 8 that included a switch with spur and bumper.

650   1100

1
9
6
0

2555W   Super O and HO Gauges $150 Retail

Contents: 2383P/2383T Santa Fe F-3 AA units; 3434 operating chicken sweeper car; 3366 operating circus car; 6414 auto loader; 6464-900 NYC boxcar; 6357-50 illuminated Santa Fe SP-type caboose; twelve curved, three straight, and one insulated straight track; twenty pieces No. 110A elevated trestle piers; 39-25 operating packet; 1044 90-watt transformer; and the complementing HO pieces along with a 0114 engine house.

Comments: This is another of the premier postwar outfits. It is commonly referred to as the "Father and Son" or "Over and Under" set. It consisted of two identical train sets with the HO set running between the trestle piers of the elevated Super O set. The components, except for the rare 6357-50 caboose, are now readily available, but the set box itself is rare. It is the standard 1960 glossy orange type, with all of the components boxed. The outfit box was oversized to accommodate the HO items, which were separated by a piece of cardboard and packed at the top.

The Santa Fe units each came in a perforated-front carton with tucked-in end flaps. The other components, except the circus car, came in Orange Perforated boxes. The circus car box is unique. It was the same size as the 3356 horse car box but was recolored and included a picture of the car and the corral. The 3366 box, because of the size and weight of its contents, was never perforated. This was the only outfit to contain the circus car, but it was catalogued as a separate-sale item in 1959-1960 and 1961.

The chicken sweeper and the circus car still retained metal trucks while the other components came with AAR trucks. The 110A trestle piers are unique to this set as they have no supporting brace at the base, and this was the only Super O set other than 13150 to include a transformer. Please refer to the original outfit instruction sheet reproduced here.

3600   6000

HOW TO ASSEMBLE
FATHER AND SON TWIN RAILROADS

MOTHER and DAUGHTER TOO!!

Designed for the mutual enjoyment of Father and Son, this combination of identical "Super-O" and HO outfits will also be interesting to Mother and Daughter.

Here is founded the basis for a Family Project. All members of the family may be called upon to assist in creating the mechanical, artistic and electrical portions of this Twin-Railroad Empire. Consider the possibility that each member of the family is inclined to be skilled in different fields. Assign the scenery project to the future Artist, wiring to the Electrical Engineer and assembly to the Mechanical Engineer.

TWO COMPLETE and SEPARATE TRAIN OUTFITS

The illustration shows how to assemble the "Super-O" track on elevated pieces with the HO loop running directly underneath and through the archways. These layouts could be placed along side of each other. In effect these outfits are two, complete and separate miniature railroads which could be split and located in different areas.

If assembled as illustrated you will require a table or platform measuring 4 feet by 6 feet. The track layout itself measures approximately 40 inches by 65 inches.

The platform should be made of plywood 3/8 or 1/2 inch thick. It should be braced with 1" x 4" face boards around the edge and across the center.

HOW TO ASSEMBLE "SUPER-O" TRACK

Begin by interlocking "Super-O" track for the upper loop. Note that the molded track base has a cylinder-and-socket joint which locks with the adjacent track section.

Ease the track sections together so that the track pins in the rails fit into the rail openings of the mating section. Make sure that the cylinder-and-socket joints are fully snapped into each other. Join the center power rails with No. 31-7 connector clips.

● Follow the illustration to establish the track pattern.

● Interlock six sections of curved track.

● Place two sections of straight track onto each end of this arc.

● Add No. 43 Power Track to one end and No. 37 Uncoupling Track to the other.

● Complete the oval by adding the remaining six sections of curved track.

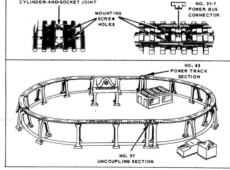

ASSEMBLING ELEVATING TRESTLE

A tie channel is slipped into the grooves on top of each bent, as shown in Figure 1. The four holes in the tie channel are so placed that at least one diagonally opposite pair will line up with the holes in the track ties when the joint is placed at the center of the bent. A pair of #4 x 1/2 sheet metal screws are inserted through the track ties and screwed into the tie channel. To avoid distortion of the track, do not screw down too tightly. But just enough to hold the channels.

1961

THE BEGINNING OF THE END

1961 saw the introduction of the non-perforated, solid orange component box with a picture of a steam engine and an F-3 on the face for rolling stock and passenger cars. This box will be referred to as *Orange Picture* in the text. Perforations also disappeared from new-issue corrugated containers, and the use of sleeves was discontinued. The O27 display-style outfit box was the half-orange, half-white type introduced in 1960 that included a sketch of a 4-6-2 steam engine on the upper portion of the lid, but only Types A and B were utilized for the low- to moderate-priced sets. The better O27 sets came in a conventional solid orange box made of coated stock with all of the contents component boxed. The introduction of the new Orange Picture box led to the demise of the Type C outfit box. There was no need to component box items in a display-style outfit box if the components could no longer be viewed. Most of the low and moderate O27 sets still had individually numbered instruction sheets.

The Super O outfit box underwent yet another change. The motive power design, which originated in 1957, was deleted from the sides in favor of a simple solid orange field on coated stock that was identical to the better O27 outfit box. The No. 48 insulated straight was no longer standard outfit issue as Lionel, in an attempt to further cut track costs, experimented with a half-straight in one outfit. This was a portent of things to come as the half-straight package would become the standard in 1962 and 1963.

The early version of the plastic AAR truck was still the norm in 1961, as were operating couplers at both ends. No cars, other than passenger, would see a metal truck again until 1969. Sometime toward the end of the product year, the metal knuckle on AAR trucks was replaced with a plastic knuckle, but it was still attached to the coupler by means of a silver knuckle pin. The coupler and truck information mentioned above is very important to follow because it assists in properly dating items. Many of the items catalogued in 1961 were also available in subsequent years and underwent changes as Lionel continued to reduce production costs.

The space age frenzy was taking a stronger hold on the product line as four O27 sets and two Super O ones were entirely space age-related. Lionel prudently avoided the mixture of car types in outfits that was so prevalent in 1959 and 1960. Even the mighty 2383 Santa Fe succumbed to the space phenomenon.

New space age items that debuted in 1961 were the 3509 and 3519 satellite launching cars, and the 3665 Minuteman missile launcher. Other interesting new items were the 3545 TV monitor car, 6416 boat loader, and the 6445 Ft. Knox bullion car. Three new road name cabooses were also introduced. They were the 6058 C & O and 6059 M St. L in the SP-type, and the 6130 Santa Fe work caboose. Inventory on the old metal truck 6427 porthole caboose was finally depleted, and it was replaced by the 6437 with Pennsylvania markings and AAR trucks.

Two important tender changes were instituted in 1961. The 2046W tender was "mothballed" after a decade of service and was replaced with the similar 736W that came with Pennsylvania lettering and AAR trucks. The 6026W was also discontinued and replaced with the 233W which retained Lionel Lines markings, but came with AAR trucks. Early examples were equipped with two contact roller assemblies that later gave way to a single-roller pickup. The 233W, not to be confused with 234W, always came with an operating coupler.

The 229 M St. L, 230 C & O, and 231 Rock Island were new road names in the Alco series, while the 616 Santa Fe and the 2359 Boston and Maine were new additions to the diesel switcher and Geep series. The highlight of the year was the reissue of the Pennsylvania GG-1. The 1961 edition came with a painted gold stripe, heat-stamped lettering, and ventilators that were the same height.

VG   LN

1123 Advance Catalogue   O27 Gauge
No Retail

Contents: 1060 steam locomotive; 1050T slope-back tender; 6406 gray or maroon General-type flatcar with gray-bumpered auto; 6042 blue gondola with two canisters; red or yellow unlettered SP-type caboose without end rails; eight curved and two straight track; and a 1026 25-watt transformer.

Comments: The outfit box was a Type A white background display style with new graphics and deep red print. Refer to page 123 for a picture of this style of outfit box. The unboxed contents were separated by loose cardboard dividers instead of channels. The new graphics included a picture of a small Hudson-type steam engine and a Santa Fe F-3. These graphics were identical to those that would be adopted in 1963 for the Type A and in 1964 for the Type D display-style outfit boxes. The rolling stock was equipped with arch bar trucks with fixed couplers. What was catalogued as a 6406 is an unstamped General-type flatcar. These inexpensive Advance Catalogue sets are difficult to obtain in collector condition. They are far more collectable than most of the consumer catalogue starter sets.   **165**   **275**

	VG	LN

1124 Advance Catalogue — O27 Gauge / No Retail

Contents: 1060 steam locomotive; 1060T streamlined tender; 3409 flatcar with helicopter; 6076 red Lehigh Valley hopper; red or yellow unlettered SP-type caboose without end rails; eight curved and two straight track; and a 1026 25-watt transformer.

Comments: The outfit box was a Type A white background display style with the unboxed contents separated by loose cardboard dividers instead of channels. Please refer to outfit 1123 for a more detailed description of the set box. The rolling stock was equipped with arch bar trucks with fixed couplers. The 1060T tender has the same body mold and Lionel Lines markings as the 1130T but it is referred to as 1060T when fitted with arch bar trucks. The 3409 is an extremely scarce car and is common only to this set. These inexpensive Advance Catalogue sets are difficult to obtain in collector condition. **135 225**

Outfits 1125 (1961) and 11011 (1962) were Advance Catalogue outfits packaged in boxes with special graphics that were later adopted for the 1963 consumer catalogue line. Why did Lionel use dated graphics from what were their lowest-end sets for the 1963 line? The answer was probably economics. Toy train sales were suffering and Lionel opted to use existing graphics rather than sustain the expense of drafting new ones. Refer to page 133 for a picture of the contents of outfit 11011. M. Sokol Collection.

1125 Advance Catalogue — O27 Gauge / No Retail

Contents: 1065 UP Alco A unit; 6630 black flatcar with IRBM launcher; 6480 exploding boxcar; 6120 yellow unstamped work caboose; eight curved and two straight track; and a 1026 25-watt transformer.

Comments: The outfit box was a Type A white background display style, with the unboxed contents separated by loose cardboard dividers. Please refer to outfit 1123 for a more detailed description of the set box. The rolling stock was equipped with arch bar trucks with fixed couplers. This is one of the most desirable of the Advance Catalogue sets as all of the contents are somewhat scarce, and diesel outfits usually generate more collector interest than their steam counterparts. **210 350**

1641 — O27 Gauge / $25 Retail

Contents: 246 steam locomotive with headlight and Magnetraction; 244T slope-back tender; 3362 helium tank unloading car; 6162 blue gondola with three canisters; 6057 SP-type caboose; eight curved and one straight track; 1008-50 camtrol uncoupling section; and a 1010 35-watt transformer.

Comments: This set came in a half-orange, half-white Type A display-style outfit box with unboxed contents. It is one of only two sets to contain the new 3362, which required the use of the camtrol for operation. The 244T came with Lionel Lines markings and an operating coupler. It was the same tender that was included with outfit 1627S from 1960. Please refer to page 124 for a picture of this outfit. **90 150**

1642 — O27 Gauge / $29.95 Retail

Contents: 244 steam locomotive with headlight and smoke; 1130T Lionel Lines non-whistle tender; 3376 giraffe car; 6405 flatcar with yellow van; 6119-100 work caboose; eight curved and one straight track; 1008-50 camtrol uncoupling section; and a 1025 45-watt transformer.

Comments: This set came in a half-orange, half-white Type A display-style outfit box with the usual unboxed contents. The 6405 was new to the product line in 1961. It is a collectable item especially when obtained with a component box. Starter steam outfits, unless absolutely mint, are of minimal collector interest. **135 225**

1643 — O27 Gauge / $29.95 Retail

Contents: 230 C & O Alco A unit; 3509 manual satellite launching car; 6050 savings bank car; 6175 flatcar with rocket; 6058 C & O SP-type caboose; eight curved and one straight track; 1008-50 camtrol uncoupling section; and a 1025 45-watt transformer.

Comments: This set came in either a yellow or a half-orange, half-white Type A display-style outfit box with unboxed contents. The 6050 was new, and the 3509 was a limited production car. This is the only catalogued set to include the

246 steam freight set 1641 in a Type A display-style box. This set included a camtrol that was used both as an uncoupling mechanism as well as a means by which to unload the helium tank car. The inclusion of the manually operated camtrol allowed Lionel to delete a more costly remote-controlled uncoupling section from their low-end sets. B. Myles Collection.

	VG	LN

230 Alco and the complementing road name 6058 caboose. The 230 differed from the 1960 edition of the 225 in that it came with a closed pilot and no front coupler. A starter diesel outfit is far more collectable than most steam counterparts. Please see pages 126 and 127 for further information.

250   400

1644   O27 Gauge $39.95 Retail

Contents: 1862 General with headlight; 1862T tender; 3370 sheriff and outlaw car; 1866 mail-baggage car; 1865 passenger car; twelve curved and four straight track; 1020 90° crossing; and a 1025 45-watt transformer.

Comments: This set came in a half-orange, half-white Type A display-style outfit box. The inclusion of the new 3370 and a Figure 8 track plan makes this set just different enough from previous issues. It was the General sets for which the arch bar trucks were developed. The non-illuminated passenger cars came with non-self-centering, fixed die-cast couplers. Early issues of the General passenger cars were painted yellow on gray body molds whereas the later examples were often painted on yellow molds, and, in some instances, left unpainted. Refer to page 128 for a picture of this outfit.

450   750

1645   O27 Gauge $39.95 Retail

Contents: 229 M St. L Alco A unit; 3410 flatcar with manual release helicopter; 6465 Cities Service two-dome tank

car; 6825 flatcar with trestle; 6059 M St. L SP-type caboose; eight curved and three straight track; 1008-50 camtrol uncoupling section; 1073 60-watt transformer; and a 147 horn controller.

Comments: This set came in a half-orange, half-white Type A display-style outfit box with unboxed contents. The 6465 Cities Service is one of the more desirable tank cars and the 3410 was the new manual counterpart to the remote-controlled 3419. The M St. L was a new road name in the Alco series and was not paired with a B unit in 1961. Beware of a broken and/or repaired strut as it is exceptionally fragile.

175   300

1646   O27 Gauge $39.95 Retail

Contents: 233 steam locomotive with headlight, smoke, and Magnetraction; 233W Lionel Lines whistle tender; 6162 blue gondola with three canisters; 6343 barrel ramp car; 6476 red Lehigh Valley hopper; 6017 SP-type caboose; eight curved and three straight track; 1008-50 camtrol uncoupling section; 1073 60-watt transformer; and a 147 whistle control.

Comments: This set usually came in an over-stickered yellow Type A display-style outfit box from 1960 that was originally marked "1631WS". The engine and tender in this outfit came boxed! The engine came in a perforated-front corrugated carton with tucked-in end flaps, while the tender came in an overstamped Orange Perforated box, and had "233W" heat stamped on the side. The 233W tender had an operating coupler and was renumbered from 243W to corre-

124

spond with the 233 engine. The 6343 barrel ramp car was new for the 1961 product year.

	VG	LN
	150	250

capabilities operable. A 6029 would have otherwise sufficed for the 3665 and 3519. This is a scarce set, and as with all of the military/space sets, the components are extremely fragile.

	VG	LN
	900	1500

1961

1647   O27 Gauge $49.95 Retail

Contents: 45 olive U.S.M.C. missile launcher; 3665 Minuteman car; 3519 satellite launching car; 6830 flatcar with submarine; 6448 exploding boxcar; 6814 medical caboose; eight curved and three straight track; 6019 uncoupling/operating section; and a 1073 60-watt transformer.

Comments: This set came in the new solid orange conventional two-tier outfit box with all of the contents individually boxed. The remote-controlled satellite car was catalogued in blue, but is not known to exist in that color. The 3665, 3519, and the 6448 were new issue and came in Orange Picture boxes. The 6814 was a carry-over item and is extremely difficult to find in a crisp white condition with all of its miscellaneous pieces, while the non-operating 6830 submarine is a more collectable car than the 3830 operating version.

It is interesting to note that a 6019 had to be included with this set in order to make the engine's missile launching

1648   O27 Gauge $49.95 Retail

Contents: 2037 steam locomotive with headlight, smoke, and Magnetraction; 233W Lionel Lines whistle tender; 6062 black gondola with cable reels; 6465 Cities Service two-dome tank car; 6519 Allis Chalmers car; 6476 red Lehigh Valley hopper; 6017 SP-type caboose; eight curved and three straight track; 1008-50 camtrol uncoupling section; and a 1063 75-watt transformer.

Comments: This set came in the new solid orange conventional two-tier outfit box with the contents individually boxed. All of the components were repeat items. The 233W with AAR trucks was the replacement tender for the discontinued 6026W. The 6465 box for the Cities Service had a "-110" suffix on the end flaps, and as this was a transition year, this set usually came with a combination of the new Orange Picture and carry-over Orange Perforated boxes. The 6519 is

233 steam freight set 1646 in a Type A display-style box. Notice here that both the engine and tender were component boxed, which was an exception for Type A packaging. B. Myles Collection.

VG   LN

**1
9
6
1**

extremely fragile and the brakewheels are almost always broken.   250   425

1649   O27 Gauge $49.95 Retail

Contents: 218P/218C Santa Fe Alco AB units; 6343 barrel ramp car; 6445 Ft. Knox car; 6475 pickle vat car; 6405 flatcar with yellow van; 6017 SP-type caboose; eight curved and three straight track; 1008-50 camtrol uncoupling section; and a 1063 75-watt transformer.

Comments: This outfit came in the new two-tier solid orange set box with all of the components individually boxed. This was one of only two sets that offered the 218C as part of the outfit, and the only one in which it was boxed. The 218C came in an Orange Picture box while the engine came in a corrugated carton with tucked-in end flaps. The Ft. Knox car was new for 1961 and is a very collectable piece of rolling stock. The 6343 and the 6405 were also new for 1961, and they, along with the 6445, came in Orange Picture boxes. Beware of a broken and/or repaired strut on the Alco unit as it is exceptionally fragile.   450   750

1650   O27 Gauge $59.95 Retail

Contents: 2037 steam locomotive with headlight, smoke, and Magnetraction, 233W Lionel Lines whistle tender,

---

VG   LN

6544 missile firing car, 6470 exploding boxcar, 3330 flatcar with submarine kit, 3419 flatcar with operating helicopter, 6017 SP-type caboose, eight curve, three straight, 6029 uncoupling section, and a 1063 75-watt transformer.

Comments: This outfit also came in the new two-tier solid orange set box with all of the components individually boxed. The engine came in a corrugated carton while the other repeat items, since this was a transition year, came in a combination of Orange Perforated and new Orange Picture boxes. The 233W with AAR trucks was the replacement tender for the discontinued 6026W. The components are extremely fragile, and the brakewheels are almost always broken on the scarce 6544. The 3330 with submarine in kit form is another scarce car, and is nearly impossible to find complete and unassembled. Note that a 6029 was included with this set to operate the 3419.   350   600

1651   O27 Gauge $69.95 Retail

Contents: 218P/218T Santa Fe Alco AA units; two 2412 Vista Domes, 2414 Pullman, and 2416 observation with blue-striped Santa Fe markings; eight curved and three straight track; 6029 uncoupling section; and a 1063 75-watt transformer.

Comments: This was the top-of-the-line O27 outfit for 1961. It came in a new solid orange two-tier conventional type set box with all of the contents individually boxed. Lionel

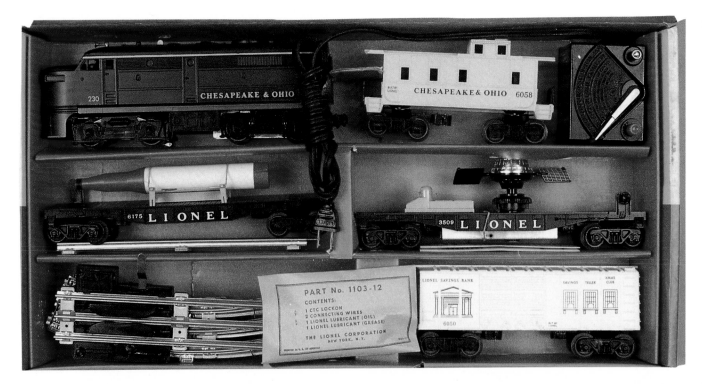

Outfit 1643 headed by a 230 C & O Alco unit came in a Type A display-style box with unboxed contents. The picture shows a half-orange and half-white box, but this set also came in a yellow background box that was either factory stamped or over-stickered 1643. Refer to page 127 for additional photographs. The 6058 caboose was one of the few matching road name cabooses that Lionel issued in the postwar era. Also note that the front coupler was eliminated on the 230 engine. The previous 225 issue from 1960 in outfit 1629 came with an open pilot and a fixed, self-centering coupler. B. Myles Collection.

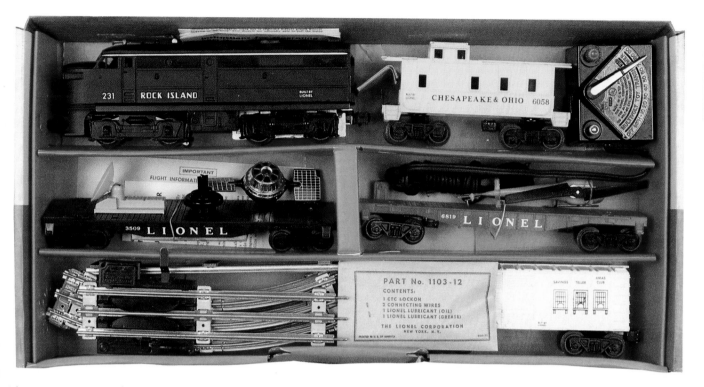

This is a variation of the 1961 catalogued outfit 1643, with paperwork dated 1962, that was normally headed by a 230 C & O Alco unit. This set substituted a very scarce 231 Rock Island without a red stripe and a 6819 helicopter car for the 6175 flatcar with rocket. This set came in a half-orange, half-white Type A display-style box that was factory stamped "1643". The additional premium that should be paid for this set is only the difference in value between a 230 Alco and the black 231 Rock Island, approximately $250. B. Myles Collection.

	VG	LN		VG	LN

continued its practice of including a remote-controlled uncoupling track with their O27 passenger sets. This was the third consecutive year that the blue-striped Santa Fe cars were catalogued. The 1961 edition replaced the previously included 3428 operating U.S. Mail car with a 2414 Pullman. The passenger car boxes could have been either Orange Perforated or the new 1961 issue. The 218P came in a non-perforated corrugated carton with tucked-in end flaps while the 218T came in an Orange Picture box. Beware of broken and/or repaired struts on the Alco units as they are exceptionally fragile. **400   650**

An end view of two different 1643 outfit boxes. The top example was an over-stickered 1960-issue box that Lionel was in the process of depleting while the bottom box was a regular half-orange, half-white 1961 issue. M. Sokol Collection.

1652   O27 Gauge $35 Retail

Contents: 236 steam locomotive with headlight, smoke, and Magnetraction; 1130T Lionel Lines non-whistle tender; 6050 savings bank car; 6476 red Lehigh Valley hopper; 6017 SP-type caboose; eight curved and three straight track; 1008-50 camtrol uncoupling section; and a 1073 60-watt transformer.

Comments: This outfit came in a yellow background Type A display style box with unboxed contents. The 236 was one of the better Scout-like engines as it was equipped with not only a headlight, but also smoke and Magnetraction. The rolling stock and tender all came with AAR trucks and operating couplers. This outfit arouses minimal collector interest. **90   150**

1809   O27 Gauge $29.95 Retail

Contents: 244 steam locomotive with headlight and smoke; 1130T Lionel Lines non-whistle tender; 3370 sheriff and outlaw car; 3376 giraffe car; 1877 flatcar with horses; and a 6017 SP-type caboose.

Comments: This set was referred to as the "Western" gift pack as it included neither track nor transformer. It came in a half-orange, half-white Type A display-style outfit box with the contents unboxed. The 3370 was new for 1961. The 244 Scout-like engine is as common as a penny, but becomes

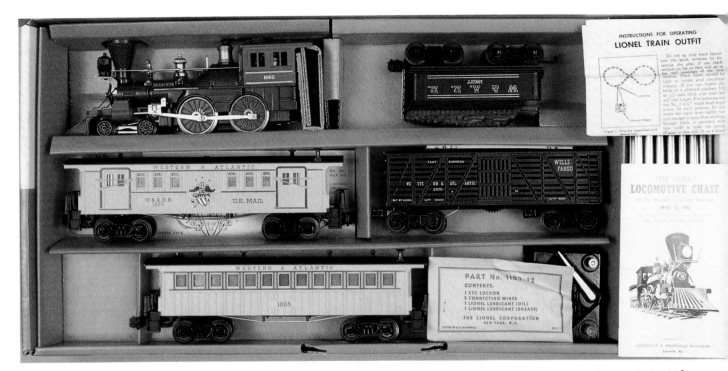

The O27 Gauge 1862 General set 1644 in a Type A display-style box. This set included a Figure 8 track plan with the 90° crossing packed under the interior liner, and a booklet entitled The Great Locomotive Race. Notice that the tender was packed upside down. This is not an error; the compartment for the tender was designed in this manner. Refer to page 104 for an end view of the outfit box. B. Myles Collection.

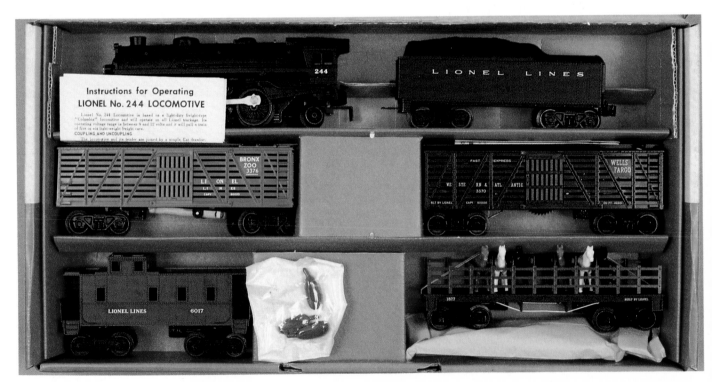

244 steam freight set 1809 in a Type A display-style box. This outfit was termed the "Western" gift pack as it included neither track nor transformer. The long manila envelope on the bottom right contained the telltale mechanism to operate the giraffe car and the packet of blue cartridges contained smoke fluid. M. Sokol Collection.

231 Rock Island outfit 1810 in a Type A display-style box. This set was termed the "Space Age" gift pack as it included neither track nor transformer. Note the cellophane packet in the upper left corner that contained lubricant in orange capsules. B. Myles Collection.

	VG	LN		VG	LN

more collectable if acquired with the set box. Refer to page 128 for a picture of this outfit.   **175**   **300**

1810   O27 Gauge $35 Retail

Contents: 231 Rock Island Alco A unit; 3665 Minuteman car; 3519 satellite launching car; 3820 olive U.S.M.C. flatcar with operating submarine; and a 6017 SP-type caboose.

Comments: This set was referred to as the "Space Age" gift pack as it included neither track nor transformer. It came in a half-orange, half-white Type A display-style outfit box with the contents unboxed. This is the only catalogued set to be headed by the new Rock Island Alco. The 3665 and 3519 were also new items, while the 3820 was a leftover from the 1960 "Land-Sea-and-Air" gift pack. The 231 was also available for separate sale, when it came in a corrugated carton with tucked-in end flaps. Beware of a broken and/or repaired strut as it is exceptionally fragile.   **240**   **400**

2528WS   Super O Gauge $49.95 Retail

Comments: This was a carry-forward set from 1959 and 1960. Sales on the General were slow, and the cataloguing of this set was merely an attempt to deplete unsold inventory. Refer to **1959** for more detailed information.

	VG	LN
Type B box	500	850
Type C or tan box	600	1000

2570   Super O Gauge $49.95 Retail

Contents: 616 Santa Fe NW-2 switcher; 6822 searchlight car; 6828 flatcar with Harnischfeger crane; 6812 track maintenance car; 6736 Detroit & Mackinac hopper; 6130 Santa Fe work caboose; twelve curved and two straight track; and a 39-25 operating packet.

Comments: The outfit box was the new 1961 issue with all of the contents individually boxed. The 6822 was a new item, and the 6130 was a new caboose for 1961. The catalogue makes no mention of this, and strangely enough it did not reappear in a catalogue until 1965. The 6812 and 6736 were repeat items and may have come in Orange Perforated boxes. The repeat 6828 construction crane came unassembled in its own white, black, and yellow thin cardboard box; the box was placed on top of the black flatcar and then repackaged in an oversized Orange Picture box.   **500**   **850**

2571   Super O Gauge $49.95 Retail

Contents: 637 steam locomotive with headlight, smoke, and Magnetraction; 736W Pennsylvania whistle tender; 3419 flatcar with operating helicopter; 6445 Ft. Knox car; 6361 timber transport; 6119 red cab work caboose; twelve curved and two straight track; and a 39-25 operating packet.

VG   LN

1961

Comments: The outfit box was the new solid orange two-tier type with all of the contents individually boxed. This set, as with other 1961 component boxed sets, is likely to show up with a combination of both Orange Perforated and the new Orange Picture boxes. The 6445 was new and is a collectable piece of rolling stock, while the better O Gauge streamlined whistle tender was now lettered "Pennsylvania", not "Lionel Lines", and became 736W.   **350   600**

2572   Super O Gauge $59.95 Retail

Contents: 2359 Boston and Maine GP-9; 6544 missile firing car; 3830 flatcar with operating submarine; 6448 exploding boxcar; 3519 satellite launching car; 3535 security car; twelve curved and four straight track; and a 39-25 operating packet.

Comments: This set came in the new solid orange two-tier outfit box with all of the components individually boxed in a mixture of both Orange Perforated and the new Orange Picture type. The Boston and Maine was a new road name Geep. It came in a corrugated carton with tucked-in end flaps, and the very early issues had a perforated front. The 3535 security car is scarce and was a component in only two sets. It was an odd looking item; the chassis was a black flatcar that utilized a 3620 searchlight hood and mechanism, the cab was one that had been previously used on the 520 electric from 1956, and the guns on top were the same as those used with the Pyro military vehicles that came with flatcars 6804 and 6809. The 1961 edition of this car came in an Orange Picture box. This is a difficult set to obtain in collector condition as all of the cars, especially the 6544, are extremely fragile. The 3519 was new and the 6448 was a new recolored exploding boxcar.   **650   1100**

2573   Super O Gauge $75 Retail

Contents: 736 Berkshire steam locomotive with headlight, smoke, and Magnetraction; 736W Pennsylvania whistle tender; 3545 TV monitor car; 6416 boat transport; 6475 pickle vat car; 6440 flatcar with vans; 6357 illuminated SP-type caboose; twelve curved and four straight track; and a 39-25 operating packet.

Comments: This set came in a new solid orange two-tier conventional type outfit box with individually boxed components. The Berkshire came in a corrugated carton with tucked-in end flaps while the tender and rolling stock, except for the caboose, came in Orange Picture boxes. The caboose was in the process of being depleted. It came in an Orange Perforated box and this was the last time that an illuminated SP-type caboose appeared in a set. The boat transport and the TV monitor car were new and are valued collector pieces. The 6440 was also a new item. It was a cheapened version of the old 6430 that did not include a mounting rack for the vans. The 736W was a nearly new tender. It was the old reliable 2046W that was now lettered "Pennsylvania" and fitted with AAR trucks.   **575   975**

VG   LN

2574   Super O Gauge $89.95 Retail

Contents: 2383P/2383T Santa Fe AA with F-3 units; 3665 Minuteman car; 3419 flatcar with operating helicopter; 3830 flatcar with operating submarine; 448 missile firing range set with 6448 exploding boxcar; 6437 illuminated Pennsylvania porthole caboose; twelve curved, three straight, and one half-straight track; No. 109 twelve-piece trestle set; 943 exploding ammo dump; and a 39-25 operating packet.

Comments: This set came in the new solid orange two-tier outfit box with individually boxed components. It is very collectable as it contains a combination of fragile cars and military accessories along with a partial trestle set. The Santa Fe units each came in their own corrugated carton with tucked-in end flaps, while the other components came in Orange Picture boxes. The 6437 Pennsylvania caboose was new in 1961 and was the AAR truck replacement for the finally-depleted 6427. The 3665 Minuteman car was a new military item as was the 448 accessory. The 6448 exploding boxcar came component boxed inside the larger 448 box. Lionel reverted to an old habit of including a Pennsylvania road name caboose with a Santa Fe engine in this outfit. The 1961 catalogue illustration always erroneously presented the 6437 with Lionel Lines markings. The Pennsylvania road name was reintroduced on the porthole caboose to match the reissue of the GG-1 in outfit 2575. That Lionel gave some thought to issuing a Santa Fe caboose as a porthole example is illustrated on page 42 of the 1960 consumer catalogue.   **1100   1850**

2575   Super O Gauge $100 Retail

Contents: 2360 Pennsylvania solid stripe GG-1; 6530 fire prevention car; 6828 flatcar with Harnischfeger crane; 6464-900 NYC boxcar; 6827 flatcar with Harnischfeger power shovel; 6736 Detroit & Mackinac quad hopper; 6560 red cab crane; 6437 illuminated Pennsylvania porthole caboose; twelve curved and six straight track; and a 39-35 operating packet.

Comments: This set came in a new solid orange two-tier conventional type outfit box with individually boxed components. The GG-1 came in a standard corrugated carton made by the Mead Company that utilized a full wraparound liner. All of the rolling stock other than the caboose were repeat items and came in a mixture of Orange Perforated and Orange Picture boxes. The GG-1 reappeared in an outfit for the first time since 1957, and this was the first of three similar sets from the early 1960s. The engine was the painted gold-striped variation with even-height ventilators and heat-stamped lettering. The 6437 caboose with Pennsylvania lettering came in an Orange Picture box and was the new AAR truck replacement for the finally-depleted 6427. The Harnischfeger items each came unassembled in its own white, black, and yellow thin cardboard box; they were placed on top of the black flatcars and then repackaged. This outfit, as with all other GG-1 sets, is highly coveted by serious collectors.   **1500   2500**

	VG	LN

2576   Super O Gauge $100 Retail

Contents: 2383P/2383T Santa Fe AA F-3 units; 2561 Vista Valley observation, 2562 Regal Pass Vista Dome, 2562 Regal Pass Vista Dome, and 2563 Indian Falls Pullman with red-striped Santa Fe markings; twelve curved and six straight track; and a 39-25 operating packet.

Comments: This "Super Chief" streamliner set can truly be called rare. The outfit box was a plain tan corrugated type with only "2576" rubber stamped on the ends. The 2383P and 2383T units each came in a perforated-front corrugated carton with tucked-in end flaps, while the passenger cars still came in Orange Perforated boxes. The cataloguing of this outfit was no more than a futile effort by Lionel to deplete existing inventory and to help the dealers move stock. This was the third and last year that the 2560 series cars were catalogued, and they are every bit as scarce and prized as the 1957 Canadian Pacific cars.   **3000   5000**

1961

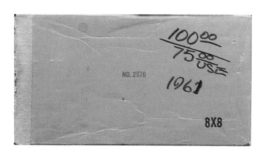

An end view of the rare 2576 Super O set box that contained the 1961 edition of the Santa Fe red-striped passenger set. Occasionally Lionel would use a nondescript outfit box such as this to package outfits with low sales projections. Also note the marked down sale price of $75. By today's standards, $75 would purchase little more than the track included with this set. M. Sokol Collection.

1962

The Descent Hastens

Rockets and missiles were flying everywhere as space age outfits and cars dominated the catalogue. New space age items were the 6463 rocket fuel tank car, 3349 turbo missile launcher, 6413 Mercury capsule carrier, 3619 reconnaissance copter car, 3470 aerial target launcher, 3413 Mercury capsule launcher, and the 6512 cherry picker car. The 6414 auto loader returned as a set component in 1962 with gray-bumpered vehicles as the standard load.

New motive power was virtually nonexistent. The 2365 Chesapeake & Ohio was a new road name Geep, the 232 New Haven was a new road name in the Alco series, and the Texas Special was reissued, with Magnetraction, as 211 after last being catalogued in 1958. The new 633 Santa Fe diesel switcher was a disappointment as it did not even include a front coupler. (To be of use, a diesel switcher must have couplers at both ends.)

Two interesting and collectable motorized units made their debut in 1962. They were the 59 Minuteman and the 65 handcar. Other new rolling stock included the 3357 cop and hobo car, 6473 rodeo car, 6501 jet motorboat car, and the scarce 6500 red and white airplane flatcar. The 6017-235 was a new Santa Fe-lettered non-illuminated SP-type caboose, and this was the introductory year for the -725 orange New Haven boxcar which, for all intents, was the last issue in the 6464 series. It was often misnumbered in the catalogues, and even the box was consistently misnumbered "6464-735". (A properly numbered original box for this item does not exist.) Finally, the 2520 series Presidential passenger cars with gold paper stripes were introduced to replace the discontinued 2560 series.

The corrugated engine and component boxes remained the same as in the previous year. 1962 saw the introduction of the five-digit outfit numbering system. A brief explanation of the fifth digit is as follows: Any fifth digit "1" or "2" designated a display-style outfit box with unboxed contents while any last digit "8" indicated a conventional set box with individually boxed components. The half-orange, half-white O27 display-style outfit box also remained the same as in 1961, but only Type A was utilized for the low and moderate sets; the better O27 and the Super O sets still used the conventional two-tier solid orange box.

Early AAR trucks were still the norm, but the metal knuckle that had been part of the original 1957 design was replaced with a plastic knuckle that was still attached by means of a silver knuckle pin. It is important to follow these minor truck and coupler changes because they assist the collector in properly dating items. Many items catalogued in 1962 were also available in subsequent years and underwent changes as Lionel continued to lower the quality of the product line. As an additional cost savings measure all of the 1962

Super O sets now included a half-straight section. The half-straight when joined with the No. 37 and No. 43 equaled a whole straight. This cost reduction had to be absolutely minimal because all that was saved was 3-1/4 inches of product, the difference in length between a full and a half section of Super O track!

Also note that no cars requiring power blades were contained in any of the nine Super O sets offered in 1962. This allowed Lionel to include only the basic 39-25 operating packet with most outfits; nevertheless, a 39-35 was included with the two GG-1 sets since a power blade was required to activate the pickup shoe assembly necessary to operate the coil-type couplers on the engine. As sales were no doubt disappointing, all of the 1962 Super O sets are scarce, some extremely rare, and all highly desirable today.

	VG	LN

11001 Advance Catalogue — O27 Gauge / No Retail

Contents: 1060 steam locomotive; 1060T streamlined tender; 6042 blue gondola with two canisters; 6402 gray or maroon General-type flatcar with cable reels; 6167 red unstamped SP-type caboose; eight curved and two straight track; and a 1026 25-watt transformer.

Comments: This outfit came in both a white background, Type A display-style box with 1961 Advance graphics, and a scaled-down version of the solid tan two-tier conventional box, also with unboxed contents. The tender and rolling stock all came with arch bar trucks with fixed couplers, and the 6402 is nothing more than an unstamped General-type flatcar. These inexpensive Advance Catalogue sets are difficult to obtain in collector condition. They are far more collectable than most of the consumer catalogue starter outfits.

75   125

11011 Advance Catalogue — O27 Gauge / No Retail

Contents: 222 Rio Grande Alco A unit; 3510 red manual satellite launching car; 6076 black or red Lehigh Valley hopper; 6120 yellow, unstamped work caboose; eight curved and two straight track; and a 1026 25-watt transformer.

Comments: This outfit box was a white background Type A display style with 1961 Advance graphics. All of the rolling stock had arch bar trucks with fixed couplers. The scarce red satellite car had only "Lionel", not "3510", stamped

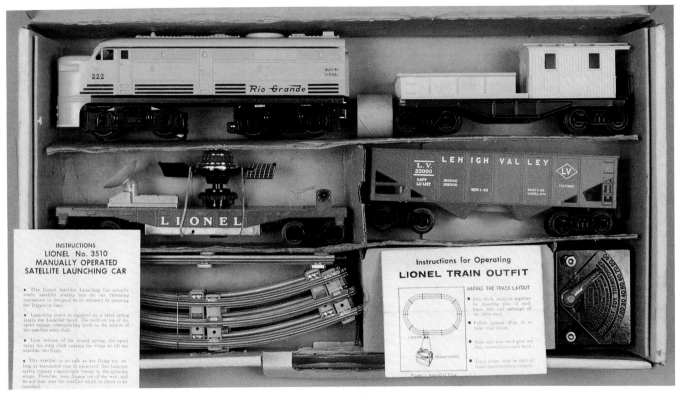

222 Rio Grande Advance Catalogue freight set 11011 in a Type A display-style box with cardboard dividers. This is one of the most desirable of the Advance Catalogue sets as it contained two scarce cars, namely the red 3510 satellite car and the unstamped yellow 6120 work caboose. (See page 123 for a picture of the set box lid.) B. Myles Collection.

	VG	LN

on the sides. This is one of the most desirable Advance Catalogue sets, as it is the only one to contain the 222 and 3510, and has the undervalued yellow work caboose. These inexpensive Advance Catalogue sets are difficult to obtain in collector condition. Please refer to page 123 for a picture pertaining to this outfit.   **210   350**

11201   O27 Gauge $19.95 Retail

Contents: 242 steam locomotive with headlight; 1060T streamlined tender; 6042-75 gondola with cable reels; 6502 black flatcar with girder; 6047 SP-type caboose; eight curved and two straight track; and a 1010 35-watt transformer.

Comments: This outfit was packed in a Type A display-style box with unboxed contents, but it is unique. Even though this outfit appeared in the consumer catalogue, it had characteristics common to an Advance Catalogue set. The outfit box was of the same style used for Advance Catalogue sets in 1961 and 1962. The 242 was a new locomotive that was a grade above the 1060. The tender and the rolling stock all came with arch bar trucks with fixed couplers. The "-75" suffix does not appear on the gondola; it was the means by which Lionel distinguished this car's coupler, truck type, and load. The flatcar, whether black or blue, has only "Lionel" stamped on the side. Please see page 134 for a picture of this outfit.

90   150

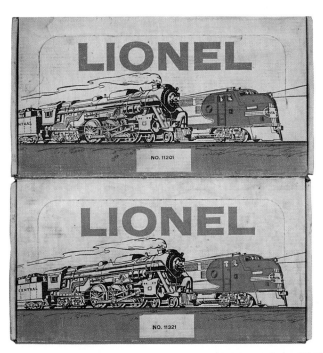

Outfit 11201 (top) was a consumer catalogue set from 1962, but came in a Type A display-style box with graphics and reddish-colored print that was used for Advance Catalogue sets in 1961 and 1962. In 1963 the Advance Catalogue graphics, shown on outfit 11321 (bottom), were adopted for all display-type consumer catalogue sets, and the printing reverted to orange. M. Sokol Collection.

1962

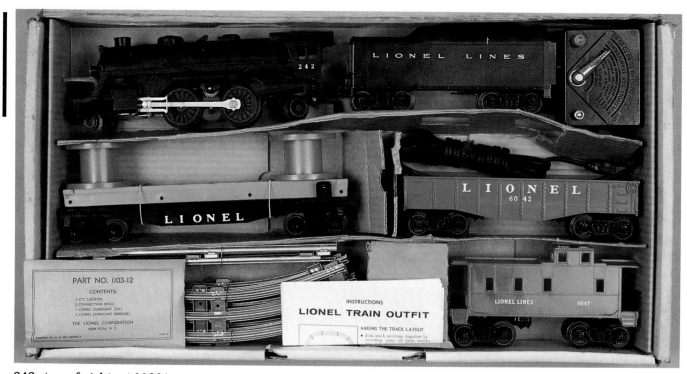

242 steam freight set 11201 in a Type A display-style box with cardboard dividers. This was a catalogued set but it had characteristics common to an Advance Catalogue set; the tender and rolling stock all came with arch bar trucks with fixed couplers. Please refer to page 133 for a picture of the set box lid. B. Myles Collection.

633 Santa Fe diesel switcher set 11212 in a Type A display-style box. The 633 was a "Spartan" engine as it did not even have a front coupler, but it was a one-year-only production item and is extremely desirable on the collector market. B. Myles Collection.

	VG	LN

11212　　O27 Gauge　　$25 Retail

Contents: 633 Santa Fe NW-2 switcher; 3349 turbo missile launcher; 6825 flatcar with trestle bridge; 6057 SP-type caboose; eight curved and one straight track; 1008-50 camtrol uncoupling section; and a 1010 35-watt transformer.

Comments: This outfit came in a half-orange, half-white Type A display-style box with the contents unboxed. The 633 was a new diesel switcher and it did not have a front coupler as issued from the factory. In spite of the low-end features, this is a scarce set. Diesel outfits arouse collector interest far more than their steam counterparts. Page 134 shows a picture of this outfit.　　**250　400**

11222　　O27 Gauge　　$29.95 Retail

Contents: 236 steam locomotive with headlight, smoke, and Magnetraction; 1050T slope-back tender; 3357 cop and hobo car; 6343 barrel ramp car; 6119 red cab work caboose; eight curved and one straight track; 1008-50 camtrol uncoupling section; and a 1025 45-watt transformer.

Comments: This set came in a half-orange, half-white Type A display-style outfit box with unboxed contents. It is rather nondescript and of limited interest to the advanced collector, yet the 3357 was new issue for 1962. Note that the 236 Scout-like engine came with headlight, smoke, and Magnetraction. The 1050T number assigned to the tender implied that it had arch bar trucks which were usually reserved for Advance and uncatalogued sets.　　**120　200**

11232　　O27 Gauge　　$29.95 Retail

Contents: 232 New Haven Alco A unit; 3410 flatcar with manual release helicopter; 6062 black gondola with cable reels; 6413 Mercury capsule carrier; 6057 orange unpainted SP-type caboose; eight curved and one straight track; 1008-50 camtrol uncoupling section; and a 1025 45-watt transformer.

Comments: This set came in a half-orange, half-white Type A display-style outfit box that was usually over-stickered with unboxed contents. This was the only set to contain the 232 New Haven and the complementing orange 6057 caboose. The 6413 and 3410 are both collectable cars, and the engine and caboose are not so common. Low-end diesel outfits stir much greater collector interest than their steam counterparts.　　**250　400**

11242　　O27 Gauge　　$39.95 Retail

Contents: 233 steam locomotive with headlight, smoke, and Magnetraction; 233W Lionel Lines whistle tender; 6465 Cities Service two-dome tank car; 6476 red Lehigh Valley hopper; 6162 blue gondola with three canisters; 6017 SP-type caboose; eight curved and three straight track; 1008-50 camtrol uncoupling section; 1073 60-watt transformer; and a 147 whistle controller.

Comments: This set came in a half-orange, half-white Type A display-style outfit box with unboxed contents. The components were all common run-of-the-mill items. Starter steam outfits, unless absolutely mint, are of minimal collector interest.　　**135　225**

232 New Haven set 11232 in a Type A display-style box. One of the shortcomings of Lionel in the postwar era was their failure to make more road name cabooses as companion pieces to engines. At least the New Haven was given a complementary orange caboose. M. Sokol Collection.

211 Texas Special space age set 11252 in a half-orange, half-white Type A display-style box. The Texas Special was reintroduced in 1962 with Magnetraction after last being catalogued in 1958. This is a scarce set and difficult to obtain in collector condition. M. Sokol Collection.

	VG	LN		VG	LN

11252　　　O27 Gauge　　　$39.95 Retail

Contents: 211P/211T Texas Special Alco AA units; 3509 manual satellite launching car; 6448 exploding boxcar; 3349 turbo missile launcher; 6463 rocket fuel tank car; 6057 SP-type caboose; eight curved and three straight track; 1008-50 camtrol uncoupling section; and a 1025 45-watt transformer.

Comments: This set came in a half-orange, half-white Type A display-style outfit box with unboxed components. As with all military and space age sets, the pieces are extremely fragile and difficult to obtain in collector condition. This was the year in which the Texas Special was reintroduced with Magnetraction and given the 211 number. The rolling stock, except for the exploding boxcar, was all new. The manual 3509 is much more scarce than the remote 3519. **600　1000**

11268　　　O27 Gauge　　　$49.95 Retail

Contents: 2365 Chesapeake & Ohio GP-7; 3619 reconnaissance copter car; 3470 aerial target launcher; 3349 turbo missile launcher; 6501 flatcar with jet motorboat; 6017 SP-type caboose; eight curved and three straight track; 6029 uncoupling section; and a 1073 60-watt transformer.

Comments: At $49.95 this was a better O27 set, and it came in a conventional two-tier solid orange box with component boxes. The engine came in a corrugated carton with tucked-in end flaps while the balance of the contents came in Orange Picture boxes. Note that a 6029 was included with this set to activate the 3619. The Chesapeake & Ohio without horn was a new road name in the Geep series. All of the rolling stock were also new items for 1962; none are rare, but they are difficult to find in collector condition. The balloons that came with the 3470, if not missing, are usually fused together as a result of age, and a mint example of the 6501 must include a foil packet of baking soda. Even the lowly 6017 caboose has a unique feature in this outfit — it came in an Orange Picture box which, believe it or not, is scarce. This outfit would be an excellent investment for the military/space collector.

775　1300

11278　　　O27 Gauge　　　$49.95 Retail

Contents: 2037 steam locomotive with headlight, smoke, and Magnetraction; 233W Lionel Lines whistle tender;

VG   LN

6473 rodeo car; 6162 blue gondola with three canisters; 6050-110 red Swift savings bank car; 6825 flatcar with trestle bridge; 6017 SP-type caboose; eight curved and three straight track; 1008-50 camtrol uncoupling section; 1073 60-watt transformer; and a 147 whistle controller.

Comments: The outfit box was a solid orange conventional two-tier type with component boxes. The engine came in a corrugated carton with tucked-in end flaps while the balance of the contents came in Orange Picture boxes. The 6473 rodeo car was new as was the Swift boxcar with a coin slot. Even the ordinary 6017 caboose had a unique feature when included in this outfit — it came in an Orange Picture box which, believe it or not, is scarce.   **210   350**

11288   O27 Gauge $49.95 Retail

Contents: 229P/229C M St. L Alco AB units; 3413 Mercury capsule launcher; 6512 cherry picker car; 6413 Mercury capsule carrier; 6463 rocket fuel tank car; 6059 M St. L SP-type caboose; eight curved and three straight track; 1008-50 camtrol uncoupling section; 1073 60-watt transformer; and a 147 horn controller.

Comments: The outfit box was the conventional two-tier solid orange type with component boxes. This was the only set in which a 6059 M St. L caboose ever came boxed; it was a red-painted example. The rolling stock was all new for 1962, and is both collectable and fragile. Like New condition boxes add a premium to the value of this outfit. The 6512 cherry picker and the 3413 were companion cars, and were often paired together in outfits. The M St. L B unit was also new for 1962. It came in an Orange Picture box while the powered unit came in a corrugated carton with tucked-in end flaps. Beware of a broken and/or repaired strut on the Alco unit as it is extremely fragile.   **725   1200**

11298   O27 Gauge $59.95 Retail

Contents: 2037 steam locomotive with headlight, smoke, and Magnetraction; 233W Lionel Lines whistle tender; 6544 missile firing car; 3419 flatcar with operating helicopter; 6448 exploding boxcar; 3330 flatcar with submarine kit; 6017 SP-type caboose; eight curved and three straight track; 6029 uncoupling section; and a 1063 75-watt transformer.

Comments: The outfit box was a solid orange two-tier conventional type with component boxes. The engine came in a corrugated carton with tucked-in end flaps, and this was a little more than a run-of-the-mill 2037 set. It contained two scarce carry-over items, the 6544 and the 3330, which still came in Orange Perforated boxes.

The 6544 is rarely found without broken brakewheels, and the submarine is seldom found complete and unassembled. Even the 6017 caboose had a unique feature when included in this outfit. It came in an Orange Picture box which, surprisingly, is scarce. The tender and other rolling stock came in Orange Picture boxes.   **400   675**

11308   O27 Gauge $69.95 Retail

Contents: 218P/218T Santa Fe Alco AA units; two 2412 Vista Domes, 2414 Pullman, and 2416 observation with blue-striped Santa Fe markings; eight curved and three straight track; 6029 uncoupling section; and a 1063 75-watt transformer.

Comments: This set came in a conventional two-tier solid orange outfit box with all of the contents individually boxed. This was the fourth consecutive year in which the blue-striped cars were catalogued, and the third in which they were pulled by the red and silver Santa Fe units. The passenger cars and the 218T came in Orange Picture boxes while the powered unit came in a corrugated carton with tucked-in end flaps. Beware of broken and/or repaired struts on the Alco units as they are extremely fragile.   **400   650**

**12502   O27 Gauge Gift Pack
$35 Retail**

Contents: 1862 General with headlight; 1862T tender; 3376 giraffe car; 1877 flatcar with horses; 1866 mail/baggage car; and a 1865 passenger car.

Comments: Since this was a gift pack, it came with neither track nor transformer. It was packaged in a half-orange, half-white Type A display-style outfit box, and was the fourth and last of the O27 Gauge General sets. Sales of the General were slow. This set was catalogued solely to deplete existing inventory. This edition included the operating giraffe car which made it just a bit different from previous issues. From a collector's point of view, this is the most desirable of the 1862 General sets.   **600   1000**

**12512   O27 Gauge Gift Pack
$39.95 Retail**

Contents: 45 olive U.S.M.C. missile launcher; 3413 Mercury capsule carrier; 3619 reconnaissance copter car; 3470 aerial target launcher; 3349 turbo missile launcher; and a 6017 SP-type caboose.

Comments: This set came with unboxed contents in a half-orange, half-white Type A display-style outfit box titled "The Enforcer" and, along with the 1805 from 1960 and 11385 from 1963, is considered one of the more rare and most desirable of the space age outfits. The engine was a repeat, but all of the rolling stock were new issue for 1962 and came with operating couplers at both ends. The components were extremely fragile, and the balloons with the 3470, if not

An end view of "The Enforcer" gift pack outfit 12512. Refer to page 138 for a picture of the contents. M. Sokol Collection.

45 U.S.M.C. mobile missile launcher space set 12512 in a Type A display-style box. It was titled "The Enforcer" and was catalogued as a gift pack that included neither track nor transformer. It is one of the rarest of the military / space related outfits. Note the unique cardboard filler on the extreme right; it held the circular missiles for the 3349 and the dish for the 3470. The miscellaneous packets and paperwork were stored underneath the filler. A side view of the set box is shown on page 137. B. Myles Collection.

	VG	LN

missing, are usually fused together with age. Please refer to page 137 for a picture pertaining to this outfit.

1200   2000

13008   Super O Gauge $49.95 Retail

Contents: 637 steam locomotive with headlight, smoke, and Magnetraction; 736W Pennsylvania whistle tender; 3349 turbo missile launcher; 6448 exploding boxcar; 6501 flatcar with jet motorboat; 6119 red cab work caboose; twelve curved, one straight, and one half-straight track; and a 39-25 operating packet.

Comments: This set came in a conventional two-tier solid orange outfit box with component boxes. The engine came in a corrugated carton with tucked-in end flaps while the other components came in Orange Picture boxes. The 3349 and the 6501 were new issue, and this was one of only two sets to include the scarce jet motorboat car. A mint example of the 6501 must include a foil packet of baking soda.

300   500

	VG	LN

13018   Super O Gauge $49.95 Retail

Contents: 616 Santa Fe NW-2 switcher; 6500 black flatcar with red/white airplane; 6650 flatcar with IRBM launcher; 3519 satellite launching car; 6448 exploding boxcar; 6017-235 Santa Fe SP-type caboose; eight curved, one straight, and one half-straight track; and a 39-25 operating packet.

Comments: The collectable 616 was available in only two sets, and this was the only catalogued set to include the very scarce 6500. The airplane on the flatcar could have been either white-over-red or red-over-white, and this was the first time ever that a Super O outfit included a caboose, other than a work type, that was non-illuminated. The -235 Santa Fe caboose is also scarce and was common only to this set. The outfit box was the conventional solid orange two-tier type with component boxes. All items, even the Santa Fe switcher, came in Orange Picture boxes.

900   1500

VG LN

VG LN

13028 Super O Gauge $59.95 Retail

Contents: 2359 Boston and Maine GP-9; 3665 Minuteman car; 3349 turbo missile launcher; 3820 olive U.S.M.C. flatcar with operating submarine; 3470 aerial target launcher; 6017-100 Boston and Maine SP-type caboose; eight curved, one straight, and one half-straight track; 39-25 operating packet; and a 943 exploding ammo dump.

Comments: This was the second consecutive year in which the 2359 headed a space age set. The contents came component boxed in a conventional solid orange two-tier outfit box. The 3349 and 3470 were new-issue cars and the balloons with the 3470, if not missing, are usually fused together because of age. This olive 3820 is a scarce car, and it came in a 3830 box! Evidently Lionel still had excess inventory on the 3820 that was originally issued for the Land-Air-and-Sea gift pack in 1960, and decided to include it in this outfit. This set has also been known to contain a regular 3830 blue flatcar with operating submarine. This was the second Super O outfit to include a caboose, other than a work type, that was non-illuminated. The engine came in a corrugated carton with tucked-in end flaps while the other items came in Orange Picture boxes. **650 1100**

13036 Super O Gauge $59.95 Retail

Contents: 1872 General with headlight, smoke, and Magnetraction; 1872T tender; 6445 Ft. Knox car; 3370 sheriff and outlaw car; 1876 illuminated mail/baggage car; 1875W illuminated passenger car with whistle; twelve curved, one straight, and one half-straight track; and a 39-25 operating packet.

Comments: This was the fourth and last year in which the 1872 General was catalogued but was only the second set ever offered. The outfit box was the solid orange conventional two-tier type with all of the contents individually boxed. This is the most valuable of the catalogued General sets, due in part to the fact that it included the collectable 6445. Sales on the General were slow. Evidently Lionel assembled this outfit solely to deplete existing inventory as the perforated-front boxes that contained the engine, tender, and passenger cars date these items to 1960. The passenger cars were illuminated and came with arch bar trucks and self-centering operating couplers. The 1875 Pullman was not included with any of the General sets. It was available only as a separate-sale item, and is the scarcest of all the General items. **900 1500**

13048 Super O Gauge $75 Retail

Contents: 736 Berkshire steam locomotive with headlight, smoke, and Magnetraction; 736W Pennsylvania whistle tender; 6822 searchlight car; 6414 auto loader; 3362 helium tank unloading car; 6440 flatcar with vans; 6437 illuminated Pennsylvania porthole caboose; twelve curved, one straight, and one half-straight track; and a 39-25 operating packet.

Comments: This was another of the fifteen postwar 736 sets, but with above average rolling stock. The outfit box was a conventional two-tier solid orange type with component boxes. The engine came in a corrugated carton with tucked-in end flaps while the other contents came in Orange Picture boxes. The 6440 was catalogued in blue, but does not exist in that color as part of regular production. It was merely a less expensive version of the "old" 6430 that does not include a mounting rack for the vans. The 6414 auto loader came with four gray-bumpered yellow cars. **575 975**

13058 Super O Gauge $89.95 Retail

Contents: 2383P/2383T Santa Fe AA F-3 units; 3619 reconnaissance copter car; 3413 Mercury capsule launcher; 6512 cherry picker car; 470 missile launching platform with 6470 exploding boxcar; 6437 illuminated Pennsylvania porthole caboose; twelve curved, three straight, and one half-straight track; and a 39-25 operating packet.

Comments: The mighty Santa Fe headed another space age line of cars that was mainly recycled from the O27 line; at least the 470 missile launching platform made it interesting. The outfit box was the solid orange two-tier conventional type with component boxes. The Santa Fe units each came in a corrugated carton made by the Mead Company with tucked-in end flaps, while the rolling stock came in Orange Picture boxes. The 3619, 3413, and 6512 were new items and, as with most military and space age items, are all extremely fragile and collectable. The 470 missile launching platform was originally issued in 1959. It came in a corrugated carton with lift-up top and included a component-boxed 6470. Early issues of this accessory came in a yellow background box that was eventually replaced by one with an orange field. **1350 2250**

13068 Super O Gauge $100 Retail

Contents: 2360 Pennsylvania solid-stripe GG-1; 6464-725 orange New Haven boxcar; 6828 flatcar with Harnischfeger crane; 6416 boat transport; 6827 flatcar with Harnischfeger power shovel; 6530 fire prevention car; 6475 pickle vat car; 6437 illuminated Pennsylvania porthole caboose; twelve curved, five straight, and one half-straight track; and a 39-25 operating packet.

Comments: The engine was the painted gold-striped variation with even-height ventilators and heat-stamped lettering that was reintroduced in 1961. The outfit box was the standard 1962 issue with all of the components individually boxed. The engine came in a conventional corrugated carton made by the Mead Company with full wraparound liner, while the rolling stock came in Orange Picture boxes. At first glance, this set looks very similar to outfits 2575 and 13138 from 1961 and 1963 respectively. It included a -725 orange New Haven boxcar which was the last new issue in the 6464 series. The Harnischfeger crane and power shovel each came unassembled in its own white, black, and yellow thin cardboard box; the box was placed on top of the black flatcar and then repackaged in an oversized Orange Picture box. This outfit, as with all other GG-1 sets, is highly coveted by collectors. **1500 2500**

	VG	LN

1962

13078   Super O Gauge $125 Retail

Contents: 2360 Pennsylvania solid-stripe GG-1; 2521 President McKinley observation; two 2522 President Harrison Vista Domes; 2523 President Garfield Pullman; twelve curved, five straight, and one half-straight track; and a 39-35 operating packet. (Presidential series cars came with gold paper stripes.)

Comments: This outfit was listed but not illustrated in the 1962 consumer catalogue; however, it was illustrated in the Advance Catalogue. Projected sales on this set must have been very low. The outfit box was a plain tan conventional two-tier style. It is one of the rarest of postwar sets with the outfit box itself contributing greatly to its total value. Please refer to outfit 13088 for additional comments on the Presidential passenger cars.   **2500   4200**

13088   Super O Gauge $120 Retail

Contents: 2383P/2383T Santa Fe AA F-3 units; 2521 President McKinley observation; two 2522 President Harrison Vista Domes; 2523 President Garfield Pullman; twelve curved, five straight, and one half-straight track; and a 39-25 operating packet. (Presidential series cars came with gold paper stripes.)

Comments: The Presidential cars were developed to replace the discontinued red-striped 2560 series passenger cars. Even though they were new in 1962, they were not touted as such in the catalogue. The outfit box was a plain tan conventional two-tier style. The striping on the passenger cars was no longer the metal type originally introduced for the Congressional cars but was instead made of a gold-colored paper base. The Presidential cars were catalogued for five consecutive years in three different Santa Fe sets and came in four distinctly different box styles. The 1962 issues usually came in Orange Picture boxes that had been printed over perforated-front stock! Since these "raw" boxes were no doubt excess inventory dating from 1960, this is another prime example of exhausting old items — boxes in this case. The Santa Fe units each came in corrugated cartons with tucked-in end flaps that were made by the Mead Company. To collectors, this is the most desirable of the Santa Fe Presidential passenger sets.   **1600   3000**

1963

WALLOWING IN MIRE

1963 was another dismal product year and the overuse of suffixes makes analysis difficult; in today's market, however, it is an extremely desirable one. Most 1963 outfits are coveted by advanced collectors. This is the most collectable year of the decade. Some of the more important items that made their debut in 1963 were the 6407 flatcar with rocket, 6469 liquefied gas car, 6446 N & W cement car, 6446-60 red Lehigh Valley covered hopper, 6447 non-illuminated Pennsylvania porthole caboose, and the 6429 work caboose. The 6315 chemical tank car was reissued, but now it was unpainted and carried Lionel Lines markings instead of Gulf.

The only new engine of merit was the 617 Santa Fe diesel switcher, which was the more highly detailed replacement for the discontinued 616. This is ironic. Lionel's policy through the years had been to eliminate trim and shave costs. Here they did an about-face and upgraded an engine without increasing the $27.50 separate-sale price. Lionel showed further good business sense by cataloguing an equitable balance of traditional and space age outfits, avoiding the mixture of car types that was prevalent in previous years.

The Orange Picture box was still the norm for component-boxed rolling stock and passenger cars while the low and moderate O27 sets, those ending with a "1", continued to be packaged unboxed in Type A display-style outfit boxes, but with "almost new" graphics. This "almost new" design pictured a small Hudson and a Santa Fe F-3 on the lid. It was the same design that had been developed for the Advance Catalogue sets in 1961 and 1962 but the color was changed from deep red to an orange print. The better O27 sets, those ending with a "5", came in a tan conventional outfit box with a strange combination of both boxed and unboxed contents that had last been seen in 1957.

The Super O outfit box was still the solid orange type that first appeared in 1961, and all Super O components were individually boxed, hence the last digit "8" of the outfit number. Six Super O sets were offered, and all contained a half-section of straight track and the basic 39-25 operating packet. This was the last year that offered a selection in Super O.

Some very important changes took place in 1963 on the AAR trucks. The early version, which originated in 1957, was

1062 steam freight outfit 11311 in a Type A display-style box with cardboard dividers. This was one of only three catalogued sets to include rolling stock that did not have heat stamping. Although the red flatcar was unnumbered, it was catalogued as "6409" and came with fixed couplers and three pipes. M. Sokol Collection.

1
9
6
3

	VG	LN

still standard equipment, *but* the old-style knuckle was replaced by a self-contained Delrin knuckle which eliminated the need for a knuckle pin. Earliest examples had integral copper metal springs that were soon replaced by less expensive plastic springs. In an effort to further reduce costs, O27 rolling stock began to appear with the combination of one fixed and one operating coupler. There is also the distinct possibility that the late version of the AAR trucks, those with the axle ends visible when viewed from the bottom, may have surfaced late during the product year. The coupler and truck information mentioned above should not be taken lightly as it assists in properly dating items.

11311	O27 Gauge	$14.95 Retail

Contents: 1062 steam locomotive with headlight; 1061T unstamped slope-back tender; 6409-25 red flatcar with pipes; 6076-100 gray unstamped hopper; 6167 red unstamped SP-type caboose; eight curved track; and a 1026 25-watt transformer.

Comments: The 1062 was an upgrade from the 1060 and 1061 as it had a two-position E-unit and a headlight. This set came in a Type A display-style outfit box with the new 1963 graphics. The tender and rolling stock came with an odd assortment of trucks and couplers. The tender came unstamped with early AAR trucks and a fixed coupler on a tab frame.

The hopper came with arch bar trucks with fixed couplers while the caboose came with early AAR trucks and one fixed coupler. The full-sized red flatcar had only "Lionel" stamped on the sides. It came with early AAR trucks and two fixed couplers along with three pipes. These inexpensive starter sets are difficult to obtain in collector condition. Page 141 shows a picture of this outfit. **105 175**

11321	O27 Gauge	$16.95 Retail

Contents: 221 Denver & Rio Grande Alco A unit; 3309 turbo missile launcher; 6076-75 black Lehigh Valley hopper; 6042-75 blue gondola with cable reels; 6167-50 yellow unstamped SP-type caboose; eight curved and two straight track; and a 1026 25-watt transformer.

Comments: This set came with unboxed contents in the new 1963 Type A display-style outfit box. The rolling stock came with an odd assortment of trucks and couplers. The hopper and turbo missile launcher came with arch bar trucks with fixed couplers. The caboose also had arch bar trucks but included only one fixed coupler, while the gondola came with fixed coupler, early AAR trucks. The 3309 was unstamped, as was its 3349 counterpart, and the description of these two cars has often been confusing. The 3349 always came with operating couplers at both ends with either early or late AAR trucks, and included a missile rack. The 3309 came with a combina-

237 steam freight outfit 11351 in a Type A display-style box with cardboard dividers. The red flatcar, although unnumbered, was catalogued as 6408 and came with one operating and one fixed coupler and five pipes. Notice the folded packet of blue smoke cartridges in the upper left corner and the placement of the transformer cord.

VG LN

tion of either two fixed couplers or one fixed and one operating coupler, and usually included a missile rack. Because it was a frequent component of uncatalogued sets, the 3309 also surfaces with arch bar trucks with fixed couplers as it did in this outfit. Low-end diesel outfits stir collector interest far more than their steam counterparts. Please see page 133 for further details. **175 300**

11331   O27 Gauge $19.95 Retail

Contents: 242 steam locomotive with headlight; 1060T streamlined tender; 6473 rodeo car; 6476-25 Lehigh Valley hopper; 6142 gondola with two canisters; 6059 M St. L SP-type caboose; eight curved and one straight track; 6139 uncoupling section; and a 1010 35-watt transformer.

Comments: This set came with unboxed contents in the new 1963 Type A display-style outfit box. The "-25" suffix applied to the hopper indicated that it had fixed couplers while the other rolling stock usually came with early AAR trucks and had one fixed and one operating coupler. The 1060T number assigned to the tender implied that it had arch bar trucks which were usually reserved for Advance and uncatalogued sets. Low-end steam sets, unless absolutely mint, are of limited interest to experienced collectors. **105 175**

11341   O27 Gauge $25 Retail

Contents: 634 Santa Fe NW-2 switcher; 3410 flatcar with manual release helicopter; 6407 flatcar with rocket; 6014-335 white Frisco savings bank car; 6463 rocket fuel tank car; 6059 M St. L SP-type caboose; eight curved and one straight track; 6139 uncoupling section; and a 1010 35-watt transformer.

Comments: This set came with unboxed contents in the Type A display-style outfit box with the new 1963 graphics. The rolling stock usually came with early AAR trucks and had one fixed and one operating coupler. This set is very desirable as it is only one of two to contain the rare 6407. The remainder of the rolling stock are all collectable pieces with the coin-slot Frisco boxcar often being overlooked. The 634 was a new number for the Santa Fe switcher and it now included a fixed front coupler. Occasionally an Orange Picture box surfaces for the 6407. The box is more rare than the car, which was boxed only when available for separate sale. **725 1200**

11351   O27 Gauge $29.95 Retail

Contents: 237 steam locomotive with headlight and smoke; 1060T streamlined tender; 6050-110 red Swift savings bank car; 6465-150 orange Lionel Lines two-dome tank; 6408 red flatcar with pipes; 6162 blue gondola with three canisters; 6119-100 red cab work caboose; eight curved and one straight track; 6139 uncoupling section; and a 1025 45-watt transformer.

Comments: This set came with unboxed contents in the 1963 Type A display-style outfit box, and surfaces with a variety of operating and fixed coupler combinations. The 237 engine is one of the few Scout types that included a smoke unit.

VG LN

The 6408, with AAR trucks and only "Lionel" stamped on the sides, came with five pipes and had one operating and one fixed coupler, as opposed to two fixed couplers and three pipes on the 6409 from outfit 11311. The 1060T number assigned to the tender implied that it had arch bar trucks, which were usually reserved for Advance and uncatalogued sets. The 6050 Swift boxcar came with a coin slot on top, hence the phrase "savings bank car". Page 142 shows a picture of this outfit. **120 200**

11361   O27 Gauge $35 Retail

Contents: 211P/211T Texas Special Alco AA units; 3665 Minuteman car; 3413 Mercury capsule launcher; 6470 exploding boxcar; 6413 Mercury capsule carrier; 6257-100 red SP-type caboose with stack; eight curved and three straight track; 6139 uncoupling section; and a 1025 45-watt transformer.

Comments: This set came with unboxed contents in the new 1963 Type A display-style outfit box. It is a scarce set, and as with all space-related items, the components are exceptionally fragile. The rolling stock usually came with early AAR trucks and one fixed and one operating coupler. The 1962 edition of the 211 Texas Special did not have Magnetraction. Beware of broken and/or repaired struts on the Alco units as they are exceptionally fragile. The red unpainted 6257-100 caboose included a smokestack, and although it is a scarce item, it has not yet aroused much collector interest. **600 1000**

11375   O27 Gauge $39.95 Retail

Contents: 238 steam locomotive with headlight and smoke; 234W Lionel Lines whistle tender; 6822-50 searchlight car; 6465-150 orange two-dome tank car; 6414-150 auto loader; 6476-75 black or red Lehigh Valley hopper; 6162 blue gondola with three canisters; 6257-100 red SP-type caboose with stack; eight curved and three straight; 6139 uncoupling section; 1073 60-watt transformer; and a 147 whistle controller.

Comments: The outfit box was a tan conventional two-tier type with a combination of both boxed and unboxed contents separated by boxed items and cardboard dividers. The engine, tender, caboose, hopper, and tank car were generally unboxed. The rolling stock usually came with early AAR trucks and a combination of one fixed and one operating coupler, while the 234W tender came with only a fixed coupler. The red unpainted 6257-100 caboose included a smokestack, and although it is a scarce item, it has not generated much collector interest to date. This was the only O27 set headed by a Scout-type engine to ever contain a 6414 auto loader, and it was this scarce auto loader that had vehicles without bumpers, wheels, or windshields. These autos came in only two colors — red and yellow. **525 800**

11385   O27 Gauge $49.95 Retail

Contents: 223P and 218C Santa Fe Alco AB units; 3619-100 reconnaissance copter car; 3470-100 aerial target launcher; 3349-100 turbo missile launcher; 3830-75 flatcar

The contents of 223 Santa Fe Alco outfit 11385. This is the premier space age set. It came in a conventional two-tier outfit box with an unusual combination of both boxed and unboxed contents. Rare and scarce items included in this set were the 6407 flatcar with rocket, the light blue variation of the 3470 aerial target launcher, and the dark yellow variation of the 3619 reconnaissance copter car. Sets packaged in this manner are a nightmare to repack. Note all the miscellaneous items included with a set; in this instance a 147 horn/whistle controller was included because the 1073 transformer lacked a horn/whistle control button. M. Sokol Collection.

	VG	LN

with operating submarine; 6407 flatcar with rocket; 6257-100 red SP-type caboose with stack; eight curved and three straight track; 6139 uncoupling section; 1073 60-watt transformer; and a 147 horn controller.

Comments: This is the premier space age set. The outfit box was a tan conventional two-tier type, and the rolling stock, except for the 3349, came with a combination of one fixed and one operating coupler. The 3830 and the 3349 were the only components that were individually boxed. This set has also been known to contain a component-boxed red 6017-235 Santa Fe SP-type caboose, and does have three extremely desirable items: the scarce dark yellow variation of the 3619, the also scarce light blue variation of the 3470, and the 6407 which is the rarest of all the space age cars. Interestingly, a 6407 box is even more rare than the car itself as it appeared only when the 6407 was available for separate sale. Beware of a broken and/or repaired strut on the fragile Alco unit, and also note that the balloons that came with the aerial target launcher are, if not lost, usually fused together because of age.

1500   2500

	VG	LN

11395   O27 Gauge $59.95 Retail

Contents: 2037 steam locomotive with headlight, smoke, and Magnetraction; 233W Lionel Lines whistle tender; 6464-725 orange New Haven boxcar; 6469 liquefied gas car; 6536 M St. L quad hopper; 6440 flatcar with vans; 6560 red cab crane; 6119-100 red cab work caboose; eight curved and three straight track; 6029 uncoupling section; 1073 60-watt transformer; and a 147 whistle controller.

Comments: This set offered another unusual combination of both boxed and unboxed components in a tan two-tier conventional type outfit box. All of the rolling stock had early AAR trucks, with the New Haven boxcar, M St. L hopper, and the crane equipped with operating couplers at both ends. The 6440 and the 6469 usually came with one fixed and one operating coupler. The -725, 6469, and 6536 were the unboxed components. The new liquefied gas car is both scarce and collectable. It came with a component box in outfit 13098, and as a separate-sale item as well. The M St. L hopper was "old" inventory, last catalogued in 1959, that Lionel was trying to deplete.

550   900

	VG	LN

11405   **O27 Gauge**   **$69.95 Retail**

Contents: 218P/218T Santa Fe Alco AA units; two 2412 Vista Domes, 2414 Pullman, and 2416 observation with blue-striped Santa Fe markings; eight curved and three straight track; 6029 uncoupling section; 1073 60-watt transformer; and a 147 horn controller.

Comments: This was the fifth and last year in which the blue-striped cars would be catalogued. The outfit box was a conventional tan two-tier type. The four passenger cars usually came in Orange Picture boxes while the 218 Santa Fe Alcos were left unboxed at the bottom of the outfit box, separated by a cardboard divider and held in place by another piece of folded cardboard. Beware of broken and/or repaired struts on the fragile Alco units.   **400**   **650**

11415 Advance Catalogue   **O27 Gauge**   **No Retail**

1 9 6 3

Contents: 1061 steam locomotive; 1061T unstamped slope-back tender; 6502 unstamped blue flatcar with girder; 6167 yellow or red unstamped SP-type caboose; eight curved and two straight track; and a 1026 25-watt transformer.

Comments: This was the last of the special low-end sets to appear in the Advance Catalogue and, ironically, its outfit number followed the normal sequence of numbers! The outfit box itself was a miniature version of the tan conventional two-tier type. Most shoe boxes are larger that this outfit box. The entire outfit was fitted with arch bar trucks with fixed couplers, and the unboxed contents were held in place by cardboard dividers. Several cost-saving measures were taken with the 1061T tender. It came unstamped with arch bar trucks on a tab frame that eliminated the need for a screw to fasten the cab to the chassis. These inexpensive Advance Catalogue sets are difficult to obtain in collector condition.

Outfit 11415 was the last of the Advance catalogue sets. Contrary to packaging norms, it came in a miniature version of a conventional two-tier outfit box. Pay particular attention to the paperwork and other miscellaneous items that always accompanied Lionel sets. Of particular interest in the top center is a form dated "6-63" that encouraged expansion of the consumer's Lionel layout by purchasing additional track. M. Sokol Collection.

	VG	LN

They are far more collectable than most of the consumer catalogue starter outfits. See page 145 for a picture of this set.

	105	175

13098   Super O Gauge $49.95 Retail

Contents: 637 steam locomotive with headlight, smoke, and Magnetraction; 736W Pennsylvania whistle tender; 6469 liquefied gas car; 6464-900 NYC boxcar; 6414 auto loader; 6446 N & W covered hopper; 6447 non-illuminated Pennsylvania porthole caboose; twelve curved, one straight, and one half-straight track; and a 39-25 operating packet.

Comments: The outfit box was a solid orange two-tier conventional type with all of the component pieces individually boxed. The engine came in a corrugated carton with tucked-in end flaps, while the tender and rolling stock came in Orange Picture boxes with early AAR trucks and operating couplers. This was the only set to contain the very scarce, non-illuminated 6447 porthole caboose and the reissue of the 6446 N & W cement car. The 6469 is also a collectable piece and even more so when component boxed. The NYC boxcar often came with solid black doors, but since the doors can easily be changed, a premium should not be paid for a car with black doors. The 6414 auto loader came with the scarce gray-bumpered yellow autos, but has also been reported to contain four rare green vehicles. This is a scarce set that contained five very desirable items.   **1200   2000**

13108   Super O Gauge $49.95 Retail

Contents: 617 Santa Fe NW-2 switcher; 3665 Minuteman car; 3419 flatcar with operating helicopter; 6448 exploding boxcar; 3830 flatcar with operating submarine; 3470 aerial target launcher; 6119-100 red cab work caboose; twelve curved, one straight, and one half-straight track; and a 39-25 operating packet.

Comments: This is an extremely scarce space age outfit. The set box was the solid orange two-tier conventional type and all of the components were individually boxed. The roster of cars was very similar to what was offered in other sets, but this was the only outfit to contain the 617 switcher. The 617 was the replacement, with operating couplers and additional details, for the discontinued 616. It came in an Orange Picture box, as did the other components, and included two small cardboard inserts that held the engine in place. The rolling stock came with early AAR trucks and usually had operating couplers at both ends.   **725   1200**

13118   Super O Gauge $75 Retail

Contents: 736 Berkshire steam locomotive with headlight, smoke, and Magnetraction; 736W Pennsylvania whistle tender; 6446-60 covered Lehigh Valley hopper; 6827 flatcar with Harnischfeger power shovel; 3362 helium tank unloading car; 6315 Lionel Lines chemical tank car; 6560 red cab crane; 6429 die-cast work caboose; twelve curved, one straight, and one half-straight track; and a 39-25 operating packet.

Comments: The outfit box was standard 1963 issue and all of the components were individually boxed. The engine came in a corrugated carton with tucked-in end flaps while the balance of the items came in Orange Picture boxes. This was one of the best Berkshire sets of the postwar era as it contained the scarce 6446-60 and the even more scarce 6429, which were common only to this set. The 6446-60 was a red Lehigh Valley quad hopper with "6436" stamped on the side; it was given a cover and then transformed into a cement car, hence the 6446 catalogue number. The Harnischfeger power shovel came unassembled in its own white, black, and yellow thin cardboard box; it was placed on top of the black flatcar and then repackaged in an oversized box. The 6429 was a reissue of the die-cast 6419 that was last catalogued in 1958, but with AAR trucks riveted to a screw-on plate. This set also contained the unpainted light orange reissue of the chemical tank car, but with Lionel Lines markings in lieu of Gulf. Be aware of a switched cover on the hopper since, because of their design, any quad hopper can accept a cover from another piece. The correct hopper for this set has "New 3-55" stamped on the sides and must have come in a box numbered "6446-60".   **900   1500**

13128   Super O Gauge $89.95 Retail

Contents: 2383P/2383T Santa Fe AA F-3 units; 3619 reconnaissance copter car; 3413 Mercury capsule launcher; 6512 cherry picker car; 448 missile firing range set with 6448 exploding boxcar; 6437 illuminated Pennsylvania porthole caboose; twelve curved, three straight, and one half-straight track; and a 39-25 operating packet.

Comments: This outfit came in the solid orange two-tier conventional type box with all of the contents individually boxed. It was a virtual repeat of outfit 13058 from 1962 with the 448 and 6448 replacing the 470 and 6470, but as with other space-related items, is both extremely fragile and highly desirable. The Santa Fe units each came in a corrugated carton made by the Mead Company with tucked-in end flaps while the rolling stock came in Orange Picture boxes. The 6448 was component boxed inside the oversized 448 box.   **1350   2250**

13138   Super O Gauge $100 Retail

Contents: 2360 Pennsylvania solid-stripe GG-1; 6464-725 orange New Haven boxcar; 6828 flatcar with Harnischfeger crane; 6416 boat transport; 6827 flatcar with Harnischfeger power shovel; 6315 Lionel Lines chemical tank car; 6436-110 Lehigh Valley quad hopper; 6437 illuminated Pennsylvania porthole caboose; twelve curved, five straight, and one half-straight track; and a 39-25 operating packet.

Comments: The engine was the final variation of the GG-1 with a painted gold stripe, and decaled letters and numbers. The outfit box was the standard 1963 solid orange-type with all of the components individually boxed. The engine came in a conventional corrugated carton made by the Mead Company with full wraparound liner, while the rolling stock came in Orange Picture boxes. This outfit was almost a twin to 13068 from 1962, with only the new 6315 chemical tank car and the quad hopper being different. The 6416 boat loader is a desirable item as are the Harnishfeger pieces. The crane and the power shovel each came unassembled in their own white, black, and yellow thin cardboard boxes; they were placed on top of the black flatcars and then repackaged in oversized boxes. Only the basic 39-25 operating packet was included with this outfit; evidently Lionel did not care if the coil couplers that came with the GG-1 were operational. This outfit, as with all other GG-1 sets, is highly coveted by collectors.   **1450   2400**

13148   Super O Gauge $120 Retail

Contents: 2383P/2383T Santa Fe AA F-3 units; 2521 President McKinley observation; 2522 President Harrison Vista Dome; two 2523 President Garfield Pullmans; twelve curved, five straight, and one half-straight track; and a 39-25

	VG	LN
operating packet. (Presidential series cars came with gold paper stripes.)

Comments: The outfit box was a plain tan conventional type that had two tiers, with all of the components individually boxed. It was nearly identical to outfit 13088 from 1962, except that a Pullman replaced a Vista Dome. The Santa Fe along with Presidential cars would continue to be catalogued for the next three years but as outfit 12780 with O Gauge track. The Santa Fe units each came in a corrugated carton made by the Mead Company with tucked-in end flaps, while the passenger cars came in Orange Picture boxes. This was the last of Super O, except for the 13150 Hudson set that appeared in 1964.   **1600   3000**

1964

THE ABYSS

New is not a word that can casually be used to describe Lionel production in 1964. The 213 M St. L was a new road name in the Alco series, and the 212 Santa Fe was a version of the discontinued 218 that showed even further efforts at cost reduction. The blue-striped Santa Fe passenger cars were discontinued in favor of the rather Spartan 2404, 2405, and 2406 Santa Fe cars that included neither illumination nor window strips.

The 1963 artwork on the display-style outfit box was retained for the 1964 O27 line, but the box itself was changed to a lift-off top that will be called *Type D* in this text. None of the components in any of the O27 sets were individually boxed.

1964 saw the reintroduction of O Gauge after a six-year absence, and a total of nine sets were catalogued. By switching the 2383 and the 736, and by adding or deleting an LW transformer, Lionel was able to catalogue eight outfits from what was essentially only two. (Please refer to pages 6 and 7 of the consumer catalogue.) It is the consensus of several knowledgeable collectors that of these eight outfits, only four

are actually known to exist, and that they came in 1965-style outfit boxes. Sets that were actually released in 1964 can be accurately dated because they contain only Orange Picture component boxes rather than Hillside Orange Picture, and the outfit box itself is marked with a "64" above the box manufacturer's seal on the bottom of the box. They are outfits 12700, 12710, 12720, and 12730. (The existence of outfits 12740, 12750, 12760, and 12770 has never been authenticated.) In addition, the rolling stock catalogued with outfits 12740, 12750, 12760, and 12770 was the same, except for the 6464-525, as what was offered in the 12820 Virginian set from 1965.

The reissue of the 773 Hudson in outfit 13150 was the last and only Super O outfit catalogued for 1964 and for the next two years.

Orange Picture boxes were still the norm for component-boxed rolling stock and passenger cars. 1964 saw the introduction of the late AAR trucks with a self-contained Delrin knuckle and axle ends that are visible when viewed from the

1062 steam freight set 11430 in a Type D display-style box with cardboard dividers. This was one of only three catalogued sets that did not have heat stamping on the rolling stock and caboose. Unstamped rolling stock has become very collectable in recent years. B. Myles Collection.

221 Rio Grande Alco outfit 11440 in a Type D display-style box. 1964 was the introductory year for the lift-off top box. This set was very similar to outfit 11321 from 1963 but included rolling stock with one fixed and one operating coupler and a 6149 uncoupling section. B. Myles Collection.

	VG	LN		VG	LN

bottom. Please pay particular attention to truck and coupler changes as they are important in properly dating items. Sales on space age cars were definitely slow — they were catalogued en masse on page 11 of the consumer catalogue solely to deplete inventory. Many space age cars were available over-the-counter at Madison Hardware until the time of the store's sale to Richard Kughn.

the new 1964 Type D-style with lift-off top, or a miniature version of a tan conventional two-tier type. **90   105**

11420   O27 Gauge $11.95 Retail

Contents: 1061 steam locomotive; 1061T slope-back tender; 6042-250 unstamped gondola; 6167-25 unstamped SP-type caboose; eight curved track; and a 1026 25-watt transformer.

Comments: This outfit was probably intended to be an Advance Catalogue set, but it could not be shown because there was no 1964 Advance Catalogue! The contents are nearly the same as those in Advance Catalogue set 11415 from 1963. This set had the dubious distinction of being the lowest-priced postwar outfit ever offered in the consumer catalogue. The tender came on a tab frame with Lionel Lines markings. The gondola and the caboose were unpainted and unstamped, and usually had arch bar trucks with fixed couplers. Note that the gondola, even though unstamped, is referred to as a 6042, which in prior years was stamped "6042"; also pay particular attention to the suffixes attached to the 6167 caboose in this outfit and in the next two outfits as well, because they do tell a specific story. The outfit box was either

11430   O27 Gauge $14.95 Retail

Contents: 1062 steam locomotive with headlight; 1061T slope-back tender; 6176 yellow unstamped hopper; 6142 green unstamped gondola; 6167-125 red unstamped SP-type caboose; eight curved and one straight track; 6149 uncoupling section; and a 1026 25-watt transformer.

Comments: The rolling stock was unpainted, unstamped, and unexciting. It came with late AAR trucks, and had one operating and one fixed coupler while the caboose had an operating coupler. The outfit box was the Type D style that was new in 1964. The tender had no ground contact and Lionel found it appropriate to include the following note:

"The Locomotive-Tender combination in this outfit is not recommended in layouts where switches or crossings will be used. The reversing mechanism of the locomotive will not operate satisfactorily over switches and crossings. Should you desire to add a crossing or switches to your layout the above condition could be corrected by replacing the front truck of the Tender with a special electrically ground truck. This can be done at any Lionel Service Station. An alternative to replacing the truck is to purchase Tender No. 242T or No. 1062T."

Page 148 shows a picture of the components of this set. **120   200**

	VG	LN		VG	LN

11440   O27 Gauge $17.95 Retail

Contents: 221 Rio Grande Alco A unit; 3309 turbo missile launcher; 6176-50 black Lehigh Valley hopper; 6142-125 blue gondola; 6167-100 red SP-type caboose; eight curved and one straight track; 6149 uncoupling section; and a 1026 25-watt transformer.

Comments: This set was nearly identical to outfit 11321 that was offered in 1963, but the contents in 11440 had late AAR trucks with one operating and one fixed coupler. The outfit box was the new Type D display style. The -100 version of the 6167 caboose had the number heat stamped on the sides. This differentiated it from the 6167-25 and 6167-125 that were included in the previous two outfits. The descriptions of 3309 and 3349 have often been confusing. The 3349 always came with operating couplers at both ends with either early or late AAR trucks and included a missile rack, while the 3309 came with either two fixed couplers, or one fixed and one operating coupler, and usually included a missile rack. The 3309 also surfaces with arch bar trucks with fixed couplers, as it was a frequent component of uncatalogued sets, and it was this example that usually did not include a missile rack. A low-end diesel outfit such as this is far more collectable than a comparable steam set. Please see page 149 for a picture of this outfit.   **175**   **300**

11450   O27 Gauge $19.95 Retail

Contents: 242 steam locomotive with headlight; 1060T streamlined tender; 6473 rodeo car; 6142-75 green gondola with two canisters; 6176-50 black Lehigh Valley hopper; 6059 M St. L SP-type caboose; eight curved and one straight track; 6149 uncoupling section; and a 1010 35-watt transformer.

Comments: This outfit box came in the 1964 Type D display-style box. The components came with late AAR trucks and had one operating and one fixed coupler, while the gondola with a "-75" suffix included two canisters that had not been added to the -125 in the previous set. The 1060T number given to the tender implied that it came with arch bar trucks, as it was usually an Advance or uncatalogued set component. Low-end steam outfits, unless absolutely mint, are of limited interest to experienced collectors.   **90**   **150**

11460   O27 Gauge $34.95 Retail

Contents: 238 steam locomotive with smoke and headlight; 234W Lionel Lines whistle tender; 6014-335 Frisco boxcar; 6465-150 orange Lionel Lines two-dome tank car; 6142-100 blue gondola with two canisters; 6176-75 yellow Lehigh Valley hopper; 6119-100 red cab work caboose; eight curved and one straight track; 6149 uncoupling section; 1073 60-watt transformer; and a 147 whistle controller.

213 M St. L freight outfit 11480 in a Type D display-style box. Note the 90° crossing that was included with this set, which allowed for a basic Figure 8 track plan. 1964 was the introductory year for the Type D lift-off top box. M. Sokol Collection.

VG   LN

Comments: The outfit box was the standard Type D style. The 238 engine is one of the few Scout types that included a smoke unit. The components came with late AAR trucks and had one fixed and one operating coupler. The suffixes on the hopper and the gondola probably denote a color change as these same two cars were included in outfit 11450. The white Frisco boxcar was usually the scarce variation with a coin slot.   135   225

11470   O27 Gauge $29.95 Retail

Comments: The contents are the same as those in outfit 11460 except that the locomotive and tender are a 237 and 1060T. The 1073 was replaced by a 1025 45-watt transformer, and the 147 whistle controller was deleted. The 1060T number assigned to the streamlined tender implied that it came with arch bar trucks.   105   175

11480   O27 Gauge $34.95 Retail

Contents: 213P/213T M St. L Alco AA units; 6473 rodeo car; 6176-50 black Lehigh Valley hopper; 6142-150 blue or green gondola with cable reels; 6014-335 white Frisco boxcar; 6257-100 red SP-type caboose with stack; twelve curved and three straight track; 6149 uncoupling section; 90° crossover; and a 1025 45-watt transformer.

Comments: The outfit box was the new Type D display style. The track included with this outfit allowed for a basic Figure 8 plan. The components came with late AAR trucks and had one fixed and one operating coupler. There are two interesting features about this set: the -150 gondola had two cable reels instead of the usual canisters, and the -100 is a red unpainted Lionel Lines caboose with a stack. The caboose is a scarce item but has not aroused much collector interest. The 213 is one of the more scarce Alco pairs. Beware of cracked and/or repaired struts on the M St. L units as they are quite susceptible to damage. Diesel sets with common rolling stock are far more collectable than their steam counterparts. Page 150 shows a picture of this outfit.   360   600

11490   O27 Gauge $49.95 Retail

Contents: 212P/212T Santa Fe Alco AA units; 2404 Vista Dome, 2405 Pullman, and 2406 observation with Santa Fe markings in blue letters; eight curved and three straight track; 6149 uncoupling section; 1073 60-watt transformer; and a 147 horn controller.

Comments: The outfit box was the standard 1964 Type D display style. The 212 Santa Fe units were a less expensive version of the discontinued 218, Magnetraction was eliminated, and the 212 now had only a two-position E-unit. Beware of broken and/or repaired struts on the fragile Alco units.

The most interesting aspect of this set is that the passenger cars had neither illumination nor window strips. [This lack of features influenced the author's decision to subtitle 1964 "The Abyss".] Unfortunately, quality and scarcity do not always go hand-in-hand, and do not do so here. This set was

catalogued for two consecutive years, but is more collectable from a collector viewpoint than the upgraded outfit 11590 from 1966.   450   750

11500   O27 Gauge $44.95 Retail

Contents: 2029 steam locomotive with headlight and smoke; 234W Lionel Lines whistle tender; 6465-150 orange Lionel Lines two-dome tank car; 6402-50 gray General-type flatcar with cable reels; 6176-75 yellow Lehigh Valley hopper; 6014-335 white Frisco boxcar; 6257-100 red SP-type caboose with stack; eight curved and three straight track; 6149 uncoupling section; 1073 60-watt transformer; and a 147 whistle controller.

Comments: This set came in the standard 1964 Type D outfit box. The components came with late AAR trucks and had one fixed and one operating coupler. The best feature of the set is that it contained the red unpainted -100 caboose with stack. The caboose is a scarce item but has not aroused much collector interest.

The 6402 General-type flatcar was a separate-sale item that was listed but not illustrated on page 13 of the 1964 consumer catalogue. (The existence of a 6402 box is not confirmed.) This car was also listed as "6401" on page 14 of the 1965 consumer catalogue. It came without any load in a greatly down-sized Orange Picture box, and sold for $2.50. The 6401 box is scarce; its value far exceeds that of the item it contained.   165   275

11510   O27 Gauge $39.95 Retail

Comments: The components were the same as those in outfit 11500, except that a 1060T streamlined tender replaced the 234W, the 1073 was replaced by a 1025 45-watt transformer, and the 147 whistle controller was deleted. The 1060T number assigned to the tender indicated that it came with arch bar trucks.   135   225

12700   O Gauge $59.95 Retail

Contents: 736 Berkshire steam locomotive with headlight, smoke, and Magnetraction; 736W Pennsylvania whistle tender; 6464-725 orange New Haven boxcar; 6162 blue gondola with three canisters; 6414 auto loader; 6476 yellow Lehigh Valley hopper; 6437 illuminated Pennsylvania porthole caboose; eight curved and five straight track; and a UCS uncoupling/operating section.

Comments: The outfit box was a two-tier flat white conventional type with orange lettering. The engine came packed in a corrugated carton with tucked-in end flaps while the balance of the components came in Orange Picture boxes. The tender and rolling stock were all equipped with operating couplers and late AAR trucks. The only item of interest in the set is the auto loader which usually came with gray-bumpered red autos, but it may surface with the scarce but cheapened red and yellow autos that did not have wheels, bumpers, or a windshield. It is extremely difficult to obtain set 12700 with

	VG	LN

**1
9
6
4**

the outfit box. It has considerably more collector value that the companion set 12710, which included an LW transformer.

550   900

12710   O Gauge $75 Retail

Comments: The components in this outfit were the same as those included with 12700, but this set also contained an LW transformer as part of a special offer. The outfit box was the same style with orange lettering, but had dimensions completely different from 12700 in order to accommodate the component-boxed LW transformer.   **475   800**

12720   O Gauge $65 Retail

Contents: The rolling stock and caboose were the same as those included with outfit 12700 except that the 736 Berkshire and 736W tender were replaced by the 2383P and 2383T Santa Fe AA F-3 units.

Comments: The outfit box was a two-tier flat white conventional style with orange lettering. Each Santa Fe unit came in a corrugated carton made by the Mead Company with tucked-in end flaps. It is extremely difficult to obtain this set with the outfit box. It has considerably more collector value than the companion set 12730, which included an LW transformer.   **900   1500**

12730   O Gauge $79.95 Retail

Comments: The components in this outfit were the same as those included in 12720, but this set also contained an LW transformer as part of a special offer. The outfit box was the same style with orange lettering, but had dimensions completely different from the 12720 in order to accommodate the component-boxed LW transformer.   **800   1400**

12740   Existence questionable

(See introduction to chapter.)

12750   Existence questionable

(See introduction to chapter.)

12760   Existence questionable

(See introduction to chapter.)

12770   Existence questionable

(See introduction to chapter.)

	VG	LN

12780   O Gauge $120 Retail

Contents: 2383P/2383T Santa Fe AA F-3 units; 2521 President McKinley observation; 2522 President Harrison Vista Dome; two 2523 President Garfield Pullmans; eight curved and five straight track; and a UCS uncoupling/operating section. (Presidential series cars came with gold paper stripes.)

Comments: This outfit was the continuation of the Presidential series begun in 1962. For 1964 it was catalogued as O Gauge and would continue as such through 1966. How many O Gauge outfits were actually shipped in 1964 is an open question. Early editions of this set came in a plain tan conventional two-tier outfit box with "12780" rubber stamped on one end. Each Santa Fe unit came in a corrugated carton, made by the Mead Company, with tucked-in end flaps, while the passenger cars still came in Orange Picture boxes with the New York, Chicago logo. This is an important point because there were box changes made in both 1965 and 1966.

1300   2600

An end view of the O Gauge set box for the very earliest edition of the 2383 Santa Fe Presidential passenger outfit 12780. Subsequent issues came in the more common solid white outfit box with orange lettering. M. Sokol Collection.

13150   Super O Gauge $200 Retail

Contents: 773 Hudson steam locomotive with headlight, smoke, and Magnetraction; 736W Pennsylvania or 773W New York Central whistle tender; 3434 chicken sweeper car; 6361 timber transport; 3662 operating milk car; 6415 Sunoco three-dome tank car; 3356 operating horse car; 6436-110 Lehigh Valley quad hopper; 6437 illuminated Pennsylvania porthole caboose; sixteen curved, nineteen straight, and four half-straight track; 112 pair remote-control switches; two 39-25 operating packets; and a 275-watt ZW transformer.

Comments: This was the last Super O set to be offered by Lionel. The outfit box was a plain tan corrugated style that approximated the size of a footlocker. Even though the 1964 Hudson is quite common, this set can be considered truly rare because few exist today with the required outfit box. This set could have come with either the 736W or 773W tender, with the 773W New York Central being the more desirable. Earliest versions of this set have even been known to contain a 3366 circus car that was last catalogued in 1961. The operating circus car came with metal trucks in an over-stickered 3356 box, and was included only to deplete remaining inventory. The tender and rolling stock all came with operating couplers and late AAR trucks in Orange Picture boxes, while the engine came in a red-lettered corrugated carton that was dated "1964" and included a full wraparound liner.

This set was also catalogued in 1965 and 1966, but actual production or packaging during those years cannot be confirmed. Examples that have been observed contain component boxes that can be dated to 1964. Subsequent cataloguing of this outfit was probably done solely to deplete existing inventory. For comparison, the $200 price tag on this outfit was only five cents higher than what the 4110WS Electronic Set sold for in 1949! This outfit exemplifies the old adage, "Timing is everything." Since consumer interest was waning, Lionel clearly introduced the right item at the wrong time.

	VG	LN
With 736W tender	1800	3000
With 773W tender	1900	3150

1964

1965

A GRASP AT RESPECTABILITY

The O27 offerings in 1965 were slightly revamped with two repeats and five new additions, while the O Gauge roster was a watered-down version of 1964 and included only two new outfits. The Boston and Maine GP-9 and the Virginian F-M were reissued and appeared as 2346 and 2322 respectively. The Super O 773 Hudson set was catalogued again only to help move existing inventory. Sales on the Hudson were slow; a comparatively high $225 price tag and declining consumer interest were no doubt contributing factors.

Although the year was largely uneventful in terms of new production, there were some very interesting box changes. The old Lionel Corporation received a new name — it became

Outfit 11530 with a 634 Santa Fe diesel switcher freight set in the 1965 Type D display-style box with lift-off top. Transformer cords usually presented a packaging problem. Notice here how Lionel positioned the cable reels so that the transformer cord could be placed on top of the gray General-type flatcar. B. Myles Collection.

"The Lionel Toy Corporation". The new name could be seen on the Orange Picture boxes which also showed the change from "New York" and "Chicago" to "Hillside, N.J." The Hillside Orange Picture boxes are dated only to 1965.

The artwork on the Type D lift-off top display boxes was completely new. It now pictured a 2037 steam engine pulling a line of freight cars. It was used for the entire O27 line and for O Gauge outfit 12800. The other O Gauge outfit box was a solid flat white conventional style with orange lettering.

The inclusion of billboards in 1965 outfits was not consistent. Some O27 Gauge outfits that came in Type D display-style boxes contained a 1961 five-strip sheet of billboards, yet O Gauge outfits had none. This practice can best be explained by an old adage: "Out of sight, out of mind." Billboards were readily visible when the top of an O27 set was removed, but could not be seen in the sealed O Gauge outfit boxes. See **Billboards** for further explanation.

	VG	LN

11490   O27 Gauge $55 Retail

Comments: This was a repeat or probable carry-over of unsold 1964 outfits with the price increased from $49.95. This set also exists in an outfit box with the new 1965 graphics. Please refer to **1964** for more information.   450   750

	VG	LN

11500   O27 Gauge $50 Retail

Comments: This was a near repeat from 1964 with the price increased from $44.95. The 6257-100 caboose was replaced by an unpainted red or brown 6059 M St. L. Please refer to **1964** for more information.   165   275

11520   O27 Gauge $20 Retail

Contents: 242 steam locomotive with headlight; 1062T slope-back tender; 6176 black or yellow Lehigh Valley hopper; 3364 operating log car; 6142 green or blue gondola with two canisters; 6059 M St. L SP-type caboose; eight curved and one straight track; 6149 uncoupling section; and a 1010 35-watt transformer.

Comments: The outfit box was the new 1965 issue Type D display style. The contents were unboxed and came with one fixed and one operating coupler. The 1062T tender came on a tab frame and was stamped "Lionel Lines". The 3364 log dump car was stamped "3362", but was referred to as 3364 when it carried logs instead of helium tanks. An authentic box for the 3364 exists, and is more valuable from a collector's point of view than the car itself.   105   175

1965 (margin)

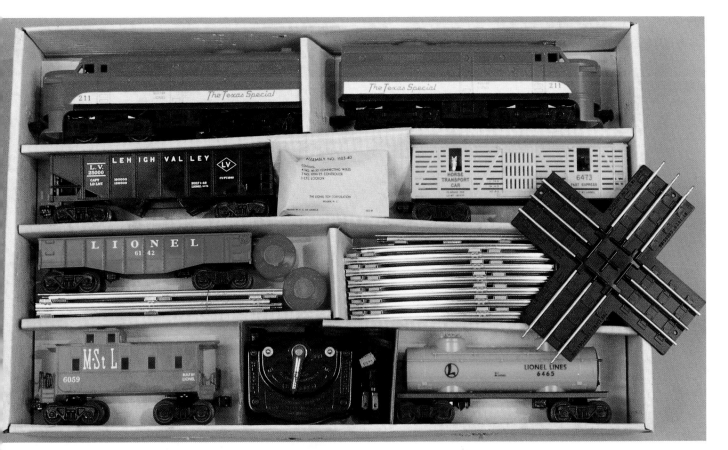

he 211 Texas Special freight set 11560 in a Type D display-style box. Note the 90° crossing that was included with this outfit at allowed for a basic Figure 8 track plan. The O27 rolling stock selection in 1965 was poor, and the same cars were utilized s set components throughout the product line. M. Sokol Collection.

1
9
6
5

VG   LN

11530   O27 Gauge $25 Retail

Contents: 634 Santa Fe NW-2 switcher; 6014 white Frisco boxcar; 6142 blue or green gondola with two canisters; 6402 gray General-type flatcar with cable reels; 6130 Santa Fe work caboose; eight curved and one straight track; 6149 uncoupling section; and a 1010 35-watt transformer.

Comments: The outfit box was the new 1965 issue Type D display style. The contents were unboxed and had one fixed and one operating coupler. The catalogue touted the 634 as new, but it was a repeat of a 1963 item. It was catalogued with safety stripes, but most often surfaces without them. The 6130 work caboose also reappeared after being last catalogued in 1961. Inexpensive diesel outfits stir collector interest far more than their steam counterparts. Please refer to page 154 for a picture of the outfit box and the contents.

150   250

11540   O27 Gauge $30 Retail

Contents: This set had the same components as outfit 11550, except that a 242T replaced the 234W tender, a 1025 45-watt transformer was substituted for the 1073, and the 147 whistle controller was deleted.

VG   LN

Comments: This was the only time that a 242T was ever mentioned in the catalogue. Listings of the 242 engine, from which the number was obviously derived, always included either a 1060T or 1062T slope-back tender, but the 242 was also a frequent component of uncatalogued sets. This streamlined tender was either stamped or unstamped, and came on a tab frame with a fixed coupler and either arch bar or late AAR trucks.

120   200

11550   O27 Gauge $40 Retail

Contents: 239 die-cast steam locomotive with headlight and smoke; 234W Lionel Lines whistle tender; 6473 rodeo car; 6465 orange Lionel Lines two-dome tank car; 6176 yellow or black Lehigh Valley hopper; 6119 red cab work caboose; eight curved and one straight track; 6149 uncoupling section; 1073 60-watt transformer; and a 147 whistle controller.

Comments: The outfit box was the new 1965 Type D display style. The contents were unboxed and had one fixed and one operating coupler. The rolling stock was all run-of-the-mill, yet the 239 was die-cast, a rarity for Scout-type engines, and was paired with a whistle tender. The 234W came with a fixed coupler that differentiated it from the 233W.

150   250

Outfit 12800 with a 2346 Boston and Maine GP-9 in a Type D display-style box with lift-off top. This was the only O Gauge set to come packaged in a Type D box. The scarce dark blue variation of the -475 boxcar was a sometime component of this set. M. Sokol Collection.

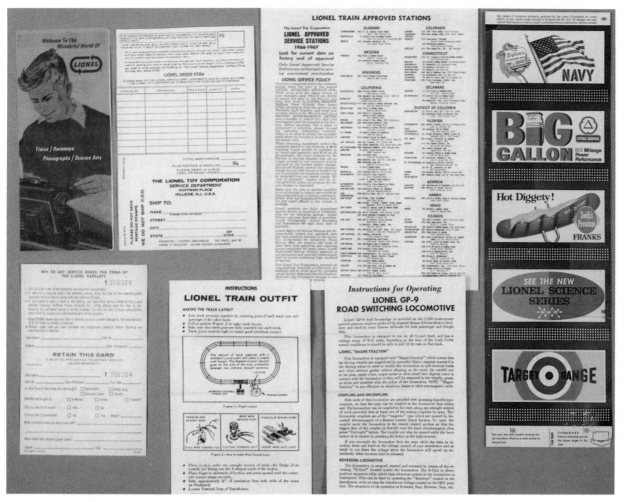

This is the miscellaneous paperwork included with outfit 12800 that was catalogued in 1965 and 1966. Pay particular attention to the accessory catalogue in the upper left corner that dates this set to 1966. Also note that this outfit contained billboards; their inclusion in 1965 and 1966 sets was not consistent. M. Sokol Collection.

	VG	LN

11560   O27 Gauge $37.50 Retail

Contents: 211P/211T Texas Special Alco AA units; 6473 rodeo car; 6176 yellow or black Lehigh Valley hopper; 6142 blue or green gondola with two canisters; 6465 orange Lionel Lines two-dome tank car; 6059 M St. L SP-type caboose; twelve curved and three straight track; 90° crossing; 6149 uncoupling section; and a 1025 45-watt transformer.

Comments: The outfit box was the new 1965 Type D display style with unboxed contents. The rolling stock were colorful but unexciting items that came with one fixed and one operating coupler. Beware of broken and/or repaired struts on the fragile Alco units. The track included with this outfit allowed for a basic Figure 8 plan. Page 155 shows a picture of this set.   **165   275**

12710   O Gauge $80 Retail

Comments: This was a repeat of the 1964 outfit with the price increased from $75. Packaging of this outfit in 1965

is confirmed by the existence of sets that show some contents in the new Hillside Orange Picture box, and by dated material such as a Service Station directory. Please see **1964** for more complete information.   **475   800**

12730   O Gauge $85 Retail

Comments: Here again a 1964 outfit was repeated, with the price increased from $79.95. Packaging of this outfit in 1965 is confirmed by the existence of sets that show some contents in the new Hillside Orange Picture box, and by dated material such as a Service Station directory. Please refer to **1964** for detailed information.   **800   1400**

12780   O Gauge $125 Retail

Comments: This was another repeat of the 1964 outfit with the price increased from $120. This was the fourth consecutive year, and the second as outfit 12780, that the Santa Fe-powered Presidential passenger set was catalogued.

	VG	LN

1965

The 1965 edition came in a two-tier flat white conventional outfit box with orange lettering. The passenger cars came in Orange Picture boxes that usually showed the 1965 changes. These boxes were the third distinctly different style to contain the Presidential cars that came with gold paper stripes. Please see **1964** for more information.   **1300**   **2600**

The box lid for outfit 12800. The Type D box was usually reserved for O27 outfits. Note the paste-on sticker at the center of the box that states that this was an O Gauge set. These graphics were utilized in 1965 and 1966. M. Sokol Collection.

12800   **O Gauge**   **$60 Retail**

Contents: 2346 Boston and Maine GP-9; 6428 U.S. Mail boxcar; 6436 Lehigh Valley quad hopper; 6464-475 Boston and Maine boxcar; 6415 Sunoco three-dome tank car; 6017-100 Boston and Maine SP-type caboose; eight curved and five straight track; and a UCS uncoupling/operating section.

Comments: This outfit came in a Type D display-style box in the new 1965 graphics. The contents, as with the O27 sets, were unboxed. The 2346 was the reissued Boston and Maine Geep that had been previously catalogued as 2359. It headed an extremely colorful set. The rolling stock came with late AAR trucks and had operating couplers at both ends. The scarce deep blue variation of the -475 Boston and Maine boxcar has been a known component of this set. The engine was also available for separate sale in a corrugated carton stamped "2346" with tucked-in end flaps. See page 157 for further information and page 156 for a picture of this outfit.   **400**   **650**

12820   **O Gauge**   **$100 Retail**

Contents: 2322 Virginian F-M; 3662 operating milk car; 6822 searchlight car; 6361 timber transport; 6464-725 orange New Haven boxcar; 6436 Lehigh Valley quad hopper; 6315 Lionel Lines chemical tank car; 6437 illuminated Pennsylvania porthole caboose; eight curved and five straight track; UCS uncoupling/operating section; and a 125-watt LW transformer.

Comments: The outfit box was standard 1965 O Gauge issue. The 2322 was the reissued twin-motored Virginian F-M that had last been catalogued in 1958. It came boxed in a corrugated carton with full wraparound liner. The rolling stock came with late AAR trucks in a combination of both Orange Picture and Hillside Orange Picture boxes. The items that most often surface in the new Hillside boxes are the 6315 chemical tank car that had a "-60" suffix as part of the stock number, and the 6437 caboose. This set was identical to outfit 12850 from 1966 except for track content. Ironically, this outfit, with less track and without remote-control switches, is more desirable as a collector item than 12850.   **900**   **1500**

13150   **Super O Gauge**   **$225 Retail**

Comments: The 1964 Hudson outfit was catalogued again with the price increased from $200. Please see **1964** for further information.

	VG	LN
With 773W tender	1900	3150
With 736W tender	1800	3000

1966

THE GRASP CONTINUES

The highlight of the entire year was the exceptional color photography of the consumer catalogue. The O27 and O Gauge outfit boxes were a repetition of 1965, and except for the inclusion of one new O Gauge steam outfit, the outfits themselves were also repeated with only a few minor changes. The Super O Hudson outfit was catalogued for the third consecutive year, which was probably no more than a futile attempt to deplete inventory and to help dealers who were backlogged with unsold stock.

There was one major change in the component boxes for rolling stock and passenger cars. The 1966 box included a cellophane see-through front. This box was also used for tenders, the 634 diesel switcher, and the 211 and 212 Alco pairs.

There were nine 6464 series boxcars catalogued in 1966. Four were carry-overs, four were reissues, and one, the -250 Western Pacific, was "almost new" because, after a twelve-year absence, it was finally catalogued with a correct stock number. The four reissues were the -375 Central of Georgia, -450 Great Northern, -650 Rio Grande, and the -700 Santa Fe.

This was a great year for the 6464 series variation collector, and some of the most scarce items from the entire series are dated to 1966. They are the red -375 and the yellow-roofed -650, which had two-phase paint schemes on gray Type IV body molds, and the Type III variations of the -250, -450, -700, and -900. These Type III boxcars were probably produced as a result of a housecleaning effort at the Lionel factory. The body molds date to the 1959-1960 era and many of them show characteristics of being repainted over what had previously been unstamped, factory-reject paint jobs. The 6431 was new issue and is a very collectable rolling stock item. The scarce 6517 Erie bay window caboose was featured in the accessory rather than in the consumer catalogue. Fortunately the rather Spartan 2404, 2405, and 2406 Santa Fe passenger cars were dropped in favor of the illuminated 2408, 2409, and 2410, which also included silhouetted window strips. The 665 steam engine was resurrected after a seven-year absence to head outfit 12840.

	VG	LN
11500 **O27 Gauge**	**$50 Retail**	

Comments: This outfit was catalogued again for the third consecutive year at the 1965 price. A yellow hopper was often substituted for the black of the previous issue. Please refer to **1964** and **1965** for additional information.

                                         165   275

	VG	LN
11520 **O27 Gauge**	**$22.50 Retail**	

Comments: This was a repeat from 1965 with the price increased from $20. Please see **1965** for more detailed information.

                                          105   175

11530 **O27 Gauge**	**$25 Retail**

Comments: Here was another repeat from 1965, but the 634 Santa Fe switcher no longer had the safety stripes on the cab sides. Please refer to **1965** for more detailed information.

                                          150   250

11540 **O27 Gauge**	**$31.50 Retail**

Comments: This was yet again a carry-over from 1965 with the price increased from $30. Please see **1965** for more information.

                                          120   200

11550 **O27 Gauge**	**$41.50 Retail**

Comments: This set was another repeat from 1965 with a black 6176 often substituted for the yellow hopper, and the price increased from $40. Please refer to **1965** for further information.

                                          150   200

11560 **O27 Gauge**	**$37.50 Retail**

Comments: Here was an exact repeat of the 1965 set, without a price increase. **1965** has additional information on this set.

                                          165   275

11590 **O27 Gauge**	**$60 Retail**

Contents: 212P/212T Santa Fe Alco AA units; 2408 Vista Dome, 2409 Pullman, and 2410 observation with illumination and Santa Fe markings in blue letters; eight curved and three straight track; 6149 uncoupling section; 1073 60-watt transformer; and a 147 horn controller.

Comments: This outfit was an upgraded version of 11490 that was offered in 1964 and 1965. The passenger cars underwent a number change necessitated by the addition of lights and silhouetted window strips. The new outfit box was the standard 1965-1966 Type D display style with lift-off top

	VG	LN

1
9
6
6

and unboxed contents. This is a scarce set and one that is in demand in the collector market.   **450**   **750**

12710   O Gauge $85 Retail

Comments: The 12710 was a repeat of the 1965 outfit with the price increased from $80. This was the last edition of the Berkshire steam outfits. There was definitely some 1966 production on this set as evidenced by examples that contained 1966 cellophane-front component boxes. Please see **1964** for more detailed information.   **475**   **800**

12730   O Gauge $90 Retail

Comments: This set was yet another repeat from 1965 with the price increased from $85. This was the last edition of the Santa Fe freight outfits. There was without question some 1966 production on this set as evidenced by examples that contained 1966 cellophane-front component boxes. Please see **1964** for more information.   **800**   **1400**

	VG	LN

12780   O Gauge $125 Retail

Comments: Here again was a carry-forward outfit from 1965 with no price increase. This was the last edition of the Santa Fe passenger outfits. Its longevity spanned fourteen years, and it was catalogued as the Presidential series for the last five of those years. There was definitely some 1966 production on this set as evidenced by examples that contained 1966 cellophane-front component boxes. The outfit box was still a two-tier flat white conventional style with orange lettering. Please see **1964** and **1965** for more detailed information.   **1300**   **2600**

12800   O Gauge $60 Retail

Comments: The 12800 was another exact repeat from 1965 with no price increase. Please refer to **1965** for additional information.   **400**   **650**

Outfit 11590 was a 212 Santa Fe passenger set in a Type D display-style box. Note the inclusion of a 147 horn controller in the lower right corner, which was essential to this outfit because the 1073 transformer did not have a self-contained whistle/horn control button. The 1966 edition of the Santa Fe passenger set included the 2408, 2409 and 2410 cars that had both illumination and silhouetted window strips that were not present on previous issues. B. Myles Collection.

	VG	LN

12840   O Gauge $80 Retail

Contents: 665 steam locomotive with headlight, smoke, and Magnetraction; 736W Pennsylvania whistle tender; 6464-375 Central of Georgia and 6464-450 Great Northern boxcars; 6431 flatcar with vans and Midge Toy tractor; 6415 Sunoco three-dome tank car; 6437 illuminated Pennsylvania porthole caboose; eight curved and five straight track; UCS uncoupling/operating section; and a 125-watt LW transformer.

Comments: The outfit box was the standard O Gauge 1965-1966 flat white conventional style with orange lettering. This was the only outfit, other than the Girls' Set, to ever contain two 6464 series boxcars. The catalogue picture mistakenly shows Type II body mold boxcars with bar-end metal trucks from the mid-1950s instead of the late issue Type IV bodies with AAR trucks, and the vans on top of the 6431 were also erroneously catalogued with Cooper-Jarrett nameplates. These cars were used solely for photographic purposes, and even the Pennsylvania tender was shown with metal trucks.

The engine came in a corrugated carton with tucked-in end flaps and had the number "665" rubber-stamped on the ends. The other components all came with late AAR trucks and operating couplers at both ends in new-issue cellophane-front boxes. The -375 and -450 boxcars were reissues for 1966 and the 6431 was also a reissue of the 6430, with the trailer mounting unit riveted to the flat. The flatcar was stamped "6430", not "6431"; the internal number change was necessitated by the inclusion of a red Midge Toy tractor that enhanced play value. The Midge tractor was packed inside the 6431 box at one end, and was held in place by a specially designed folded insert. The 6431 is an extremely scarce and collectable item.

                                                 575   950

	VG	LN

12850   O Gauge $135 Retail

Comments: The component pieces were the same as those in outfit 12820 from 1965. The outfit number was changed because this set now included a pair of T022 remote-control switches, and the amount of track was increased to ten curved and fourteen straight. The outfit box was a two-tier flat white conventional style with orange lettering. It usually contained a hodgepodge of box types, with Orange Picture, Hillside Orange Picture, and the new cellophane fronts all being used. Ironically, this outfit, with more track and remote-control switches, is more common and less desirable as a collector item than 12820. Please review the 12820 description in **1965** for further information.   **725   1300**

13150   Super O Gauge $225 Retail

Comments: This was the third consecutive year the Hudson set was catalogued. It is not known with certainty whether any sets were actually packaged in 1966 or if inventory from previous years was carried forward. After two poor illustrations, the 1966 catalogue finally did the set justice and at last pictured the 773W New York Central tender. As previously mentioned, this set in the outfit box is truly rare, thus making it one of *the* premier postwar outfits. This was also the last time that a Super O outfit would grace the pages of a Lionel catalogue. Please refer to **1964** for additional information.

	VG	LN
With 736W tender	1800	3000
With 773W tender	1900	3150

1967

THE BLACK HOLE

There was neither production nor a catalogue for the year 1967. The following memorandum, taken from an article written by William Staiger for the July 1988 issue of *The Train Collectors Quarterly*, was originally sent to employees of Joe, the Motorists' Friend stores by the company's president, Joseph R. Strine. The portion reprinted here explains Lionel production during this period with a style and flavor that is hard to match.

Please pay particular attention to the comments made about uncatalogued sets that had numbers beginning with "19". An inordinate amount of differently numbered uncatalogued sets were available during this period, and it is the author's opinion that Lionel put outfits together haphazardly using whatever inventory was on the shelves.

November 14, 1967

TO ALL STORES:

I want to give you the Lionel situation for this year. Many of you have heard all kinds of rumors but I want to make sure that all personnel connected with the selling of electric trains is in a position to explain to customers just exactly the true situation.

The Lionel Corporation for the past several years has lost money in the train division of their Company but made a considerable amount of money in the electronics business. They are not going out of the train business but are trying to revamp it so that in future years they can make money from the train end of their business. Consequently this year they have not manufactured one piece of train merchandise but have sold only their last year's carry over which amounted in round numbers to Four Million Dollars worth of merchandise. This is all which will be available this year and it is a very small percentage of their Seventeen Million Dollars in annual sales. You can see this year there will be a tremendous shortage of all Lionel trains and accessories and it is likely that people will be rushing from store to store trying to find merchandise.

We have taken every piece of our allotment plus the entire allotment of some distributors and other distributors who have decided to go out of business because their allotment was so small it was not worth bothering with. The result is that we have in the warehouse the same number of train outfits which we sold last year but like all other Lionel accounts we will be terribly short in some numbers.

Lionel will begin manufacturing in 1968 and intends to produce 10 or 12 numbers only in the O27 line. The O gauge line and Super O line will be discontinued permanently. You will receive calls for some of this merchandise 10 years from now. I recall 20 years ago they discontinued what we then called the standard gauge line which even today we are still receiving calls for standard gauge track and other parts. The same thing is going to happen on O gauge and Super O. Therefore, it will not be necessary to cut the price on any O gauge or Super O gauge merchandise you have in stock.

Under the circumstances Lionel did not print any catalogs for 1967 with the result that description of outfits and list prices remain the same as they were in 1966. We have no extra 1966 catalogs in the warehouse which means that you will not be receiving some every week as you did in prior years. This means that you must hold onto your last year's catalog for dear life because you, no doubt, want to refer to the catalog most every day when the selling season really starts.

NOW ABOUT THE AVAILABILITY OF LIONEL MERCHANDISE

The only train outfits listed in the catalog which we have in stock are 11560, 12710, 12840, 12850, and 13150. These outfits we will be willing to break up provided you sell the locomotive first. Never break up an outfit simply to sell one car.

I said before we have as many train outfits on hand as we sold last year but they are all special uncatalogued numbers with stock numbers beginning with 19. Of course, this is in keeping with our policy of former years when the same condition existed.

We have plenty of O27 track and TOC but no TOS. If you are using TOS track on the shelves of your train table in order to display your outfits I would suggest that you change over to 1018 track for this purpose. Your customers will get awfully mad if they see some TOS track in your possession and you refuse to sell it. After you have sold whatever TOS track you have in your possession you can truthfully tell your customers that you don't have any and thus avoid an unpleasant situation.

There will be a tremendous shortage of transformers. The only ones we have in stock in quantity are the LW and ZW. In order to help out your customers who want the small transformers for small trains we have purchased a quantity of Marx transformers for the benefit of those people who are looking for a $6.95 or $7.95 transformer. In taking special orders you can save yourself a lot of time and disappointment by refusing to take orders for merchandise which is just not available. In this class of merchandise is the 2383 locomotive and all passenger cars including both the O27 and O gauge sizes. We just don't have any, there will be none available and it is a waster of time to promise customers delivery or take orders. If your customer is lucky he may be able to find these items in the carry over stock of other dealers but we have no carry over in the warehouse.

Last year, and already this year, there has been a rush for freight cars, particularly those that are not supplied in any regular outfit. The only ones we have available are 6464-475, 525, 735 and 900.

Other numbers which are not available are 154, 310, 1020 and 042. We will be low on the full set of 1020, O27 hand controlled switches. We do have, however, plenty of 1022 LH and 1022 RH. These, when put together, will make a pair. After you are sold out of the complete sets of 1020 you can sell your customers one each of LH and RH. You must note, however, that we sell the 1022 for $5.95 and the LH and RH for $3.49 each making a total of $6.98 which is the price we must get from your customer. Due to the national shortage of switches this will be no problem....

Keep this letter handy so that you can refer to it, particularly the section dealing with the items which are not available.

Very truly yours,

Joseph R. Strine
President
JOE, THE MOTORISTS' FRIEND, INC.

1968

THE 23RD HOUR

Because of the disruption caused by the move to Hagerstown, Maryland during the previous year as well as generally poor business conditions, Lionel produced only *one* set in 1968. Only two engines were available for separate sale: the 2029 and the 736 Berkshire, and the Berkshire was probably carry-over inventory. The separate-sale rolling stock were all repeat items from the 1966 product year, but most now came in the new checkerboard box with "Hagerstown, Md." on the end flaps. Note that the 54 ballast tamper was recatalogued once again. Lionel was still trying to deplete inventory of this item, which was last manufactured during the very late 1950s.

11600	O27 Gauge	No Retail

Contents: 2029 steam locomotive with headlight and smoke; 234W Lionel Lines whistle tender; 6014 white Frisco boxcar; 6476 yellow Lehigh Valley hopper; 6315 Lionel Lines chemical tank car; 6560 crane; 6130 Santa Fe work caboose; 1122 remote-control left-hand switch; 260 black plastic illuminated bumper; 1020 90° crossing; twelve curved and six straight track; 6149 uncoupling section; and a 1044 90-watt transformer.

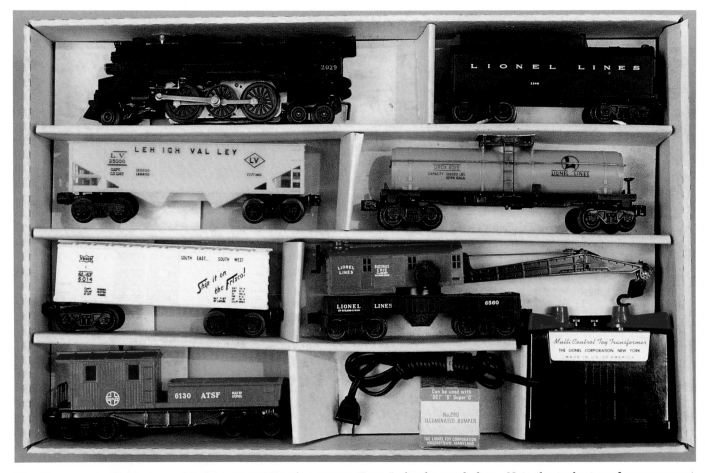

The Hagerstown 2029 steam freight set 11600 with a unique Type D display-style box. Note the inclusion of a component-boxed 260 bumper that is shown next to the transformer. B. Myles Collection.

Comments: With effrontery that almost defies belief, the catalogue touted this as "the greatest train set of all times." That statement was almost blasphemous — the engine was made in Japan when that meant "cheap." This outfit contained enough track to construct a basic Figure 8 and also included a switch with spur and bumper. The 6476 hopper was often stamped "6176" or "6076", or was even unstamped, and the now desirable Hagerstown crane had the scarce dark blue boom and base. The unpainted 6130 work caboose was also somewhat unique as the rectangular lettering and logo plate was an enlarged variation with no slats at the bottom of the cab. The rolling stock all came with late AAR trucks and usually had operating couplers at both ends. The outfit box was a Type D lift-off top display style but it was unique —

VG   LN

1
9
6
8

nothing else in the postwar era compares with it. The top lifted off to show the unboxed contents separated and protected between channels. Upon closer scrutiny, one notices an approximately two-inch "false" bottom that held the track, as well as the individually boxed switch, crossover, and bumper with "Hagerstown" on the end flaps of the boxes. The black plastic variation of the 260 bumper is both scarce and collectable. This outfit also had its own specific instruction sheet.

Collector interest in this set has increased measurably in recent times. This outfit exemplifies one of those special instances in which the set box alone is valued as much as the items it contained.   **700   1200**

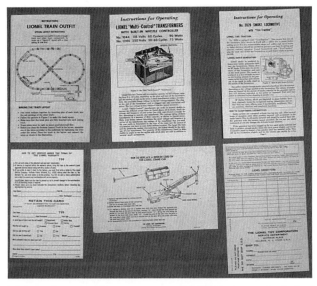

This is the miscellaneous paperwork that was included with the Hagerstown set. Pay particular attention to the center bottom illustration that explains the restringing of the 6560 crane, and the outfit instruction sheet that was unique to this set. M. Sokol Collection.

The box lid for the Hagerstown set 11600. Note the legend on the upper right side that shows a diagram of the track plan and lists the contents. M. Sokol Collection.

1969

THE LAST BREATH

At first glance one might think that Lionel was in a period of massive expansion because the number of available outfits increased 500 percent. In reality, however, the product line was a total embarrassment. A stranger to the hobby need only compare a 1969 set with one from the 1950s, and he would swear they were not made by the same company. The six outfits that were offered all came in traditional two-tier set boxes that were printed in red and blue on a white background, and marked "Hillside, N. J." In 1969 Lionel did what it should have done a score of years earlier — pasted a picture of the set, for identification purposes, on the exterior of the outfit box. None of the contents in any of the sets were individually boxed; they were protected and separated by cardboard dividers.

There was one general instruction sheet for 1969 that explained all the engines in the product line, and it was included in each outfit. Not too many years ago the 1969 sets were hard to give away, but they have suddenly become collectable and can still be obtained at very reasonable prices.

This was indeed a "last breath" as Lionel ventured to use up everything in stock. Set components varied more in 1969 than in any previous year; if it was not nailed down it probably went into an outfit box. Rolling stock had various combinations of arch bar and AAR trucks, as well as fixed and operating couplers. Most separate-sale items came in checkerboard boxes with either "Hagerstown, Md." or "Hillside, N.J." printed on the end flaps and with rubber-stamped stock numbers. Very few box sizes were utilized. The 6057 caboose and the 6014 boxcars came in the same size box as the 6464 series boxcars.

There was no new rolling stock, only reissues of old items. The 6473 rodeo car and the 3376 giraffe car reappeared, and the Gulf logo returned to the 6315 chemical tank car. The 6415 three-dome Sunoco tank car was also reissued with metal trucks, as were five 6464 boxcars. They were the -75 Rock Island, -200 Pennsylvania, -400 B & O, -425 New Haven, and the -500 Timken on Type IV body molds.

It was the decision to reissue a black New Haven boxcar that created the scarce variation with a "-725" number. The explanation for this variation is simple: after the black Type IV body molds were pressed, they were mistakenly lettered and numbered with the orange New Haven -725 heat stamp, and then packed in boxes with "-425" on the end flaps. "-425" was the original suffix for the black New Haven issued in 1956, and the intended reissue number.

1969 was the year for the scarce yellow-lettered giraffe car on a blue body mold. The explanation for this variation is also uncomplicated: Lionel catalogued and shipped the giraffe car in green with yellow letters, but some unstamped blue body molds were also part of inventory. These molds were simply run through the heat-stamping process without having

the color of the heat-stamp tape changed; hence, blue mold giraffe cars with yellow letters. The 3376 was available for separate sale. It was "stuffed" into a regular size checkerboard box and had "3376-160" rubber stamped on the end flaps.

	VG	LN

11710 **O27 Gauge** **No Retail**

Contents: 1061 2-4-2 steam locomotive; 1061T or 1062T slope-back tender; 6402 gray General-type flatcar with cable reels; 6142 gondola with canisters; 6059 M St. L caboose; eight curved and two straight track; and a 1025 45-watt transformer.

Comments: The outfit box was standard issue for 1969. The 1061 was different from earlier production in that it was upgraded from an 0-4-0 to a 2-4-2 wheel configuration. The rolling stock usually had one operating and one fixed coupler even though the outfit did not include an uncoupling section. The difference between the tenders is that the 1062T was stamped "Lionel Lines" while the 1061T was unstamped. Refer to page 167 for an end view of the outfit box.

	75	125

11720 **O27 Gauge** **No Retail**

Contents: 2024 C & O Alco A unit; 6142 gondola with two canisters; 6402 gray General-type flatcar with cable reels; 6176 yellow Lehigh Valley hopper; 6057 brown unstamped SP-type caboose; eight curved and three straight track; 6149 uncoupling section; and a 1025 45-watt transformer.

Comments: The outfit box was standard issue for 1969. All of the rolling stock had one operating and one fixed coupler. The caboose and the hopper were even offered boxed as separate-sale items. Strangely enough, the yellow hopper was referred to as 6476-185 when offered for separate sale.

	120	200

11730 **O27 Gauge** **No Retail**

Contents: 645 Union Pacific NW-2 switcher; 6402 gray General-type flatcar with boat; 6014-85 orange Frisco boxcar with blue lettering; 6176 black Lehigh Valley hopper; 6142 gondola with two canisters; 6167-85 Union Pacific SP-type caboose; eight curved and five straight track; 6149 uncoupling section; and a 1025 45-watt transformer.

Comments: The outfit box was standard issue for 1969. All of the rolling stock had one fixed and one operating coupler.

VG   LN

The unstamped flatcar with boat was still called 6402 even though it had cable reels in the previous two sets. The boxcar, hopper, and caboose were also offered for separate sale. The black hopper was referred to as 6476-160 and the orange Frisco repeated an "-85" suffix that had previously been used in the 1957-1958 era. The yellow UP caboose is collectable and is the most desirable item in the set, especially if it can be obtained with an original checkerboard box.   **175   300**

11740   O27 Gauge   No Retail

Contents: 2041P/2041T Rock Island Alco AA units; 6315 chemical tank car; 6142 gondola with two canisters; 6014-410 white Frisco boxcar; 6476 yellow hopper; 6057 brown unstamped SP-type caboose; eight curved and seven straight track; 6149 uncoupling section; and a 1025 45-watt transformer.

Comments: The outfit box was standard issue for 1969. The rolling stock came with both one operating and one fixed coupler, and two operating couplers. The cars with two operating couplers were probably carry-over items from 1968 as three of them were included in the Hagerstown set. Supposedly the 6476 hopper, even if numbered "6176" or unnumbered, had two operating couplers. The 6315 chemical tank car was catalogued as Lionel Lines but usually had the scarce Gulf markings. Mint 2041 cabs are still readily available in the marketplace. The key to this set is the outfit box itself.   **250   400**

11750   O27 Gauge   No Retail

Contents: 2029 steam locomotive with headlight and smoke; 234T Lionel Lines non-whistle tender; 6014-85 orange Frisco boxcar with blue lettering; 6476 black hopper; 6473 rodeo car; 6315 chemical tank car; 6130 Santa Fe work caboose; eight curved and seven straight track; 6149 uncoupling section; and a 1025 45-watt transformer.

Comments: The outfit box was standard issue. This set also had cars with a combination of either one fixed and one operating coupler, or two operating couplers. The Frisco boxcar repeated an "-85" suffix that had previously been used in the 1957-1958 era. The 6315 usually had the scarce Gulf markings, and the 6130 caboose with an enlarged logo rectangle was a carry-over item from the 1968 Hagerstown set. Notice here, and in the previously listed and following sets, that with the uncoupling section Lionel included *eight* pieces of straight track! This much O27 track had not been contained in an outfit since the early 1950s.   **175   300**

VG   LN

11760   O27 Gauge   No Retail

Contents: 2029 steam locomotive with headlight and smoke; 234W Lionel Lines whistle tender; 6014-410 white Frisco boxcar; 6315 chemical tank car; 6476 black hopper car; 3376 giraffe car; 6119 work caboose; eight curved and seven straight track; 6149 uncoupling section; and a 1044 90-watt transformer.

Comments: The set box was standard issue for 1969. This outfit has the dubious distinction of being "The End of the Line," but an analysis of it is quite interesting. The rolling stock had a combination of one fixed and one operating coupler, or two operating couplers, and each was available for separate sale. It has been known to come with the very desirable Pennsylvania-lettered tender and the blue giraffe car with yellow letters; the catalogue set pictures a green giraffe car in 1969 but both blues and greens were produced that year. The hopper car was again improperly catalogued as 6476, and the 6315 usually had the scarce Gulf markings. The work caboose is also intriguing. It was catalogued as 6119 because of its gray tool bin but uses a 6130 Santa Fe cab. This was no doubt a last ditch effort by Lionel to use up any and all component parts in stock.   **225   375**

An end view of two 1969 outfit boxes. Lionel finally did what it should have done a score of years sooner — pasted a picture of the set, for identification purposes, on the exterior of the outfit box. M. Sokol Collection.

Appendix A
Billboards

The billboard concept was a collaborative effort of Lionel, Standard Outdoor Advertising, and several leading national advertisers. It is not known whether the idea originated with Lionel or if it was the brainchild of Standard — none the less, it was an excellent idea.

The first billboard sheet appeared in 1949, but it was neither included in any outfits nor available for separate sale in the catalogue. The 1949 sheet was available only through a special mail-in offer which was advertised in newspapers and several magazines with nationwide circulation. For the cost of twenty-five cents, the hobbyist received the billboard sheet along with a 1949 consumer catalogue, a layout planning book for "Pop," and a miniature sound effects record. Billboards became part of outfit packaging in 1950, and their inclusion was continuous in every Lionel outfit, even Scout and low-end sets, through 1964. Only the uncut sheet itself was included, never the frames. Frames had to be purchased separately as part of No. 310 Billboard Set, which also included a folded but uncut sheet of billboards along with five

green frames. This was good business strategy — give away billboards and induce the customer to buy frames that included the same billboards!

In 1965 the inclusion of billboards in outfits became inconsistent. Some O27 outfits that came in Type D display-style packaging contained a 1961 five-strip sheet, yet most O Gauge sets were packed without billboards. It is doubtful whether any billboard sheets destined for sets were actually printed after the release of the three-cut sheet in 1962. Toy train sales were very slow in the early 1960s, so Lionel simply depleted old inventory by including the 1961 sheet with some 1964 and 1965 outfits until the supply was exhausted.

The uncut sheets that are reproduced in this appendix were included with outfits, except for the years 1949 and 1966. Because of overlapping use, some of the dates differ slightly from what has been discussed in previous analysis elsewhere. *Old* was depleted before *new* was released. The dates given here are based upon the author's longtime analysis of catalogued sets.

These two uncut sheets of Lionel billboards are from 1949 (left) and 1950 (right). The 1949 sheet was not included in any outfits; it was available only through a special mail-in offer. D. Corrigan Collection and photograph.

These two uncut sheets of Lionel billboards are from 1951 (left) and 1952 (right). The sheet was expanded in 1951 to include ten billboards. D. Corrigan Collection and photograph.

These two uncut sheets of Lionel billboards are from 1953 (left) and 1954 (right). The number of billboards on these sheets was reduced in 1953 from ten to eight. D. Corrigan Collection and photograph.

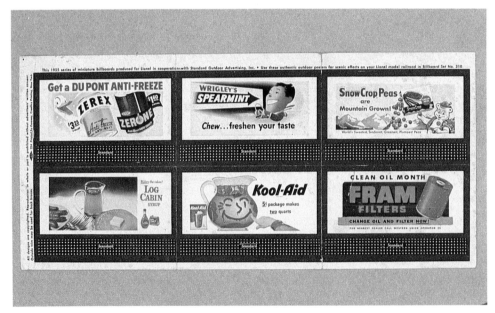

This uncut sheet of Lionel billboards covers both 1955 and 1956. A new billboard sheet was not produced in 1956. Lionel instead re-ran the existing sheet, even though the 1955 date appears in the upper left corner. The number of billboards on this sheet was also reduced to six. D. Corrigan Collection and photograph.

These four uncut sheets of Lionel billboards (left to right) are from 1957, 1958, 1959, and 1961. The 1957 sheet was dated on the white border while the other sheets were undated. The 1958 sheet regularly surfaces in 1959 sets, and the 1959 sheet was also prevalently used in 1960. The 1961 sheet, however, requires further explanation as follows: this sheet was also utilized for part of the 1962 outfits, but it was supplanted by a three-cut sheet that included a Van Camp billboard (refer to the three-cut sheet for additional details). When the supply of the three-cut Van Camp sheets was exhausted, Lionel reverted to using their existing inventory on the 1961 sheet until it was depleted sometime in 1965. D. Corrigan Collection and photograph.

This uncut sheet shows the three bill-boards offered in 1962, 1963, and 1964. Evidence suggests that Lionel still had adequate inventory of the five-cut 1961 sheet. Why then issue a new sheet? Lionel reached an agreement with Stokely/Van Camp to produce un-catalogued set 19142 to be offered on the label of a can of pork and beans that included the 638-2361 Van Camp box-car. As part of the deal, Lionel was required to include a Van Camp bill-board; hence, this three-cut sheet was used in part of 1962, all of 1963, and until depleted in 1964. D. Corrigan Col-lection and photograph.

This uncut billboard sheet shows the five bill-boards offered in 1966-1968. It was not included in any outfits, but was available for separate sale. The border was changed from the greens of previous years to a purple hue. It was sold as blister pack No. B310 for $1. D. Corrigan Collec-tion and photograph.

Appendix B

An index of outfits in numerical sequence with the engines they included and the years catalogued.

Outfit	Engine	Years	Outfit	Engine	Years
463W	224	1945	1423W	1655	1948-1949
1000W	2016	1955	1425B	1656	1948-1949
1001	610	1955	1426WS	2026	1948-1949
1105	1055	1959 Advance	1427WS	2026	1948
1107	1055	1960 Advance	1429WS	2026	1948
1109	1060	1960 Advance	1430WS	2025	1948-1949
1111	1001	1948	1431	1654	1947
1112	1001	1948	1431W	1654	1947
1113	1120	1950	1432	221	1947
1115	1110	1949	1432W	221	1947
1117	1110	1949	1433	221	1947
1119	1110	1951-1952	1433W	221	1947
1123	1060	1961 Advance	1434WS	2025	1947
1124	1060	1961 Advance	1435WS	2025	1947
1125	1065	1961 Advance	1437WS	2025	1947
1400	221	1946	1439WS	2025	1947
1400W	221	1946	1441WS	2020	1947
1401	1654	1946	1443WS	2020	1947
1401W	1654	1946	1445WS	2025	1948
1402	1666	1946	1447WS	2020	1948-1949
1402W	1666	1946	1449WS	2020	1948
1403	221	1946	1451WS	2026	1949
1403W	221	1946	1453WS	2026	1949
1405	1666	1946	1455WS	2025	1949
1405W	1666	1946	1457B	6220	1949-1950
1407B	1665	1946	1459WS	2020	1949
1409	1666	1946	1461S	6110	1950
1409W	1666	1946	1463W	2036	1950
1411W	1666	1946	1463WS	2026	1951
1413WS	2020	1946	1464W	2023	1950-1951
1415WS	2020	1946	1464W	2033	1952-1953
1417WS	2020	1946	1465	2034	1952
1419WS	2020	1946	1467W	2023	1950-1951
1421WS	2020	1946	1467W	2032	1952-1953

Outfit	Engine	Years	Outfit	Engine	Years
1469WS	2035	1950-1951	1542	520	1956
1471WS	2035	1950-1951	1543	627	1956
1473WS	2046	1950	1545	628	1956
1475WS	2046	1950	1547S	2018	1956
1477S	2026	1951-1952	1549	1615	1956
1479WS	2056	1952	1551W	621	1956
1481WS	2035	1951	1552	629	1956
1483WS	2056	1952	1553W	2338	1956
1484WS	2056	1952	1555WS	2018	1956
1485WS	2025	1952	1557W	621	1956
1489WS	2025	1952	1559W	2338	1956
1500	1130	1953-1954	1561WS	2065	1956
1501S	2026	1953	1562W	2328	1956
1502WS	2055	1953	1563W	2240	1956
1503WS	2055	1953-1954	1565WS	2065	1956
1505WS	2046	1953	1567W	2243	1956
1507WS	2046	1953	1569	202	1957
1509WS	2046	1953	1571	625	1957
1511S	2037	1953	1573	250	1957
1513S	2037	1954-1955	1575	205	1957
1515WS	2065	1954	1577S	2018	1957
1516WS	2065	1954	1578S	2018	1957
1517W	2245	1954	1579S	2037	1957
1519WS	2065	1954	1581	611	1957
1520W	2245	1954	1583WS	2037	1957
1521WS	2065	1954	1585W	602	1957
1523	6250	1954	1586	204	1957
1525	600	1955	1587S	2037-500	1957-1958
1526S	2037	1955	1589WS	2037	1957
1527	1615	1955	1590	249	1958
1529	2028	1955	1591	212 USMC	1958
1531W	2328	1955	1593	613	1958
1533WS	2055	1955	1595	1625	1958
1534W	2328	1955	1597S	2018	1958
1535W	2243	1955	1599	210	1958
1536W	2245	1955	1600	216	1958
1537WS	2065	1955	1601W	2337	1958
1538WS	2065	1955	1603WS	2037	1958
1539W	2243	1955	1605W	208	1958
1541WS	2065	1955	1607WS	2037	1958

Outfit	Engine	Years	Outfit	Engine	Years
1608W	209	1958	2103W	224	1946
1609	246	1959-1960	2105WS	671	1946
1611	614	1959	2110WS	671	1946
1612	1862	1959-1960	2111WS	671	1946
1613S	247	1959	2113WS	726	1946
1615	217	1959	2114WS	726	1946
1617S	2018	1959	2115WS	726	1946
1619W	218	1959	2120S	675	1947
1621WS	2037	1959	2120WS	675	1947
1623W	2349	1959	2121S	675	1947
1625WS	2037	1959	2121WS	675	1947
1626W	208	1959	2123WS	675	1947
1627S	244	1960	2124W	2332	1947
1629	225	1960	2125WS	671	1947
1631WS	243	1960	2126WS	671	1947
1633	224	1960	2127WS	671	1947
1635WS	2037	1960	2129WS	726	1947
1637W	218	1960	2131WS	726	1947
1639WS	2037	1960	2133W	2333	1948
1640W	218	1960	2135WS	675	1948-1949
1641	246	1961	2136WS	675	1948-1949
1642	244	1961	2137WS	675	1948
1643	230	1961	2139W	2332	1948-1949
1644	1862	1961	2140WS	671	1948-1949
1645	229	1961	2141WS	671	1948-1949
1646	233	1961	2143WS	671	1948
1647	45	1961	2144W	2332	1948-1949
1648	2037	1961	2145WS	726	1948
1649	218	1961	2146WS	726	1948-1949
1650	2037	1961	2147WS	675	1949
1651	218	1961	2148WS	773	1950
1652	236	1961	2149B	622	1949
1800	1862	1959-1960	2150WS	681	1950
1805	45	1960	2151W	2333	1949
1809	244	1961	2153WS	671	1949
1810	231	1961	2155WS	726	1949
2100	224	1946	2159W	2330	1950
2100W	224	1946	2161W	2343	1950
2101	224	1946	2163WS	736	1950-1951
2101W	224	1946	2165WS	736	1950

Outfit	Engine	Years	Outfit	Engine	Years
2167WS	681	1950-1951	2247W	2367	1955
2169WS	773	1950	2249WS	736	1955
2171W	2344	1950	2251W	2331	1955
2173WS	681	1950-1951	2253W	2340-25	1955
2175W	2343	1950-1951	2254W	2340	1955
2177WS	675	1952	2255W	601	1956
2179WS	671	1952	2257WS	665	1956
2183WS	726	1952	2259W	2350	1956
2185W	2344	1950-1951	2261WS	646	1956
2187WS	671	1952	2263W	2350	1956
2189WS	726	1952	2265WS	736	1956
2190W	2343	1952	2267W	2331	1956
2190W	2353	1953	2269W	2368	1956
2191W	2343	1952	2270W	2341	1956
2193W	2344	1952	2271W	2360-25	1956
2201WS	685	1953	2273W	2378	1956
2201WS	665	1954	2274W	2360	1956
2203WS	681	1953	2275W	2339	1957
2205WS	736	1953	2276W	404	1957
2207W	2353	1953	2277WS	665	1957
2209W	2354	1953	2279W	2350	1957
2211WS	681	1953	2281W	2243	1957
2213WS	736	1953	2283WS	646	1957
2217WS	682	1954	2285W	2331	1957
2219W	2321	1954	2287W	2351	1957
2221WS	646	1954	2289WS	736	1957
2222WS	646	1954	2291W	2379	1957
2223W	2321	1954	2292WS	646	1957
2225WS	736	1954	2293W	2360	1957
2227W	2353	1954	2295WS	746	1957
2229W	2354	1954	2296W	2373	1957
2231W	2356	1954	2297WS	746	1957
2234W	2353	1954	2501W	2348	1958
2235W	2338	1955	2502W	400	1958
2237WS	665	1955	2503WS	665	1958
2239W	2363	1955	2505W	2329	1958
2241WS	646	1955	2507W	2242	1958
2243W	2321	1955	2509WS	665	1958
2244W	2367	1955	2511W	2352	1958
2245WS	682	1955	2513W	2329	1958

Outfit	Engine	Years	Outfit	Engine	Years
2515WS	646	1958	11232	232	1962
2517W	2379	1958	11242	233	1962
2518W	2352	1958	11252	211	1962
2519W	2331	1958	11268	2365	1962
2521WS	746	1958	11278	2037	1962
2523W	2383	1958	11288	229	1962
2525WS	746	1958	11298	2037	1962
2526W	2383	1958	11308	218	1962
2527	44	1959-1960	11311	1062	1963
2528WS	1872	1959, 1960, 1961	11321	221	1963
2529W	2329	1959	11331	242	1963
2531WS	637	1959	11341	634	1963
2533W	2358	1959	11351	237	1963
2535WS	665	1959	11361	211	1963
2537W	2242	1959	11375	238	1963
2539WS	665	1959	11385	223	1963
2541W	2383	1959	11395	2037	1963
2543WS	736	1959	11405	218	1963
2544W	2383	1959-1960	11415	1061	1963 Advance
2545WS	746	1959	11420	1061	1964
2547WS	637	1960	11430	1062	1964
2549W	2349	1960	11440	221	1964
2551W	2358	1960	11450	242	1964
2553WS	736	1960	11460	238	1964
2555W	2383	1960	11470	237	1964
2570	616	1961	11480	213	1964
2571	637	1961	11490	212	1964-1965
2572	2359	1961	11500	2029	1964, 1965, 1966
2573	736	1961	11510	2029	1964
2574	2383	1961	11520	242	1965-1966
2575	2360	1961	11530	634	1965-1966
2576	2383	1961	11540	239	1965-1966
3105	1666	1947 Advance	11550	239	1965-1966
4109WS	671R	1946-1947	11560	211	1965-1966
4110WS	671R	1948-1949	11590	212	1966
11001	1060	1962 Advance	11600	2029	1968
11011	222	1962 Advance	11710	1061	1969
11201	242	1962	11720	2024	1969
11212	633	1962	11730	645	1969
11222	236	1962	11740	2041	1969

Outfit	Engine	Years	Outfit	Engine	Years
11750	2029	1969	13008	637	1962
11760	2029	1969	13018	616	1962
12502	1862	1962	13028	2359	1962
12512	45	1962	13036	1872	1962
12700	736	1964	13048	736	1962
12710	736	1964, 1965, 1966	13058	2383	1962
12720	2383	1964	13068	2360	1962
12730	2383	1964, 1965, 1966	13078	2360	1962
12740 ?	2383	1964	13088	2383	1962
12750 ?	2383	1964	13098	637	1963
12760 ?	736	1964	13108	617	1963
12770 ?	736	1964	13118	736	1963
12780	2383	1964, 1965, 1966	13128	2383	1963
12800	2346	1965-1966	13138	2360	1963
12820	2322	1965	13148	2383	1963
12840	665	1966	13150	773	1964, 1965, 1966
12850	2322	1966			

? — Question mark indicates that the existence of the outfit is questionable.

Appendix C

At last, an explanation of the "Mystery Years" of 1955, 1956, and 1957, with a complete listing of both the consumer catalogue and "special" three-digit outfit numbers.

1955

Special	Engine	Consumer	Special	Engine	Consumer
500	600	1525	514	2065	1541WS
501	610	1001	515	2037	1526S
502	1615	1527	A-20	2338	2235W
503	2028	1529	A-21	665	2237WS
504	2037	1513S	A-22	2363	2239W
505	2328	1531W	A-23	646	2241WS
506	2016	1000W	A-24	2321	2243W
507	2055	1533WS	A-25	2367	2244W
508	2328	1534W	A-26	682	2245WS
509	2243	1535W	A-27	2367	2247W
510	2245	1536W	A-28	736	2249WS
511	2065	1537WS	A-29	2331	2251W
512	2065	1538WS	A-30	2340-25	2253W

1956

Special	Engine	Consumer	Special	Engine	Consumer
513	2243	1539W	A-31	2340	2254W
700	627	1543	714	2243	1567W
701	628	1545	750†	520	1542
702	2018	1547S	800	601	2255W
703	1615	1549	801	665	2257WS
704	621	1551W	802	2350	2259W
705	629	1552	803	646	2261WS
706	2338	1553W	804	2350	2263W
707	2018	1555WS	805	736	2265WS
708	621	1557W	806	2331	2267W
709	2338	1559W	807	2368	2269W
710	2065	1561WS	808	2341	2270W
711	2328	1562W	809	2360-25	2271W
712	2240	1563W	810	2378	2273W
713	2065	1565WS	811	2360	2274W

† Note: This item was a late addition to the product line after the other outfits had already been numbered.

1957

Special	Engine	Consumer	Special	Engine	Consumer
725	202	1569	816	404	2276W
726	625	1571	817	665	2277WS
727	250	1573	818	2350	2279W
728	205	1575	819	2243	2281W
729	2018	1577S	820	646	2283WS
730	2018	1578S	821	2331	2285W
731	2037	1579S	822	2351	2287W
732	611	1581	823	736	2289WS
733	2037	1583WS	824	2379	2291W
734	602	1585W	825	646	2292WS
735	204	1586	826	2360	2293W
736	2037-500	1587S	827	746	2295WS
737	2037	1589WS	828	2373	2296W
815	2339	2275W	829	746	2297WS

Appendix D

Index of **engines** in numerical sequence with the outfits they headed and the year(s) catalogued.

44: 2527 (1959-1960)

45: 1805 (1960), 1647 (1961), 12512 (1962)

202: 1569 or 725 (1957)

204: 1586 or 735 (1957)

205: 1575 or 728 (1959)

208: 1605W (1958), 1626W (1959)

209: 1608W (1958)

210: 1599 (1958)

211: 11252 (1962), 11361 (1963), 11560 (1965-1966)

212: USMC 1591 (1958)

212: Santa Fe 11490 (1964-1965), 11590 (1966)

213: 11480 (1964)

216: 1600 (1958)

217: 1615 (1959)

218: 1619W (1959), 1637W (1960), 1640W (1960), 1649 (1961), 1651 (1961), 11308 (1962), 11405 (1963)

220: None

221: Steam 1400 and 1400W (1946), 1403 and 1403W (1946), 1432 and 1432W (1947), 1433 and 1433W (1947)

221: Rio Grande 11321 (1963), 11440 (1964)

222: 11011 (1962 Advance)

223: 11385 (1963)

224: Steam 463W (1945), 2100 and 2100W (1946), 2101 and 2101W (1946), 2103W (1946)

224: 1633 (1960)

225: 1629 (1960)

229: 1645 (1961), 11288 (1962)

230: 1643 (1961)

231: 1810 (1961)

232: 11232 (1962)

233: 1646 (1961), 11242 (1962)

236: 1652 (1961), 11222 (1962)

237: 11351 (1963), 11470 (1964)

238: 11375 (1963), 11460 (1964)

239: 11540 (1965-1966), 11550 (1965-1966)

242: 11201 (1962), 11331 (1963), 11450 (1964), 11520 (1965-1966)

243: 1631WS (1960)

244: 1627S (1960), 1642 (1961), 1809 (1961)

246: 1609 (1959-1960), 1641 (1961)

247: 1613S (1959)

249: 1590 (1958)

250: 1573 or 727 (1957)

400: 2502W (1958)

404: 2276W or 816 (1957)

520: 1542 or 750 (1956)

600: 1525 or 500 (1955)

601: 2255W or 800 (1956)

602: 1585W or 734 (1957)

610: 1001 or 501 (1955)

611: 1581 or 732 (1957)

613: 1593 (1958)

614: 1611 (1959)

616: 2570 (1961), 13018 (1962)

617: 13108 (1963)

621: 1551W or 704 (1956), 1557W or 708 (1956)

622: 2149B (1949)

623: None

624: None

625: 1571 or 726 (1957)

626: None

627: 1543 or 700 (1956)

628: 1545 or 701 (1956)

629: 1552 or 705 (1956)

633: 11212 (1962)

634: 11341 (1963), 11530 (1965-1966)

637: 2531WS (1959), 2547WS (1960), 2571 (1961), 13008 (1962), 13098 (1963)

645: 11730 (1969)

646: 2221WS (1954), 2222WS (1954), 2241WS or A-23 (1955), 2261WS or 803 (1956), 2283WS or 820 (1957), 2292WS or 825 (1957), 2515WS (1958)

665: 2201WS (1954), 2237WS or A-21 (1955), 2257WS or 801 (1956), 2277WS or 817 (1957), 2503WS (1958), 2509WS (1958), 2535WS (1959), 2539WS (1959), 12840 (1966)

671: 2105WS (1946), 2110WS (1946), 2111WS (1946), 2125WS (1947), 2126WS (1947), 2127WS (1947), 2140WS (1948-1949), 2141WS (1948-1949), 2143WS (1948), 2153WS (1949), 2179WS (1952), 2187WS (1952)

671R: 4109WS (1946-1947), 4110WS (1948-1949)

675: 2120S and 2120WS (1947), 2121S and 2121WS (1947), 2123WS (1947), 2135WS (1948-1949), 2136WS (1948-1949), 2137WS (1948), 2147WS (1949), 2177WS (1952)

681: 2150WS (1950), 2167WS (1950-1951), 2173WS (1950-1951), 2203WS (1953), 2211WS (1953)

682: 2217WS (1954), 2245WS or A-26 (1955)

685: 2201WS (1953)

726: 2113WS (1946), 2114WS (1946), 2115WS (1946), 2129WS (1947), 2131WS (1947), 2145WS (1948), 2146WS (1948-1949), 2155WS (1949), 2183WS (1952), 2189WS (1952)

736: 2163WS (1950-1951), 2165WS (1950), 2205WS (1953), 2213WS (1953), 2225WS (1954), 2249WS or A-28 (1955), 2265WS or 805 (1956), 2289WS or 823 (1957), 2543WS (1959), 2553WS (1960), 2573 (1961), 13048 (1962), 13118 (1963), 12700 (1964), 12170 (1964, 1965, 1966), 12760 ? (1964), 12770 ? (1964)

746: 2295WS or 827 (1957), 2297WS or 829 (1957), 2521WS (1958), 2525WS (1958), 2545WS (1959)

773: 2148WS (1950), 2169WS (1950), 13150 (1964, 1965, 1966)

1001: 1111 (1948), 1112 (1948)

1055: 1105 (1959 Advance), 1107 (1960 Advance)

1060: 1109 (1960 Advance), 1123 (1961 Advance), 1124 (1961 Advance), 11001 (1962 Advance)

1061: 11415 (1963 Advance), 11420 (1964 consumer), 11710 (1969)

1062: 11311 (1963), 11430 (1964)

1065: 1125 (1961 Advance)

1110: 1115 (1949), 1117 (1949), 1119 (1951-1952)

1120: 1113 (1950)

1130: 1500 (1953-1954)

1615: 1527 or 502 (1955), 1549 or 703 (1956)

1625: 1595 (1958)

1654: 1401 and 1401W (1946), 1431 and 1431W (1947)

1655: 1423W (1948-1949)

1656: 1425B (1948-1949)

1665: 1407B (1946)

1666: 1402 and 1402W (1946), 1405 and 1405W (1946), 1409 and 1409W (1946), 1411W (1946)

1862: 1800 (1959-1960), 1612 (1959-1960), 1644 (1961), 12502 (1962)

1872: 2528WS (1959, 1960, 1961), 13036 (1962)

2016: 1000W or 506 (1955)

? — Question marks indicate that the existence of the outfit has not been confirmed.

2018: 1547S or 702 (1956), 1555WS or 707 (1956), 1577S or 729 (1957), 1578S or 730 (1957), 1597S (1958), 1617S (1959)

2020: 1413WS (1946), 1415WS (1946), 1417WS (1946), 1419WS (1946), 1421WS (1946), 1441WS (1947), 1443WS (1947), 1447WS (1948-1949), 1449WS (1948), 1459WS (1949)

2023: 1464W (1950 yellow-1951 silver), 1467W (1950 yellow-1951 silver)

2024: 11720 (1969)

2025: 1434WS (1947), 1435WS (1947), 1437WS (1947), 1439WS (1947), 1430WS (1948-1949) 1445WS (1948), 1455WS (1949), 1485WS (1952), 1489WS (1952)

2026: 1426WS (1948-1949), 1427WS (1948), 1429WS (1948), 1451WS (1949), 1453WS (1949), 1463WS (1951), 1447S (1951-1952), 1501S (1953)

2028: 1529 or 503 (1955)

2029: 11500 (1964, 1965, 1966), 11510 (1964), 11600 (1968), 11750 (1969), 11760 (1969)

2031: None

2032: 1467W (1952-1953)

2033: 1464W (1952-1953)

2034: 1465 (1952)

2035: 1469WS (1950-1951), 1471WS (1950-1951), 1481WS (1951)

2036: 1463W (1950)

2037: 1511S (1953), 1513S (1954), 1513S or 504 (1955), 1526S or 515 (1955), 1579S or 731(1957), 1583WS or 733 (1957), 1589WS or 737 (1957), 1603WS (1958), 1607WS (1958), 1621WS (1959), 1625WS (1959), 1635WS (1960), 1639WS (1960), 1648 (1961), 1650 (1961), 11278 (1962), 11298 (1962), 11395 (1963)

2037-500: Girls' 1587S or 736 (1957-1958)

2041: 11740 (1969)

2046: 1473WS (1950), 1475WS (1950), 1505WS (1953), 1507WS (1953), 1509WS (1953)

2055: 1502WS (1953), 1503WS (1953-1954), 1533WS or 507 (1955)

2056: 1479WS (1952), 1483WS (1952), 1484WS (1952)

2065: 1515WS (1954), 1516WS (1954), 1519WS (1954), 1521WS (1954), 1537WS or 511 (1955), 1538WS or 512 (1955), 1541WS or 514 (1955), 1561WS or 710 (1956), 1565WS or 713 (1956)

2240: 1563W or 712 (1956)

2242: 2507W (1958), 2537W (1959)

2243: 1535W or 509 (1955), 1539W or 513 (1955), 1567W or 714 (1956), 2281W or 819 (1957)

2245: 1517W (1954), 1520W (1954), 1536W or 510 (1955)

2321: 2219W (1954), 2223W (1954), 2243W or A-24 (1955)

2322: 12820 (1965), 12850 (1966)

2328: 1531W or 505 (1955), 1534W or 508 (1955), 1562W or 711 (1956)

2329: 2505W (1958), 2513W (1958), 2529W (1959)

2330: 2159W (1950)

2331: 2251W or A-29 (1955), 2267W or 806 (1956), 2285W or 821 (1957), 2519W (1958)

2332: 2124W (1947), 2139W (1948-1949), 2144W (1948-1949)

2333: Santa Fe or NYC 2133W (1948), 2151W (1949)

2337: 1601W (1958)

2338: 2235W or A-20 (1955), 1553W or 706 (1956), 1559W or 709 (1956)

2339: 2275W or 815 (1957)

2340: Tuscan 2254W or A-31 (1955)

2340-25: Green 2253W or A-30 (1955)

2341: 2270W or 808 (1956)

2343: 2161W (1950), 2175W (1950-1951), 2190W (1952), 2191W (1952)

2344: 2171W (1950), 2185W (1950-1951), 2193W (1952)

2345: None

2346: 12800 (1965-1966)

2348: 2501W (1958)

2349: 1623W (1959), 2549 (1960)

2350: 2259W or 802 (1956), 2263W or 804 (1956), 2279W or 818 (1957)

2351: 2287W or 822 (1957)

2352: 2511W (1958), 2518W (1958)

2353: 2190W (1953), 2207W (1953), 2227W (1954), 2234W (1954)

2354: 2209W (1953), 2229W (1954)

2355: None

2356: 2231W (1954)

2358: 2533W (1959), 2551W (1960)

2359: 2572 (1961), 13028 (1962)

2360: 2274W or 811 (1956), 2293W or 826 (1957), 2575 (1961), 13068 (1962), 13078 (1962), 13138 (1963)

2360-25: 2271W or 809 (1956)

2363: 2239W or A-22 (1955)

2365: 11268 (1962)

2367: 2244W or A-25 (1955), 2247W or A-27 (1955)

2368: 2269W or 807 (1956)

2373: 2296W or 828 (1957)

2378: 2273W or 810 (1956)

2379: 2291W or 824 (1957), 2517W (1958)

2383: 2523W (1958), 2526W (1958), 2541W (1959), 2544W (1959-1960), 2555W (1960), 2574 (1961), 2576 (1961), 13058 (1962), 13088 (1962), 13128 (1963), 13148 (1963), 12720 (1964), 12730 (1964, 1965, 1966), 12740 ? (1964), 12750 ? (1964), 12780 (1964, 1965, 1966)

6110: 1461S (1950)

6220: 1457B (1949-1950)

6250: 1523 (1954)

? — Question marks indicate that the existence of the outfit has not been confirmed.

Appendix E

A chronological listing of the postwar passenger sets by series.

THE TINPLATE SETS

Years	Outfit	Engine	Components
Blue Series			
1946	1400	221-221T	2430, 2430, 2431
1946	1400W	221-221W	2430, 2430, 2431
1947	1432	221-221T	2430, 2430, 2431
1947	1432W	221-221W	2430, 2430, 2431
Green Series			
1946	1402	1666-2466T	2440, 2440, 2441
1946	1402W	1666-2466W	2440, 2440, 2441
1946	2100†	224-2466T	2440, 2440, 2441
1946	2100W†	224-2466WX	2440, 2440, 2441
1947	1434WS	2025-2466WX	2440, 2440, 2441
1948-1949	1426WS	2026-6466WX	6440, 6440, 6441

† *Outfits 2100 and 2100W are also known to exist with brown cars that are numbered "2442" and "2443".*

Years	Outfit	Engine	Components
Brown Series			
1947	2120S	675-2466T	2442, 2442, 2443
1947	2120WS	675-2466WX	2442, 2442, 2443
1948	2136WS	675-2466WX	2442, 2442, 2443
1949	2136WS	675-6466WX	6442, 6442, 6443

STREAMLINED O27-TYPE 2400 SETS

Years	Outfit	Engine	Components
Green with Yellow Trim Series			
1948-1949	1430WS	2025-6466WX	2400, 2401, 2402
1948-1949	2140WS	671-2671W	2400, 2401, 2402
Yellow Anniversary Series			
1950	1464W	2023AA	2481, 2482, 2483
Silver with Gray Roof Series			
1950	2150WS	681-2671W	2421, 2422, 2423
1951	1464W	2023AA	2421, 2422, 2423
Silver with Silver Roof Series			
1952	1484WS	2056-2046W	2421, 2422, 2423, 2429
1952-1953	1464W	2033AA	2421, 2422, 2423
1953	1502WS	2055-2046W	2421, 2422, 2423
Silver with Red Stripe Series			
1956	1562W	2328	2442, 2442, 2444, 2446

Note: The 2445 Elizabeth was not included with the set but was available for separate sale.

Years	Outfit	Engine	Components

Silver with Red Letters Series

1954	1516WS	2065-2046W	2432, 2434, 2436
1954	1520W	2245AB	2432, 2435, 2436
1955	1534W	2328	2432, 2434, 2436
1955	1536W	2245AB	2432, 2432, 2436
1955	1538WS	2065-2046W	2432, 2434, 2435, 2436
1956	1552	629	2432, 2432, 2436
1957	1578S	2018-1130T	2432, 2434, 2436
1957	1586	204AA	2432, 2432, 2436
1958	1600	216	6572, 2432, 2436 Mooseheart
1958	1608W	209AA	2432, 2432, 2434, 2436 Mooseheart

Note: The 1957 Advance Catalogue shows the 2436 as a "Summit" while the consumer catalogue shows it as a "Mooseheart."

Santa Fe with Blue Stripe Series

1959	1626W	208AA	3428, 2412, 2412, 2416
1960	1640W	218AA	3428, 2412, 2412, 2416
1961	1651	218AA	2412, 2412, 2414, 2416
1962	11308	218AA	2412, 2412, 2414, 2416
1963	11405	218AA	2412, 2412, 2414, 2416

Santa Fe with Blue Letters Series

1964-1965	11490	212AA	2404, 2405, 2406 (non-illuminated)
1966	11590	212AA	2408, 2409, 2410 (illuminated)

THE GENERAL SETS

1959-1960	1612	1862-1862T	1865, 1866
1959-1960	1800	1862-1862T	1865, 1866, 1877
1959-1961	2528WS	1872-1872T	1875W, 1876, 1877
1961	1644	1862-1862T	1865, 1866, 3370
1962	12502	1862-1862T	1865, 1866, 1877, 3376
1962	13036	1872-1872T	1875W, 1876, 3370, 6445

Note: The 1875 coach was not included with either of the O Gauge General sets but was available for separate sale.

THE MADISON SETS

1946	2110WS	671-2466W	2625, 2625, 2625 (Irvington only)
1946	2114WS	726-2426W	2625, 2625, 2625 (Irvington only)
1947	2124W	2332	2625, 2625, 2625 (three names)
1947	2126WS	671-671W	2625, 2625, 2625 (three names)
1948-1949	2144W	2332	2625, 2627, 2628
1948-1949	2146WS	726-2426W	2625, 2627, 2628
1950	2148WS	773-2426W	2625, 2627, 2628 (with silhouettes)

Years	Outfit	Engine	Components

THE BUDD SETS

Years	Outfit	Engine	Components
1957	2276W	404	2559, 2559
1958	2502W	400	2550, 2559

EXTRUDED-ALUMINUM O GAUGE 2500 SETS

The Super Speedliner Series

Years	Outfit	Engine	Components
1952	2190W	2343AA	2531, 2532, 2533, 2534
1953	2190W	2353AA	2531, 2532, 2533, 2534
1954	2222WS	646-2046W	2530, 2531, 2532
1954	2234W	2353AA	2530, 2531, 2532, 2533
1955	2244W	2367AB	2530, 2531, 2533
1956	2270W	2341	2531, 2532, 2533
1957	2292WS	646-2046W	2530, 2531, 2532, 2533
1958	2518W	2352	2531, 2533, 2534
1958	2526W	2383AA	2530, 2531, 2532, 2532

The Congressional Series

Years	Outfit	Engine	Components
1955	2254W	2340	2541, 2542, 2543, 2544
1956	2274W	2360	2541, 2542, 2543, 2544

The Canadian Pacific Series

Years	Outfit	Engine	Components
1957	2296W	2373AA	2551, 2552, 2552, 2552

The Super Chief Series

Years	Outfit	Engine	Components
1959-1960	2544W	2383AA	2530, 2561, 2562, 2563
1961	2576	2383AA	2561, 2562, 2562, 2563

The Presidential Series

Years	Outfit	Engine	Components
1962	13078	2360	2521, 2522, 2522, 2523
1962	13088	2383AA	2521, 2522, 2522, 2523
1963	13148	2383AA	2521, 2522, 2523, 2523
1964-1966	12780	2383AA	2521, 2522, 2523, 2523

Appendix F

Scarce and/or collectable cars in numerical sequence by type
with descriptions and the outfits in which they were included.

6464 SERIES BOXCARS

Number	Description	Outfits
-1	Silver WP	1505WS
-25	Great Northern	1515WS, 2203WS
-50	Tuscan M St. L	1535W, 2201WS, 2219W
-75	Green RI	2211WS
-100	Blue feather WP	2223W
-100	Yellow feather WP	2223W
-125	NYC Pacemaker	2239W
-150	MP Eagle	2247W, 2281W
-175	Silver RI	2217WS
-200	Pennsylvania	None
-225	Black SP	1517W
-250	Blue feather WP	None
-275	State of Maine	1537WS, 2237WS, 2249WS, 2251W, 2519W, 2537W
-300	Rutland	2243W, 2253W
-325	B & O Sentinel	None
-350	Tuscan Katy	None
-375	Central of Georgia	12840
-400	B & O Timesaver	1555WS
-425	Black NH	1553W, 1573, 1601W, 1605W, 1607WS, 2259W, 2279W, 2507W
-450	Great Northern	1589WS, 12840
-475	Boston and Maine	1577S, 1615, 1621WS, 1637W, 2275W, 2509WS, 12800
-500	Timken	2287W, 2505W
-510	Girls' Pacemaker	1587S
-515	Girls' Katy	1587S
-525	Red M St. L	1585W, 2283WS, 2291W, 2501W
-650	Rio Grande	1581
-700	Santa Fe	None
-725	Orange NH	11395, 12700, 12710, 12720, 12730, 12820, 12850, 13068, 13138

Number	Description	Outfits
-725	Black NH	None
-825	Alaska	2539WS
-900	Jade NYC	2555W, 2575, 13098

OPERATING BOXCARS

3428	U.S. Mail	1626W, 1640W
3474	WP 9-1/4 inch	1511S, 1483WS
3484	Pennsylvania	2205WS, 2207W, 2209W
3484-25	Santa Fe	None
3494-1	NYC Pacemaker	1541WS
3494-150	MP Eagle	None
3494-275	State of Maine	1559W, 2289WS
3494-550	Monon	None
3494-625	Soo	None

MISCELLANEOUS BOXCARS

6014	White Bosco	1603WS
6014	Red Airex	None
6024	Shredded Wheat	1581, 1585W, 1589WS
6044	Blue Airex	1105 Advance, 1107 Advance
6428	U.S. Mail	12800
6454	Baby Ruth	None
6468X	Tuscan double-door	1535W ?
6468-25	New Haven double-door	1579S, 2263W, 2507W
6530	Fire prevention car	1639WS, 2575, 13068

TANK CARS

2855	Sunoco single-dome	2113WS, 2129WS
6045	Gray Lionel Lines	1105 Advance
6045	Cities Service	None
6315	Dark orange Gulf (early)	2269W, 2287W
6315	Gulf unpainted (late)	11740, 11750, 11760
6425	Gulf three-dome	1551W, 2275W, 2285W, 2513W
6463	Rocket Fuel	11252, 11288, 11341
6465	Black Gulf	1607WS
6465-110	Cities Service	1631WS, 1645, 1648, 11242
6469	Liquefied gas	11395, 13098
6475	Pickle vat	1637W, 1649, 2547WS, 2573, 13068

Number	Description	Outfits
3435	Traveling aquarium	1623W, 2531WS, 2537W, 2553WS
3512	Fireman and ladder car	1623W, 1625WS, 2529W, 2539WS, 2541W, 2551W
3562-1	Black barrel car	1521WS, 2225WS
3562-75	Orange barrel car	2281W, 2291W, 2511W
3672	Bosco with stand	2535WS, 2553WS

FLATCARS WITH LOADS

Number	Description	Outfits
1877	Flatcar with horses	1800, 1809, 2528WS, 12502
6151	Flatcar with Range Patrol truck	1590
6262	Flatcar with wheels	1549, 1561WS
6311	Flatcar with three pipes	1529
6343	Barrel ramp	1646, 1649, 11222
6362	Flatcar with rail trucks	1551W, 1559W, 2255W
6405	Flatcar with yellow van	1642, 1649
6418	Double-truck girder car	2271W, 2285W
6431	Flatcar w/vans & tractor	12840
6440	Flatcar with vans	2573, 11395, 13048
6467	Miscellaneous car	1563W, 2257WS, 2265WS
6477	Miscellaneous car with pipes	1605W, 2279W
6518	Double-truck transformer car	2269W, 2293W, 2525WS
6660	Flatcar with boom crane	1593, 1607WS
6670	Flatcar with boom crane	1617S
6802	Flatcar with girder	1605W, 1619W, 2501W
6810	Flatcar with Cooper-Jarrett van	1601W
6816	Flatcar with dozer	1617S, 1639WS, 2541W
6817	Flatcar with scraper	1639WS, 2531WS
6818	Flatcar with transformer	1593, 1597S, 1603WS, 1607WS
6821	Flatcar with crates	1613S, 1635WS
6826	Flatcar with Christmas trees	1613S, 1635WS
6827	Flatcar with power shovel	2551W, 2575, 13068, 13118, 13138
6828	Flatcar with truck crane	2551W, 2570, 2575, 13068, 13138

Number	Description	Outfits

MILITARY AND SPACE-RELATED ITEMS

Number	Description	Outfits
3309	Turbo missile launcher	11321, 11440
3413	Mercury capsule launcher	11288, 11361, 12512, 13058, 13128
3470	Aerial target launcher	11268, 11385, 12512, 13028, 13108
3509	Satellite car (manual)	1643, 11252
3510	Red satellite car (manual)	11011 Advance
3519	Satellite car	1647, 1810, 2572, 13018
3540	Radar scanner	2545WS, 2549W
3545	TV monitor	2573
3619	Reconnaissance copter car	11268, 11385, 12512, 13058, 13128
3665	Minuteman launcher	1647, 1810, 2574, 11361, 13028, 13108
6175	Flatcar with rocket	1637W, 1643, 2545WS
6407	Flatcar with rocket	11341, 11385
6413	Mercury capsule carrier	11232, 11288, 11361
6480	Exploding boxcar	1125 Advance
6512	Cherry picker	11288, 13058, 13128
6519	Allis Chalmers car	1619W, 1621WS, 1631WS, 1648, 2505W, 2517W, 2525WS, 2541W
6544	Missile firing trail car	1633, 1650, 2572, 11298
6630	Black IRBM launcher	1125 Advance
6640	Olive IRBM launcher	1805
6803	Flatcar w/military units	1591
6804	Flatcar w/military units	1595
6805	Atomic energy disposal car	2505W, 2509WS, 2517W, 2521WS
6806	Flatcar w/military units	1595
6807	Flatcar with amphibious duck	1591
6808	Flatcar w/military units	1595
6809	Flatcar w/military units	1591
6823	Flatcar with missiles	2527, 2535WS, 2543WS
6844	Missile-carrying flatcar	2527

Number	Description	Outfits

CABOOSES — PORTHOLE

Number	Description	Outfits
6417	without NY Zone	2293W
6417-25	Lionel Lines	2221WS, 2227W, 2229W, 2231W
6417-50	Gray Lehigh Valley	2223W
6417-50	Tuscan Lehigh Valley	None
6427-60	Virginian	2513W
6427-500	Girls'	1587S
6447	Non-illuminated	13098

CABOOSES — WORK

Number	Description	Outfits
6119	Red with red bin	1527
6119-25	Orange	1549, 1557W, 2255W, 2529W
6119-50	Brown	1549 ?
6120	Yellow unstamped	1125 Advance, 11011 Advance
6130	Santa Fe	2570, 11530, 11600, 11750
6219	C & O	1629
6419-100	N & W	2295WS, 2525WS
6420	Searchlight	None
6429	AAR trucks (1963)	13118
6814	White medical	1647, 2527
6824	Olive medical	1805

CABOOSES — SP-TYPE

Number	Description	Outfits
6007	Semi-scout	1461S
6017	Gray Lionel Lines	1595
6017-50	U.S.M.C.	1591
6017-100	Boston and Maine	1615, 12800, 13028
6017-185	Gray ATSF	1619W, 1637W
6017-200	U.S. Navy	1633
6017-235	Red ATSF	13018
6027	Alaska	1611
6057-50	Orange Lionel Lines	11232
6058	C & O	1643
6167-85	Yellow UP	11730
6357-50	ATSF illuminated	2555W

? — Question marks indicate that the inclusion of the car in the outfit was a sometime occurrence or a probability. For example, the 6520 searchlight car with green generator was definitely 1949 production and is likely to surface in four sets.

Number	Description	Outfits
6557	Smoking	2519W, 2521WS, 2543WS
6657	Rio Grande	2291W, 2517W

CABOOSES — MISCELLANEOUS

Number	Description	Outfits
3535	Security car	2549W, 2572
6517-75	Erie bay window	None

Glossary

A unit: lead unit for certain diesel locomotive designs, such as F-3 units; has cab for crew.

AA: combination of two A unit diesel locomotives.

AAR trucks: trucks designed by the Association of American Railroads; Lionel's plastic version was introduced in 1957.

AB: combination of an A and B unit.

ABA: combination of an A unit, a B unit, and a second A unit.

Advance Catalogue: a catalogue for wholesale and retail distributors that indicated what would most likely be available for sale.

Alco: an acronym for American Locomotive Company, manufacturer of locomotives for full-size railroads; made the FA units popularized in O27 by Lionel.

arch bar truck: the inexpensive plastic truck that was developed for the General components in 1959; also the most commonly used truck for inexpensive Advance and uncatalogued sets.

B unit: trailing unit for certain diesel locomotive designs, such as F-3 diesels; has no cab or windshield.

Bakelite: synthetic resin or plastic used in the early manufacture of toy trains; e.g., Madison passenger cars.

bar-end truck: a metal truck in which the side frame is pressed against a bolster that resembles a bar; it replaced the staple-end truck.

bay window caboose: caboose with no cupola, but with extended side windows.

Berkshire: type of steam locomotive with a 2-8-4 wheel arrangement.

box cab: electric-outline locomotive with a rectangular body, such as the 520 introduced in 1956.

Budd RDC: self-propelled Rail Diesel Car; resembles a passenger car; modeled by Lionel as 400 and 404.

C unit: a term used by Lionel in catalogues and on boxes to identify their B units.

camtrol: plastic track-mounted device for O27 that allows manual uncoupling.

coach: basic passenger car; usually has windows along entire length of each side.

coil coupler: type of coupler that was activated by a sliding shoe; more costly to manufacture than magnetic couplers.

Columbia: type of steam locomotive with a 2-4-2 wheel arrangement.

combine: car used in passenger trains with combination of uses, such as baggage-passenger combination, or baggage-Railway Post Office combination.

consumer catalogue: a catalogue that was offered to the general public to promote Lionel trains.

couplers: mechanical devices used to connect cars; made in many different variations on toy trains; Lionel used knuckle couplers for postwar production.

die-cast: metal cast in a die or mold; sometimes brittle.

die-cut: a box or insert cut by mechanical means to make openings for the contents.

dummy: non-powered locomotive; for example, the B units in many AB combinations sold by toy train companies were dummies as were non-powered A units.

ECU-1: Electronic Control Unit; a box-like device that was included with the Electronic Sets to control train function.

EMD: Electro-Motives Division of General Motors; maker of the F-3.

EP-5: specific type of electric locomotive with a cab on each end; no walkways; e.g., 2350 New Haven.

F-3: specific type of diesel locomotive; rounded nose, no walkways; popularized by Lionel; e.g., 2343 Santa Fe.

FA: specific type of Alco diesel locomotive; eight wheels, rounded nose; popularized in O27 by Lionel; e.g., 2023 Union Pacific.

Fairbanks-Morse (F-M): manufacturer of locomotives for the real railroads; produced the "Trainmaster" made popular by Lionel; e.g., 2321 Lackawanna.

feedwater heater: accessory on a steam locomotive, usually on the front above the headlight.

fixed coupler: a coupler that does not operate; has components that are fixed in place; either plastic or die-cast.

frame: bottom part of a car or locomotive, to which wheels or trucks are attached.

GG-1: popular electric locomotive used by the Pennsylvania Railroad; created by famed industrial designer Raymond Loewy; modeled by Lionel and others; e.g., 2332.

GP-7 or GP-9: specific types of diesel locomotives; boxy, walkways around sides; modeled by Lionel; e.g., 2028 Pennsylvania and 2349 Northern Pacific.

GE: abbreviation for General Electric, manufacturer of locomotives for real railroads; Lionel's model of the 44-ton center-cab diesel was based upon a GE design.

gauge: distance between the rails; specific names are used to describe the commonly used sizes, such as HO Gauge, O Gauge, Standard Gauge, etc.

Geep: railroader's slang for GP-series locomotives.

heat-stamped: process of lettering toy trains using heat and colored tape; usually makes a slight impression on plastic or metal surfaces.

Hudson: steam locomotive with a 4-6-4 wheel arrangement. Larger examples such as 773 are referred to as NYC type while smaller Hudsons such as 665 are called Santa Fe type.

lithographed: process of applying paint or ink to sheet metal; commonly used by early toy manufacturers and in the production of early trains; no longer in favor, but continued in usage for low-priced items.

magnetic coupler: the replacement for the coil coupler; introduced in 1948 and activated by an electromagnet.

Magnetraction: special design element of Lionel locomotives using magnetized components to improve traction (pulling power); introduced in 1949 on 622 and 6220 diesel switchers.

Manumatic: Lionel's trade name for a manual uncoupler; developed for the Scout series introduced in 1948.

NW-2: specific type of diesel switcher modeled by Lionel; e.g., 6250 Seaboard.

Northern: type of steam locomotive with a 4-8-4 wheel arrangement; the 746 N & W was the only Northern that Lionel made during the postwar era.

O27 track: Lionel's lightweight track that is 7/16" high; eight sections form a circle with a diameter of 27 inches measured from outer rail to outer rail.

O track: Lionel's heavier weight track that is 11/16" high; eight sections form a circle with a diameter of 31 inches measured from outer rail to outer rail.

OPS: Office of Price Stabilization; established in early 1950s in an attempt to control rampant inflation; OPS stickers and stamps showed that stringent pricing guidelines had been issued.

observation: passenger car usually used at the end of a train; open platform or rounded end with large windows for "observation" of scenery by passengers.

P unit: designation used for powered diesel locomotives.

Pacific: type of steam locomotive with a 4-6-2 wheel arrangement; Lionel did not make a Pacific engine in the postwar era but used an artist's rendering of one on some early 1960s display-style outfit boxes.

porthole caboose: center-cupola caboose with round porthole windows that was modeled after the Pennsylvania N5C.

powered: refers to a locomotive with a motor; used when necessary to distinguish between an operating locomotive and a dummy unit.

Pullman: specific type of passenger car originally designed by George Pullman; often used as a generic term for better-grade passenger cars.

RCS uncoupling/operating section: Remote Controlled uncoupling Section without an electromagnet.

rectifier: another term often used in reference to some electric locomotives; commonly used to refer to Lionel's 2329 Virginian.

reefer: slang term for a refrigerator car, such as those used to ship meats and other perishables.

rubber-stamped: process of lettering toy trains using rubber pads.

SP-type caboose: Southern Pacific square cupola caboose with cupola oriented towards the rear; introduced in late 1947 and produced with several road names and a variety of trim.

scale: proportion of a model to its prototype; for example, an O scale model is 1/48 actual size; therefore O scale is also referred to as 1/48 or 1:48 scale; most Lionel models were slightly less than scale.

Scout: term that refers to sets or components in sets that included a "Lionel Scout" tender and components with both Scout trucks and couplers; scout engines include 1001, 1110, and 1120.

Scout-like: term that has come to mean all small, inexpensive engines with a 0-4-0 or 2-4-2 wheel alignment.

Scout-type: term that is interchangeable with "Scout-like."

semi-Scout: term used to describe rolling stock and the 6001T and 6066T tenders that have the combination of Scout trucks and magnetic couplers.

staple-end truck: a metal truck with the side frames attached with what appears to be a staple that is bent outwards.

steam switcher: type of small steam engine with an 0-4-0 wheel arrangement that was used for yard duty, not main line service.

stock car: commonly called a "cattle car"; used for hauling livestock.

streamlined: locomotives and other trains featuring aerodynamic designs; highly popular in the 1930s.

switcher: type of light-duty locomotive usually used in railroad yards.

Super O: Lionel's specialized track system introduced in 1957 that consists of plastic ties with a copper contact strip in place of the third rail; twelve sections form a circle with a diameter of 38 inches measured from outer rail to outer rail.

T unit: designation used for trailing or non-powered diesel engines.

tender: commonly called a "coal car" by non-railroaders; used to haul fuel for a steam locomotive.

three-rail: track system popularized by Lionel; features two outside running rails (electrically grounded) and a single rail along the center that provides the positive current.

tinplate: toys made from tin-coated steel; also used loosely to describe items that are caricatures of real trains rather than scale models.

transformer: the electrical power source for a model train. Lionel manufactured numerous types ranging from a lowly 1011 with 25 watts of power to a high of 275 watts in the ZW model that could run four trains simultaneously.

truck: assembly that mounts the wheels beneath a railroad car.

truss rods: steel support rods used on the underframes of freight and passenger cars on early railroads; once associated with hobos, who slept on the truss rods beneath the cars.

turbine: Lionel's model of the Pennsylvania railroad 6-8-6 S-2 steam turbine.

two-rail: track arrangement similar to that used on the real roads; commonly used by American Flyer (for its S Gauge models) and by most scale model railroad manufacturers.

UCS: uncoupling/operating section of track that allows automatic operation of couplers by means of an electromagnet; replacement for the RCS; introduced in 1949.

uncoupler: track-mounted device that allows uncoupling of cars, either manually or by remote control.

Index

(C) – indicates a color photograph
(B&W) – indicates a black and white photograph
(box) – indicates a photograph of a box

Outfit	Page	Outfit	Page	Outfit	Page	Outfit	Page	Outfit	Page
2120S	33	2221WS	64	2501W	99	11288	137	12800	130, 158
2120WS	33	2222WS	64	2502W	99	11298	137	12800 (C)	156
2121S	33	2223W	65	2503WS	99	11308	137	12800 (box) (C)	158
2121WS	33	2223W (C)	65	2505W	99	11311	142	12820	158
2123WS	33	2225WS	66	2507W	99	11311 (C)	141	12840	161
2124W	34	2225WS (C)	66	2509WS	99	11321	142	12850	161
2124W (B&W)	34	2227W	66	2511W	100	11321 (box) (C)	133	13008	138
2125WS	34	2229W	66	2513W	100	11331	143	13018	138, 146
2126WS	34	2231W	66	2515WS	100	11341	143	13028	139
2127WS	35	2234W	67	2517W	100	11351	143	13036	139
2129WS	35	2234W (box) (C)	67	2518W	100	11351 (C)	142	13048	139
2131WS	35	2235W	72	2519W	101	11361	143	13058	139
2133W	38	2237WS	72	2521WS	101	11375	143	13068	139
2135WS	39, 44	2239W	72	2523W	101	11385	143	13078	140
2136WS	39, 44	2241WS	72	2525WS	101	11385 (C)	144	13088	140
2137WS	39	2243W	73	2527	108, 117	11395	144	13098	146
2139W	39, 44	2244W	74	2527 (C)	120	11405	145	13118	146
2140WS	39, 44	2245WS	74	2527 (box) (C)	120	11415	145	13128	146
2141WS	39, 44	2245WS (C)	73	2528WS	109, 118, 129	11415 (C)	145	13138	146
2143WS	44	2247W	75	2528WS (C)	108, 109	11420	149	13148	147
2144W	40, 44	2247W (box) (C)	68	2528WS (box) (C)	104	11430	149	13150	152, 158, 161
2145WS	40	2249WS	75	2529W	109	11430 (C)	148	A-20	72
2146WS	41, 44	2251W	76	2531WS	109	11440	150	A-21	72
2147WS	44	2251W (box) (C)	68	2533W	110	11440 (C)	149	A-22	72
2148WS	48	2253W	76	2535WS	110	11450	150	A-23	72
2148WS (box) (C)	48	2253W (C)	74	2537W	110	11460	150	A-24	73
2149B	45	2254W	76	2539WS	110	11470	151	A-25	74
2150WS	49	2254W (C)	75	2541W	110	11480	151	A-26	74
2151W	45	2255W	81	2543WS	110	11480 (C)	150	A-27	75
2153WS	45	2257WS	81	2544W	111, 118	11490	151, 155	A-28	75
2155WS	45	2259W	81	2544W (box) (C)	120	11500	151, 155, 159	A-29	76
2159W	49	2261WS	81	2545WS	111	11510	151	A-30	76
2161W	49	2263W	81	2547WS	118	11520	155, 159	A-31	76
2163WS	49, 53	2265WS	81	2549W	118	11530	156, 159		
2165WS	49	2267W	82	2551W	119	11530 (C)	154		
2167WS	49, 53	2269W	82	2553W	121	11540	156, 159	**BILLBOARDS**	
2169WS	50	2269W (box) (C)	82	2555W	121	11550	156, 159	1949	168
2171W	50	2270W	82	2571	129	11560	157, 159	1950	168
2173WS	50, 53	2270W (C)	83	2572	130	11560 (C)	155	1951	169
2173WS (box) (C)	53	2271W	83	2573	130	11590	159	1952	169
2175W	50, 53	2273W	83	2574	130	11590 (C)	160	1953	170
2175W (box) (C)	47	2273W (box) (C)	82	2575	130	11600	164	1954	170
2177WS	55	2274W	84, 90	2576	131	11600 (C)	164	1955	170
2179WS	56	2276W	90	2576 (box) (C)	131	11600 (box) (C)	165	1956	170
2183WS	56	2276W (box) (C)	90	2625W	102	11710	166	1957	171
2185W	50, 53	2277WS	90	4109W	29, 35	11710 (box) (C)	167	1958	171
2185W (box) (C)	53	2279W	90	4110WS	41, 45	11720	166	1959	171
2187WS	56	2281W	91	4110WS (C)	40	11730	166	1961	171
2189WS	56	2283WS	91	5270	129	11740	167	1962	172
2190W	56, 60	2285W	91	11001	132	11750	167	1963	172
2190W (box) (C)	56	2287W	91	11011	132	11750 (box) (C)	167	1964	172
2191W	57	2287W (box) (C)	91	11011 (C)	133	11760	167	1966-1968	172
2193W	57	2289WS	91	11011 (box) (C)	123	12502	137		
2201WS	60, 64	2289WS (C)	92	11201	133	12512	137		
2203WS	60	2291W	92	11201 (C)	134	12512 (C)	138		
2205WS	60	2291W (C)	93	11201 (box) (C)	133	12512 (box) (C)	137		
2207W	60	2292WS	92	11212	135	12700	151		
2209W	61	2293W	93	11212 (C)	134	12710	152, 157, 160		
2211WS	61	2295WS	93	11222	135	12720	152		
2213WS	61	2296W	94	11232	135	12730	152, 157, 160		
2217WS	64	2296W (C)	94	11232 (C)	135	12740	152		
2219W	64	2297WS	95	11242	135	12750	152		
				11252	136	12760	152		
				11252 (C)	136	12770	152		
				11268	136	12780	130, 152, 157		
				11278	136	12780 (box) (C)	152		

(C) – indicates a color photograph
(B&W) – indicates a black and white photograph
(box) – indicates a photograph of a box